LIVING IN THE AGE OF THE JERK

Technology innovation, pandemics and
our future Join the debate

Acknowledgements

With grateful thanks to Neil Strudwick for the wonderful illustrations.

With special thanks to Jon Dean, Peter Robinson, Rafael Gordon, Sally Shorthose and Tina Lawton for their support since the beginning of our journey writing our book.

And thanks to Debbie Baxter

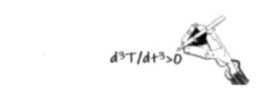

$d^3T/dt^3 > 0$

CONTENTS

Introduction

Within the lifetime of most readers of this book,
technology will have changed humanity so much, that
a case could be made for saying we are no
longer the same species. The dangers, including a
potential return of totalitarianism, are many. But,
if we play it right, we could return to
Eden, a technological Eden.

A perfect storm is brewing. Technology blows from the west. Fear of disease blows from the east. Circulating the world is the threat of climate change. Fascism threatens to add to the mix and rain upon us all. Never before has humanity been so close to descending into a dystopian nightmare.

Some storms never reach land. Technology could becalm the threat. Technology is set to change at a pace for which there is no precedent. This is simultaneously a fantastic opportunity and an insidious threat. Never before has humanity been so close to realising the dream of utopia.

 As these words are written, the world is in the midst of its biggest extended crisis, triggered by a pandemic, since the Second World War. But before these words were written, it was apparent to all who observe these things that technology was set to embark on a period of extraordinary change.

Indeed, technology was and still is changing so fast that we say it is on the trajectory of the jerk. We shall explain what we mean shortly.

1

The Covid-19 crisis has added a whole new level of complication and danger.

The risk is that we become so focused on the threat of disease spreading across the globe, that we miss both the opportunity and challenge created by technology, like a character in a horror movie so preoccupied with the danger ahead that they forget to look behind.

The bad side of technology could combine with the very worst aspects of human nature to compound the danger. A return of fascism, disease even more deadly than Covid-19, social unrest on a massive scale, an end to privacy and a revolution or global conflict are among the dangers.

On the other hand, if we can all work together, learn from the lessons of history and act with reason, and openness, we can mould this technology revolution and turn it into something wonderful.

Approximately 250 years-ago, the world's population was around 700 million, and different peoples and places were strange, even mysterious. For most of these people, life was hard, short, and often miserable.

Then we experienced an industrial revolution, then we encountered another, and then eventually a third, and everything changed. Eventually, people became wealthier and healthier, but sometimes, in the immediate aftermath of an industrial revolution, the world descended into chaos.

Today, the world seems like a small place, people from across the planet watch the same movies, eat similar food, buy the same branded goods and often converse in the same language. Today, 7.5 billion people live on this planet, and thanks to the internet and other communication technologies these people are drawn together like never seen before – the family of humanity is becoming closer. It's as if we are becoming global citizens.

Yet, intolerance and conflict are never far away. We risk repeating the errors of history. Climate change and the problem of providing for today's global population is creating disease – Covid-19 will almost certainly not be the only health-related emergency to bestride the globe over the next decade or two. Lies go global. The message of hate charges social unrest. Pandemics threaten lives and our way of life. We look back to an older time that never existed, and long for a more localised planet, where national identities are celebrated, lives were short and immersed in grinding poverty, wars between nations were more common, and except for the Black Death, and a very long list of other diseases that have changed the course of history, viruses didn't go global!

In so doing, we risk taking our eye off the ball. Technology creates both opportunity and danger. If we focus on the wrong risks, we risk missing the opportunity and only getting the downside.

We are at the beginning of two successive periods of innovation; a revolution of automation followed by a revolution of augmentation. The automation revolution has already begun, and it will continue for roughly ten years. During this period, we will see more technological change than we saw in the previous century.

The augmentation revolution will immediately follow, it may even overlap with the first period. Indeed, we would argue that this revolution has also already begun. It will be the most dramatic period of innovation ever.

Techopia — will technology create utopia or dystopia? It is up to us!

Consider three simple truths.

- Just about all change that has occurred over the last seven thousand years was in some way created by technology.
- But for us, our species, the human race, and our particular version of that species, Homo sapiens sapiens, has not changed; our DNA is almost identical to that of our ancestors from seven, twenty or even hundred thousand years ago. Society has changed massively; the economy has changed completely, culture is barely recognisable from a few centuries ago, let alone seven thousand years ago. But the bodies and brains we are born with are virtually unchanged.
- There is nothing new about accelerating technology and occasional periods when this acceleration accelerates. But the inevitable consequence of this is that we race ever more quickly to a new dawn — a dawn that could bring utopia or dystopia.

3

We are not equipped to deal with this change; neither are we given the cognitive abilities to understand it truly. But the change is occurring all the same. We can fight it, we can ignore it, we can retreat behind national borders, or we can sit back, and hope things will sort themselves out, but within those routes lies disaster. Or we can embrace it but with our eyes wide open, fully aware of the dangers.

There are eight ways this could pan out.

 Technology may liberate us; free us to spend our time doing the things that matter, focus on our empathy and destroy the barriers that separate us. Television screenwriter and producer, Gene Roddenberry envisioned such a cultural and egalitarian society where scarcity is eliminated, and the peoples of the planet are united in the TV series Star Trek.

If we are not careful, we could lurch into a world of extreme inequality and risk the return of fascism. If you want to delve into fiction to imagine such a futuristic scenario, think of Star Wars, with the rule of the Sith and abject poverty alongside wealth.

 Alternatively, computers, robots and other technologies will make our life too easy. Struggle and challenge are part of being human. We could be waited upon day and night by robot servants, creating a lazy, slothful society, that would horrify our ancestors. Like in the movie Wall-E, we lose our lust for life.

Or we could throw ourselves into computer games, escape into virtual reality, like in the movie The Matrix, where we would socialise in virtual space, maybe even holiday there. But is that desirable?

 Or we could give up privacy, descend into a kind of police state, where our thoughts are no longer private, Big Brother is spying on us. An Orwellian world as portrayed in the book 1984.

Or technology may amplify us, turn us into bionic men and women, armed with enhanced intelligence, strength and health; as envisioned in the 1970s TV series; The Six million-dollar man.

Or we could head into conflict, world war, revolution or (less likely) face an existential threat from the machine; scenarios potentially found in films like Apocalypse Now or to the somewhat less probable Terminator.

 Or we could unite, technology may bring us together, create an emergent system, charged by collective intelligence as envisioned by Isaac Asimov in the Foundation Series with Gaia, or by James Cameron when he created Avatar. Fiction has many such examples; not all are benign.

In practice, these eight scenarios will overlap — we may never experience one such scenario to its extreme.

But within the lifetime of most people alive today, our fate will be inextricably sealed. We will be irreversibly heading for a specific combination of those scenarios.

The time for us all to take control and shape our fate to create the most benign outcome possible is now.

So who, what is this Jerk?

Imagine a car. If its speed increases from zero to sixty miles per hour in ten seconds, then from sixty to 120 mphin twenty seconds, it is accelerating. Now consider a rocket and imagine that, at first, its acceleration is quite slow as it lifts off its launcher, then it accelerates at a faster rate. It takes a few minutes before acceleration peaks. This is a Jerk. It refers to the acceleration of acceleration.

It is also possible to have a negative jerk; this describes the rapid reversal of acceleration. For example, from your speeding car travelling at 100 kph, you spot a traffic jam ahead, and you slam on the brakes.

Unfortunately, you skid into the vehicle in front and reach an abrupt halt. This would be a negative jerk.

People often say technology is accelerating. We disagree; it is more than that. Right now, it is accelerating at an accelerating rate; it is jerking.

You can go back further; the jerk describes evolution too. Life began almost four billion years ago, and at first, things changed very, very slowly. Roughly 1.8 billion years ago, the first complex organism evolved, and evolution accelerated. Approximately 535 million years ago, we saw another significant change, something those who study evolution call the Cambrian explosion – the acceleration of evolution accelerated – or as we like to say, it jerked.

Of course, there were occasions when things went into a sharp reversal. There was a negative jerk when the meteorite wiped out the dinosaurs. But this soon changed to a positive jerk, as the vacuum created by the end of the dinosaurs created an opportunity for mammals. There was an explosion in activity as evolution accelerated, but at a rate that was much faster than before the meteorite.

When nature created an ape that talked, we saw another type of evolution: a cultural/technology evolution, and ever since then, change in culture and technology has accelerated.

Now and again, something big happened, and with that, this acceleration accelerated. It happened when our early ancestors learned how to write, which triggered a rush of new innovations. It happened again with the invention of the printing press. In its wake, we saw civil wars, revolutions, and industrial revolutions.

Most recently it happened with the internet and world wide web. It will happen again with augmented and virtual reality, enhanced by artificial intelligence, (AI) new communication channels like nothing we have seen before.

Take a look at the last two or three hundred years, and you will find that there have been a series of industrial revolutions, each one creating a new jerk. Some of these industrial revolutions were followed by an economic boom, a period of rising prosperity. Others were followed by economic hardship, the rise of totalitarian governments, and world war. Sometimes we saw an actual revolution.

This book focuses on what we call the Fifth Industrial Revolution, in which we will experience the acceleration of the fourth industrial revolution that is currently well underway. This acceleration is will be driven by new technological innovations such as Artificial Intelligence (AI), Quantum computers, augmented reality (AR), gene editing, digital evolution and brain to computer interfaces to name a few. The fifth industrial revolution will end up with technology that augments us. For the first time we will be truly different from the ape that bestrode the plains of Africa 70,000 years ago and then conquered the world.

That's why we are all living in the age of the jerk.

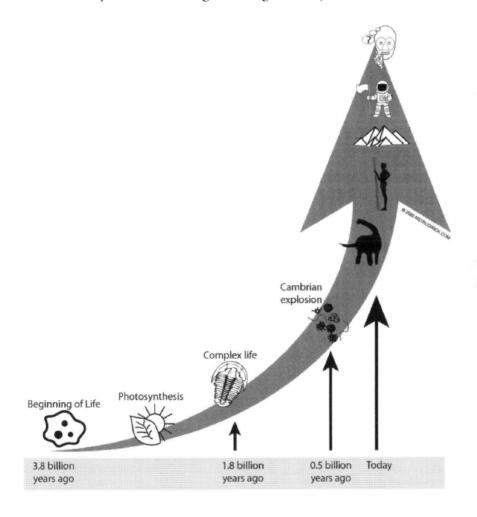

"We shall escape the absurdity of growing a whole chicken in order to eat the breast or wing, by growing these parts separately under a suitable medium. Synthetic food will, of course, also be used in the future. Nor need the pleasures of the table be banished. The new foods will be practically indistinguishable from the natural products from the outset, and any changes will be so gradual as to escape observation." – **Winston Churchill, The Strand Magazine 1931**

For many ages to come, the old Adam will be so strong in us that everybody will need to do some work if he is to be contented. We shall do more things for ourselves than is usual with the rich to- day, only too glad to have small duties and tasks and routines. But beyond this, we shall endeavour to spread the bread thin on the butter-to make what work there is still to be done to be as widely shared as possible. Three-hour shifts or a fifteen-hour week may put off the problem for a great while. For three hours a day is quite enough to satisfy the old Adam in most of us! – **John Maynard Keynes, Economic Possibilities for our Grandchildren (1930)**

The power of exponential

Put an imaginary grain of rice on a metaphorical chessboard. Then two on the second square, four on the third, eight on the fourth, etcetera. By the end of the first row, you will have 256 grains. By the end of row two 64,000 grains, and by the end of the chessboard you will have 18,446,744,07 3,709,551,616 grains.

That is when it gets interesting. Because if you were to then grab a second metaphorical chessboard, by the middle of the first row of the second chessboard, you would need a container the size of the Earth to contain all the rice. By the third row of the second chessboard, you would need a container one cubic light-second in size.

By the end of the fourth row of the fifth chessboard, you would need a container the size of the observable universe, and a few squares later a container the size of the universe.

Now imagine a computer that doubles in power every six to twelve months. With quantum computers, this exponential rate may even increase. Imagine that!

"The Pentium IIs we used in the first year of Google performed about 100 million floating point operations per second. The GPUs we use today perform about twenty trillion such operations –a factor of about 200,000 difference – and our very own TPUs are now capable of 180 trillion (180,000,000,000,000) floating point operations per second. If we are successful with our 72-qubit prototype, it would take millions of conventional computers to be able to emulate it. A 333-qubit error-corrected quantum computer would live up to our name, offering a 10,000,000, 000,000,000,000,000,000,000,000,00 0,000,000,000,000,000, 000,000,000,000,000,000,000,000,000,00 0,000,000,000,000, 000,000,000 times speedup." – **Sergey Brin, co-founder of Google, 2017 founders' letter.**

What is technology?

"Technology is understood to consist of the principles, processes, and nomenclatures of the more conspicuous arts, particularly those which involve applications of science, and which may be considered useful, by promoting the benefit of society, together with the emolument of those who pursue them," -Jacob Bigelow, Elements of Technology, 1829.

"Technology includes all tools, machines, utensils, weapons, instruments, housing, clothing, communicating and transporting devices and the skills by which we produce and use them." -Read Bain, 1937

"The ability to imitate and use tools is something that started among monkeys but has been brought to a much greater level among the apes. And those two talents were ultimately to lead to the transformation of the world" -David Attenborough, Life of Mammals

"Technology refers to methods, systems, and devices which are the result of scientific knowledge being used for practical purposes." -Collins Dictionary

"Technology is the reason most of us are alive to complain about technology" - Gary Kasparov

Prologue

Technology liberates, and it enslaves. It can create inequality leading to social unrest, fashioning the conditions that lead to the rise of fascism, but it can also enlighten and reduce poverty.

Occasionally, in the story of humanity, something remarkable happens, and it changes the world. The change is not always for the better, but it is undoubtedly dramatic. Such changes are rare, indeed. During the lifetime of most readers of this book, we won't merely see a single development that will profoundly transform the world. Instead, we will see many.

Consider the checklist of such breakthroughs seen in the past – learning how to make fire, development of agriculture, the discovery of electricity and how to harness it. Maybe we could include the discovery of penicillin in this list. Other innovations have been catalysts, for change for example, the invention of writing, or the printing press. You may be able to think of a few more examples, but there are not many.

The latter years of the 20th Century saw another – the Internet. The technology itself didn't physically produce much utility – not like fire or electricity, but just like the invention of writing and the printing press, it spreads ideas, it mixes them and enables change.

If the printing press was the catalyst of religious and industrial reform, leading not only to industrial revolutions, but bloody revolutions too, the internet is having an even more profound impact. What is so remarkable about the age we are living in is that we are set to see several advances, each on its own sufficient to create seismic change.

There is artificial intelligence (AI), genome sequencing, a DNA editing tool known as CRISPR/cas9, quantum computing, augmented and virtual reality, stem cell research and nanotechnology. Applications that are emerging include real-time language translation, AI-based personal assistants that will support us, augment us, challenge us and maybe nudge us. Other technologies relating to neural science may actually enhance our brain. They provide interfaces directly from brain to computer, or even read our minds and they may have an even more profound impact.

What are the implications? They are as far-reaching as you can imagine.

The Covid-effect

Without the Covid-19 crisis, both the public and private sector were going to adopt the revolutionary digital technologies. However, there were barriers to this adoption. Public attitudes were often cautious, driven by a fear of change, a desire to protect the known. Businesses, often encumbered with a legacy of processes that were hard to change, were being dragged into this new technology age. [1]

Covid-19 and lockdowns have forced these changes upon us more rapidly. Many people have found these technology changes not as onerous as anticipated. Remote working has been tried at scale – and for its users, it was not as bad as expected. Virtual meetings and even virtual conferences have become everyday routine – and many have been surprised by how painless this way of working is. Others have been forced to apply more automation – it will be hard to reverse this change. More consumers bought products online and found themselves asking why they hadn't done this before. Families and friends, unable to meet in person, experienced online video communication – they had no idea how fun it would be.

There is another side to the crisis. The virus discriminated – it seemed to be more deadly to people from poorer backgrounds, poorer health and across much of the West to people of ethnic minorities. [2]

---

[1] *Xiao and Fan*
[2] *Public Health England, Beyond the data: Understanding the impact of COVID-19 on BAME groups*

The crisis also highlighted how the workers who provide essential services are often poorly paid. It became clear that many roles that pay high salaries were of far less social importance.

The economic hit created by Covid-19 may exacerbate inequality even further.

The role of technology

History shows, what to many people is intuitively apparent, that technology creates wealth. Before the era of industrial revolutions that began between 200 and 300 years ago, economic growth per person was tiny. Before these revolutions, most people lived in a kind of grinding poverty. The era of industrial revolutions was accompanied by massive increases in population, but income per person grew even faster. GDP per capita in 1760 was roughly $1,803 measured in 1992 purchasing power. GDP per capita in the UK today is roughly nine-times higher than in 1760 after allowing for inflation.[3] [4]

But the impact of these industrial revolutions was not always benign.[5] It seems that the 19th Century saw increased inequality and the benefits from technology did not always trickle down into improved wealth, and indeed health, for ordinary folk.

Other technologies such as the printing press sowed the spread of ideas – propelled innovation and probably culture. The printing press is regarded as a critical driver of the Renaissance as well as new religious beliefs.[6]

But while the outcomes of this spread of ideas were often positive, it also led (for better or worse) to revolutions and conflict, both within and between nations.

New technologies may have been key drivers in leading to the world wars of the 20th Century. New technologies certainly made the world seem like a smaller place and conflicts that may have been

---

[3] *Roderick Floud, Paul Johnson, The Cambridge Economic History of Modern Britain: Volume 1*
[4] *Max Roser, GDP per capita in England*
[5] *Graeme Snooks, Was the Industrial Revolution Necessary?*
[6] *Rita Santillan, The effect of the printing press in the Renaissance in the 15th century, Italy*

regional in the past have scaled and become global. Technology has also fashioned terrifying new weapons.

The most significant age of innovation experienced to date ended around 1914.[7] With it, an age sometimes called the first age of globalisation ended too.[8] In the aftermath of the First World War, the world drew in on itself. The Treaty of Versailles was based on the principle that Germany must pay for its role in the war. Global institutions such as the League of Nations were given limited support. The US, for example, never joined. Nor did many other major globally significant players. In 1929, the Wall Street crash heralded the start of the Great Depression in the US. In 1930, the US introduced the Smoot Hawley Tariff Act,[9] which imposed tariffs on 20,000 goods imported into the US.

The world reacted to the challenges of the post First World War era by engaging in self-defeating behaviour. Although fascism took root in Germany and Italy with disastrous consequences, it drew popular support across much of the world, including the UK and US. And the world experienced its Second World War.

After the Second World War, the Marshall Plan provided enormous economic support to war-ravaged Europe, especially Germany. It was the antithesis of the Treaty of Versailles

Other international institutions such as the European Coal and Steel Community, (forerunner of the EU), the UN and the General Agreement on Tariffs and Trade (GATT)), the predecessor of the WTO were formed, and The Universal Declaration of Human Rights was agreed. The WHO can trace its origins back to before this time, but it wasn't until after the Second World War that it became more influential.

These international bodies helped create stability. The significant innovations of Victorian Times and of the early 20th Century finally began to be fully utilised, and the so-called advanced world enjoyed its strongest quarter of a century of growth ever recorded. Inequality fell too.

---

[7] *Smil, Vaclav. Creating the Twentieth Century: Technical*
[8] *Stephen D King, Grave new world*
[9] *The battle of Smoot-Hawle: The Economist*

When, by the mid-1970s, the West had finally managed to fulfil most of the potential productivity created by the innovations of the past, economic growth slowed, inequality increased, and politics shifted towards the right.

Then in 2008, the global economy saw a crash that brought back memories of 1929. Many feared a repeat of the disaster that was the 1930s. This fate was avoided, but only to an extent, as economic policymakers papered over the cracks that had been emerging since the mid-1970s. Central banks reacted to a crisis that was caused by too much debt, by cutting interest rates, leading to more debt. The issue of inequality was not dealt with and has grown deeper over the last decade. Widespread anger has grown with it. When the Second World War came to an end, the response was different. Politicians and their advisors developed ideas that applied the lessons of Post First World War. In 1944, at Bretton Woods, a new international economic framework was conceived. It created a system for managing international trade and the flow of money, and the IMF and World Bank were formed.

Before the Covid crisis, the authors already feared a possible return of fascism, especially if new technologies were allowed to develop in such a way as to create even more inequality.

The Covid crisis has exacerbated this danger.

We are also witnessing a backlash against globalisation, a growing view that China must be made to pay, bringing back memories of the Treaty of Versailles, the undermining of global institutions such as WHO, WTO and EU and a growing protectionist sentiment.

Such movements threaten to repeat the economic nightmare that was the 1930s. The possibility of an outcome of social unrest and conflict should be terrifying.

Other Threats

The occurrence of viruses spreading across the world, claiming millions of lives, predates modern technologies and modern globalisation by thousands of years. The Black Death is an obvious example – responsible for 200 million deaths at a time when the global population was a fraction of the current size.

And such viruses can spread from West to East or vice versa, or indeed from West and then around the world. The reason, for example, why both Cortes and Pizarro were able to respectfully conquer the Aztecs and Incas, each with a small band of men, was in large part due to the spread of Smallpox and Measles brought in by the Europeans[10]

If you want to look for something or someone to blame for viruses spreading out, claiming vast numbers of lives, blame the invention of agriculture seven or so thousand years ago, which led to a closer mingling of people and animals and was also associated with rapidly growing human populations. Before agriculture, we were typically healthier (we were undoubtedly taller), but because hunter-gatherers societies are quite good at limiting population growth, they have often been conquered by agricultural communities primarily because of their greater numerosity.

Today, climate change and population growth pressures mean that humans and the rest of the animal kingdom are encroaching on each other's turf, creating strains that foster the evolution of new diseases. As a consequence of this, Covid-19 is just one example of a Coronavirus that has spread globally this Century – both SARS and MERS, being other examples.

And more will follow. The Covid-19 outbreak was not a once in 100-year event. It was the first event of that scale in 100 years but is likely to be followed by many more such occurrences.

Yet, new Coronaviruses do not pose the greatest disease-related threats to humanity during this half of the 21st Century. We have been busily enabling more dangerous threats from bugs caused by over-use of antibiotics.

It has been estimated that the accidental discovery of penicillin in 1928 by Alexander Fleming saved between 80 million and 200 million lives.[11]

Subsequent overuse of antibiotics, especially its indiscriminate use within agriculture, threatens to destroy their effectiveness, and given that the entire global population today is over seven billion, meaning as many people are vulnerable to superbugs, the loss of such effectiveness could claim hundreds of millions of lives.

---

[10] Jared Diamond: Guns, Germs and Steel
[11] *Bacteria in Photos,*

Technology and globalisation provide the fix

However, the end of effective antibiotics does not represent the biggest threat to humanity this century.

We should consider climate change, over fishing, plastic pollution; the list is long

However, it is technology which poses the greatest long-term threat, because it is changing so fast – accelerating at an accelerating rate, jerking – disrupting all in its path risking a dystopian world, the stuff of nightmares.

Although rapidly changing technology poses enormous risks, it also represents an extraordinary opportunity.

Technologies such as renewable energy, energy storage and new ways to create food using less land and water can simultaneously allow us to defeat climate change whilst creating an age of plenty – where no one should experience poverty.

Technologies provides our only hope of winning the war against disease.

The good news is that technologies are developing that can indeed win these wars. But the advancement of such technologies requires global cooperation. China, for example, is becoming a key player in the development of technology. A Chinese company is working on a battery for an electric car that could have a lifetime of 100 million miles.[12] Chinese companies are also radically transforming the solar power industry,[13] while in the field of healthcare, Chinese companies are collaborating with firms from both East and West to create new antibiotics or alternative treatments to superbugs.[14]

If we were to attempt to ostracise China from the global economy, as we did with Germany, post First World War, we are very likely to punish ourselves. But for technology to benefit us all, we need globalisation for another reason. Technology advances often follow a course known as a learning rate – as total production of a technology increases its cost falls, and its sophistication advances.

---

[12] *Bloomberg News, Chinese giant that powers Tesla says it has million-mile electric-car battery ready to launch*

[13] *Charlotte Edmond, China's lead in the global solar race - at a glance*

[14] *Michael Berger, An alternative to antibiotics - weakening superbugs' grip*

To understand a learning rate, we can turn to an American aeronautical engineer of the early 20th Century, Theodore Paul Wright. To cite, Ramez Naam, an expert on the disruptive compact of renewables, "Wright observed that every doubling of production of US aircraft brought down prices by 13%." [15]

This is known as Wright's Law.

Computer power advances, the falling cost of energy renewables and storage and genome sequencing are all experiencing learning rates. With computer processing power, the learning rate is also called Moore's Law. Learning rates apply in other areas – such as stem cell research or editing DNA. The greater the size of the market for these technologies, the greater the scope for the learning rate to make the technologies affordable for ordinary people.

We need a global market for technologies in order to make them at scale. To defeat climate change and hunger and plastic pollution, we need a global market for the technologies that can help us achieve these victories.

This is global market that must include China, especially as it seems set to become the largest economy in the world.

The Danger of Groupthink

The internet and burgeoning communication technologies such as virtual and augmented reality supported by AI, could eventually enlighten us and bring us closer together.

But they carry risks too. Among those risks are groupthink and linked to that group polarization. [16]

All of us are inclined to comply with the group that we attach ourselves too. Our inbuilt biases mean we latch onto ideas that support preconceived notions. When these tendencies are multiplied out across large numbers of people, we get groupthink.

Groups can behave like they have a kind of collective conscience (they don't, but it is as if they do.) Group polarisation occurs when a group exaggerates the views of a majority – for example, a group of people who are, on an individual basis, mildly inclined to take

---

[15] Naam, Ramaz: How to decarbonize America
[16] *Stone, James A. F.; Risky and cautious shifts in group decisions*

the odd calculated risk, can become reckless in the extreme. New communication technologies will exaggerate this risk further still.

We need education that can teach us how to make technology enhance us, become a purveyor of factual information and enlighten us. We also need education to teach us how to rise above groupthink so that it does not corrupt us. Group dynamics can create great insights, but they can be enormously dangerous. In the past, groupthink has fostered intolerance, the rise of fascism and conflict.

Wisdom of the crowds

While groupthink can be dangerous, crowds can also be extraordinarily clever and wise.

We recommend that the solution to the challenges described here require the wisdom of crowds.

But a pivotal prerequisite to creating a wise crowd and not one riddled with dangerous groupthink is diversity.

We don't only need a wise crowd; we need a gender, racially and culturally diverse crowd.

The issues described in this book are just about the most important questions there are.

And these are way too important for us to leave it to the politicians, academics and entrepreneurs to figure out a response, a solution.

If we play this right, we could be no more than a few decades from living in a form of utopia.

We could return to a kind of Eden, a digital Eden, and realise the advantages that were ours before agriculture changed us, but combine it with technology too, and see extra benefits. However, if we play it wrong, dystopia beckons.

And all of us must engage in the debate. We must take ownership of our future and that of future generations. It is the most critical debate there will ever be, and the answer does not solely lie with academics, or intellectuals, or all the people who frequent the Annual World Economic Forum at Davos for example, who consider themselves to be deep thinkers.

The responsibility lies with us all; the wisdom of the crowd holds the answer. That means you and me.

Part 1

The Jerk

Chapter 1

Five industrial revolutions, creative destruction and the threat of fascism

Could anyone have imagined that 13 years after its launch, the touchscreen smartphone would be engaged as a vital weapon in the war against a virus?

When Steve Jobs revealed the iPhone, he gave one of the most talked-about business presentations in history. Even so, he understated the significance of the product that he revealed on that day in history.

It was 9th January, 2007, and Steve Jobs strutted on stage. Too much fanfare, he teased his audience. He claimed that Apple had produced three revolutionary products, a widescreen iPod, a revolutionary mobile phone and a breakthrough internet communications device, only to then reveal that the three products were, in fact, one and the same: a product called the iPhone.

Yet the super salesman under-sold. The smartphone has profoundly changed us: the human brain now has three forms of memory: short-term memory, long-term memory, and the entire knowledge of humanity, accessed via what was once called a 'breakthrough communications device.'

The smartphone, whatever guise it wears – Apple, Samsung or some other brand, has augmented us. Our brains are no longer limited by the tools which nature gave us. Instead, nearly all of us are just a few seconds away from accessing the entire knowledge of humanity.

23

Furthermore, the speed with which we download information will increase such that it will eventually reduce so that it is virtually instantaneous – it will be as if our personal internet connection device has become an extension of our brain.

And during the Covid-19 crisis in 2020, the smartphone, along with social media, became weapons against the virus. They supported communication, and they helped reinforce the message of social distancing. For better or worse, authorities also used these technologies to track our movements to see who had been in contact with someone who had tested positive, tracing the patient-zero.

We can thank technology because if Covid-19 had emerged in the year 2000, the fight against it would have been much harder to win.

Our species is called Homo sapiens sapiens: it's an odd description, it means wise wise man. It distinguishes us from other human species now extinct, such as Homo sapiens neanderthalensis. Thanks to the smartphone and technologies to follow, a case could be made to say we are on the verge of becoming a new species,[17] a species quite different from the creature evolution designed[18] to be a social animal that hunted and gathered for a living and used its brain to collaborate with a small number of others.

It is as if we hold in the palm of our hand a device of knowledge: one internet-communications device, to rule them all. Never before have we known so much. Never before have we been so wise.

It is as if we are becoming Ipsum Homo sapiens (very wise man)!!!

Or you could say that smartphones have shortened attention spans, that they have made us less social, less empathetic, and indeed less moral, like we have all become versions of Tolkien's Gollum. Even when we don't have our smartphone with us, we might wistfully imagine it in our hands, stroking it gently.

Maybe it is worse than that. Arguably smartphones have created a nasty new breed of social deviant — keyboard warriors and trolls, and via its filter bubble, has increased bias; it has even helped create the recent surge in populism. What impact will the next generation

---

[17] Not new in the sense of changes to DNA, we won't have mutated in the evolutionary sense, but we will be artificially physically different, no longer simply human, but augmented human

[18] Metaphorically speaking evolution designed

of technology have when such technology changes us far more than smartphones have done?

That's the point about technology. It could be a tool to create a new, self-aware, wise, thoughtful and rational version of ourselves. It could amplify our connections with others to allow us to become more social and by increasing understanding, more empathetic. We would become not so much very wise humans, as augmented, compassionate and very wise humans: Homo augebatur, miserator, ipsum sapiens.

Or it could be a weapon of our undoing.

But there is one piece of economic irony associated with the iPhone and other digital services and devices; they may have changed us, but they have done very little for so-called mature economies – on aggregate.

The iPhone, phones based on Android operating systems and the Kindle were all launched in 2007. Facebook and Twitter became established as global forces at about the same time, as did the emergence of Uber and Airbnb. Yet the period since has been awful for economic expansion in most mature economies.

And the one metric that matters more than anything else for enabling economic growth, productivity, has seen an abysmal performance within all OECD economies since the financial crash of 2008.

Despite their wondrous nature, smartphones and related technologies appear to have had little macroeconomic significance.

Time lags and creative destruction

One of the lessons of advances in technology in the past has been time lags. The interval between innovation and positive economic consequences can be long. Indeed, the most significant period of innovation ever seen to date did lead to an economic boom, but only after a time lag of around 30 years, with the intervening years witnessing the rise of fascism.

Sometimes, however, another factor is vital to support the adoption of technology. The lesson of history appears to show, that technology adoption can be held back by a kind of inertia – a rigid structure to society, business, regulations, the economy and people's attitudes, that can hinder the advance of technology. We will return to this idea shortly.

Inequality

Rapid periods of innovation can be associated with a rise in inequality. This can sometimes have an adverse effect. Not only can rising inequality lead to social unrest, but it can also suck aggregate demand out of the economy, thereby starving the economy of the metaphorical oxygen that it needs to grow. Over time, rising inequality is not only negative for the poorest; it can, counter to intuition, be negative for the richest, too.

The five revolutions

If you exclude the industrial revolutions of ancient history and indeed pre-history, with, for example, the Bronze and Iron ages, you could say that there have been three industrial revolutions so far, and we are at the beginning of the fourth. The greatest one of all – the one that really will transform us – the fifth industrial revolution, has also already begun in a small way. But its full impact is yet to unravel.

It's the impact of this fifth industrial revolution, which provides such extraordinary promise, while simultaneously threatens such danger within the next couple of decades, during the lifetime of most readers of this book, which is the main topic of the scribblings contained here.

 The first industrial revolution began in the early to mid-1700s, around 1760, involved a revolution in the textile industry, perhaps starting with a device called the Spinning Jenny and the beginning of the steam age.

The second industrial revolution was probably the greatest of the revolutions yet witnessed. Vaclav Smil,[19] (a man Bill Gates describes as one of his favourite authors) defines this period as the age of symmetry. A period that lasted from 1867 to 1914. It began

---

[19] *Creating the Twentieth Century: Technical Innovations of 1867- 1914 and Their Lasting Impact (Technical Revolutions and Their Lasting Impact) Hardcover – 29 Sep 2005 by Vaclav Smil*

with the invention of dynamite, was swiftly followed by
the telephone and photographic film. The 1880s saw the
first electricity- generating plants, electric motors, steam
turbines, the gramophone, cars, aluminium production,
air-filled rubber tyres and pre-stressed concrete. The early
1900s saw the first aeroplanes, tractors, radio signals and plastics, neon
lights and assembly line production.

The third industrial revolution was about information technology
(IT) – occurring during the 1980s and 1990s, culminating in the
realisation of Bill Gates' dream of a PC on every desk.

The fourth industrial revolution can also be described
as the Age of Automation. It is not easy to say when the
third industrial revolution ended, and the fourth began. It
may not be unreasonable to say that the fourth industrial
revolution began with the emergence of broadband internet access four
years or so into this century. But it is being charged by data, robotic
process automation, artificial intelligence, robotics, the internet of
things, virtual and augmented reality and additive
manufacturing. PwC has projected that artificial
intelligence will boost the global economy by just
over $15.7 trillion a year by 2030, more than the
output of India and China combined. A consultancy
called McKinsey has predicted that the internet of things will have an
economic impact of between $3.7 trillion and $11.1 trillion a year
by 2025. These are big numbers. If they prove prophetic, the global
economy could be on the verge of experiencing one of its strongest
periods of growth ever. But maybe this resulting economic boom won't
be felt for a few years. After all, to emphasise a critical point, there are
often time lags.

The fifth industrial revolution will be extraordinary;
it is the Augmentation Revolution. It will involve the
creation of new ways of doing things, and it will change
us and transform us, for better or worse. That is why we
say that the fifth industrial revolution has already begun because the
smartphone is already augmenting us.

What's different about the augmentation revolution?

The first, third and fourth industrial revolutions created (or are creating) new ways of producing the things we already use.[20]

By contrast, the second industrial revolution created new consumer products — electric lights, motor cars, aeroplanes, the telephone and radio, for example. It did not so much revolutionise the way we produce products as introduce a new way of living.

Some economists argue that the technology change we see as this book is written is not going to prove to be as transformative as technology change seen in the past. They are too hasty, apparently ignoring the issue of time lags between innovation and wealth creation, but in a way, they may be partially right.

However, dramatic the fourth industrial revolution will be, it will not be as transformative as the second industrial revolution.

The fifth industrial revolution, the augmentation revolution, will be more like the second revolution, but its impact will be more significant still.

In time, AI will become more powerful. It will eventually build on data, and via sophisticated computer models help test and experiment rapidly, creating new cures and treatments for diseases. Likewise, nanotechnology will create revolutionary new medical treatments. It may also create clothes that never need washing or are virtually indestructible. Stem cell research may make it possible to produce meat, bypassing the environmentally disastrous business of rearing and then slaughtering animals. A new super material called graphene will create new, super strong and flexible products. Genome sequencing will create new revelations in medicine. CRISPR/cas9 is

---

[20] *Textiles were made more efficiently, office administration and business communication were made more efficient by computers, and the fourth industrial revolution will transform the way we produce goods and services, automating processes that previously had to be carried out by humans. Apps such as Airbnb are more efficiently marrying the forces of supply and demand, making more efficient use of existing resource. In the case of health tech, the fourth revolution will provide access to a wealth of information leading to the diagnosis of diseases and recommended appropriate treatments much more efficiently.*

enabling the ability to edit DNA, potentially making us healthier, and longer-lived, or manipulate the DNA of say, mosquitoes so that they no longer spread malaria. Augmented Reality (AR) and Virtual Reality (VR) could transform that most human of characteristics, the way we communicate, uniting us in a way that is currently impossible. Neural technologies will enhance our brains, while prosthetics and other implants may enhance our bodies.

This revolution began with the smartphone because this was the first device to augment us, but its extreme outcomes will occur afterwards. Indeed, some of the innovations of the fourth industrial revolution, such as AI, will make some of the more astonishing innovations of the fifth possible.

Like Beethoven's fifth symphony, the fifth industrial revolution began strongly with the iPhone, but could, if we play it right, unite humanity, in the way Beethoven dreamed with his ninth symphony.

The fifth industrial revolution could transform us into very wise, empathetic, augmented humans, or Hom augebatur, miserator, ipsum sapiens, or Homo sapiens augmented for short, or make us as extinct as our former cousins, Homo sapiens neanderthalensis.

The jerk, the negative jerk, fascism and prosperity

There are occasions when technology change occurs at a breathless pace. It happened in the eighteenth and nineteenth centuries with the first industrial revolution and then again in the second half of the nineteenth century and early twentieth, with the second industrial revolution. These periods saw such rapid change that it seems that technology didn't merely accelerate; it accelerated at an accelerating rate – it jerked.

It is jerking again today with the fourth industrial revolution and will do so again with the fifth industrial revolution – we are living in the age of the jerk.

Indeed, so rapid will the rate of technology change be in the next few years, that a case could be made for saying that even the jerk is accelerating — what is known as a snap.[21] Or maybe we can say the

---

[21] Acceleration of acceleration is a jerk. Acceleration of acceleration of acceleration is called a snap. Acceleration of acceleration of acceleration of acceleration is

fifth industrial revolution is the consequence of the jerk that the fourth industrial revolution created.

There are other occasions when we might see a rapid de- acceleration in technology change, a negative jerk.

Some commentators and observers can be fooled by the negative jerk. They proclaim the end of technological change as if the negative jerk that they are witnessing will last forever.

There is an added complication.

Imagine you are staying in a hotel with an unfamiliar shower. You turn the taps on, feel the temperature and jump in. But it has not fully heated up, and a few seconds later you screech, 'It's too hot.' You turn the hot tap down and the cold tap up. It seems about right, but then it takes time for the adjustments to work, the shower is then too cold. When there are time lags like this, it gets complicated.

While the broad sweep of history points to an acceleration in change, the rotation from positive to negative jerk is just a part of the technology cycle. Even so, politicians, economists and the markets are often fooled. Furthermore, unlike in the shower analogy, they can't simply switch off the water!

Take as an example; the combined effect of the first an second industrial revolutions. On a per-person basis, the western economy barely grew at all from the collapse of the Roman Empire to around 1820. This began to change in the aftermath of the first industrial revolution.

The industrial revolutions were surely the catalyst that made such growth possible.

Yet there is something odd, economic growth per capita didn't become significant until after the first industrial revolution had time to unwind.

But the time lag between the second industrial revolution, the greatest industrial revolution seen to date, and the resulting economic boom, was around 30 years. (Slightly shorter in the US.) The second industrial revolution was, however, followed by a world war, economic crises combined with growing inequality and then another world war.

---

called a crackle. And acceleration of acceleration of acceleration of acceleration of acceleration is called a pop.

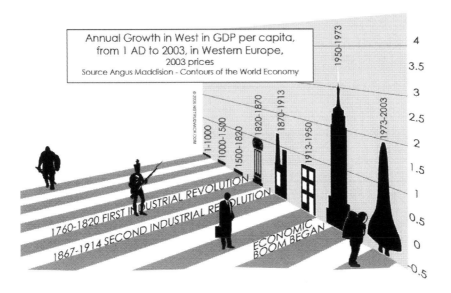

Annual Growth in West in GDP per capita, from 1 AD to 2003, in Western Europe, 2003 prices
Source Angus Maddision - Contours of the World Economy

Growth in GDP per capita, in per cent, Western Europe, US,
Source Angus Maddison, Contours of the World Economy 1-2030 AD, page 383

	Western Europe	US	World
1-1000 AD	-0.03	-	0.00
1000- 1500 AD	0.12	-	0.05
1500-1820	0.14	0.36	0.05
1820-1870	0.98	1.34	0.54
1870-1913	1.33	1.82	1.31
1913-1950	0.76	1.61	0.88
1950-1973	4.05	2.45	2.91
1973-2003	1.87	1.86	1.56

Creative Destruction

Sometimes, change is difficult. For it to occur, on occasions there first needs to be a shock.

The economist Joseph Schumpeter coined the phrase creative destruction, although he used it in a different context.[22]

To understand what we mean in the context here, consider the dinosaurs. They had ruled the world for 150 million years, but by the standards of the last 60 million years, changed very slowly.

Then a meteorite wiped them out. This created a vacuum, a gap in the market, which the mammals filled. There then followed a period of extraordinary change. The great variety of mammals we know today, the whale, and aardvark, the hippopotamus and kangaroo, the elephant and the mouse, the rat and the human, came about after the extinction of the dinosaurs

In the world of technology, the steam train revolution began in the UK, but the early railway engineers chose a four-foot eight-inch railway gauge. Later, the great engineer Isambard Kingdom Brunel tried to introduce a superior seven-foot gauge, but it was too late. The four-foot gauge was too advanced at this stage, and the UK has been left with this inferior system ever since.

Or take the QWERTY keyboard, developed to slow down typists so that the keys didn't become wedged together as they moved to strike the paper. Now we are stuck with this rather odd keyboard layout, maybe forever.

The adoption of new technologies can be held back for a similar reason. Resistant to change, cultural attitudes, fear of the new can all combine to slow up the full adoption of new technology.

It is perhaps no coincidence, the first period of significant growth in GDP per capita in the UK, didn't coincide with the first industrial revolution, but rather began soon after the Napoleonic Wars.

---

[22] Schumpeter had the relationship the other way around from how we are describing it here. He thought that innovative new companies emerge with new ideas leading to the destruction of older companies. We are talking about something quite different; destruction creates a vacuum into which new ideas and companies can flourish.

Likewise, the Second World War may have provided sufficient creative destruction to enable Europe to finally learn how to utilise the innovations of the second industrial revolution.

It is not a perfect theory, but the creative destruction that came with such periods could have been a factor in creating space to convert great technological breakthroughs into greater prosperity across an economy.

As outlined in the prologue, the Covid-19 crisis may play a similar role in allowing the innovation of the fourth industrial revolution to gain faster and broader adoption.

If there had been no Covid-19 crisis, the fourth and fifth industrial revolutions would have occurred and changed the world anyway.

But there has been a Covid-19 crisis. As a result, these revolutions are likely to occur even more quickly than would otherwise have happened.

Time lags in history

The idea of time lags between innovation and economic outcomes is important. Let us dwell on this concept for a little bit longer.

In 1987, the Nobel Prize winning economist Robert Solow famously said: "Computers are everywhere but in the productivity numbers." He was speaking at a time when the computer revolution was apparently in full flight, yet its impact on the economy was apparently undetectable.

Far be it for us to disagree with someone as brilliant as Robert Solow, and perhaps he was deliberately provocative — but he was too hasty. Productivity did indeed surge, but a few years later. It simply took time for the computer revolution to create economic growth.

It was not a new lesson. If, in 1820, an economist of Solow's stature, could have acquired data on GDP, he might have said: "The first industrial revolution is everywhere but in the economic statistics." But the economic boom did follow, indeed, for the first time in at least 2,000 years, GDP per capita began to rise sharply in the West just as the first industrial revolution was drawing to an end. [23]

---

[23] In a way this did happen. Thomas Malthus argued something similar to that point in 1798.

In 1935, an economist might have made a similar comment. They might have observed that the much- trumpeted second industrial revolution, the one that created such remarkable technology as the motor car, flight, assembly-line production and mass availability of electricity, was followed by a quarter of a century of economic and social strife.

Indeed, one economist did.

The economist Alvin Harrison wrote: "Population growth is fading. There are no new territories to settle and exploit. We can only hope for more technological advancement, so don't do anything to hamper this last great hope of ours. Except that it seems that we are: the growing power of trade unions, trade associations, and other monopolistic practices are restricting technological advance. This is a great folly."[24]

And there you have it. A period of wondrous innovation had yet to make its full mark upon the world – and yet an economist lamented the lack of innovation. He had misdiagnosed the problem.

Harrison's explanation for the economic disaster of his time is known as secular stagnation. This is a theory that has come back into fashion in modern times.

The first two industrial revolutions, fascism and boom

The first industrial revolution was remarkable, but at first, its full benefit did not trickle down into boosting wages for the general public.

We know this because records from the British army show that in the mid-years of the nineteenth century, the average height of recruits, a proxy for diet in childhood, fell.[25]

---

[24]

[25] *Health and Welfare during Industrialization Volume Author/Editor: Richard H. Steckel and Roderick Floud,*

Did technology make us shorter?

Time lags, new technology does not always make us healthier. Army records show that average male height (a proxy for health) in the british army reduced during the decades after the first industrial revolution, before the benefits of technology innovation kicked in.

68 in

67 in

66 in

65 in

64 in

63 in

62 in

1742 1752 1762 1772 1782 1792 1802 1812 1822 1832 1842 1852 1862

Other studies show that during the early stages of this revolution, factory owners had a kind of monopoly power in their local labour market. Profits rose, but wages did not rise so fast.[26]

As a consequence, economic growth was limited. This changed eventually. Later, in the nineteenth century, wages did begin to rise, as skills acquired by workers at one factory became more transferable, and such workers found they had a stronger wage bargaining position.

---

[26] *James Bessen, for example, argues that during the earlier stages of the first industrial revolution, while productivity rose, wages did not rise in tandem, contrary to what economic theory might predict. It seems that to begin with each factory that applied new technology was quite different to all other factories. They had their unique way of operating and as a result workers found that the skills they developed at one factory were not transferable — workers were taken on with little experience and swiftly trained, meaning that the employer had the upper hand in wage negotiations. This changed after trade associations created better practice, industry became more homogeneous, and skills learnt at one factory became relevant to the next. Greater competition for labour resulted and wages rose — but while employers might have lost their monopolistic power over wages, they were largely better off — productivity rose and profits increased. More to the point, as wages rose across the economy, the market for the goods that factory owners produced also increased in size*

As wages rose, aggregate demand across the economy increased, the economy grew at a faster rate, and as a result, the factory owners themselves could sell more of the goods they produced, becoming wealthier still. In short, factory owners benefited from paying workers more money, because, across the economy, other factory owners behaved similarly, increasing aggregate demand and thus the size of the economy.

In summary: It seems that at first, the first industrial revolution initially only benefited a small minority of society. Only when this changed, and there was a trickle- down effect, which then turned into a cascade of wealth creation, touching a much higher proportion of society, did the economy boom.

That takes us to the second industrial revolution and the curious delay between this revolution and economic boom. How can it make sense that the golden age of growth began more than 30 years after the golden age of innovation ended?

In part, the explanation is that there always are time lags between innovation, its adoption and the eventual impact on the economy. Of course, the occurrence of two world wars didn't help.

Between the two world wars, the Western economy saw an abysmal performance. In Europe, the economic disaster of the 1920s, combined with the legacy of World War One (Treaty of Versailles in particular) may have sowed the seeds for World War Two. In the US, the 1930s saw the Great Depression. The US response to the 1929 crash was the Smoot-Hawley Tariff Act, which imposed tariffs on over 20,000 imported goods into the US. We know that this act exacerbated the weakness of the global economy.

The evil that was fascism grew on both sides of the Atlantic, spilling over with appalling consequences in certain European countries and Japan.

But what were the underlying causes of these often-destructive actions during this period? If you want to argue that the underlying cause was the First World War, then what was the underlying cause of the 1914-1918 war?

Maybe, the true underlying reason for the economic misery of this period is that we had not learned how to convert the wondrous innovations of the second industrial revolution into rising wealth. In particular, it is possible that technology innovation led to rising inequality, starving the global economy of demand, sowing the seeds of social disquiet. It also created weapons that wrought terror, while advances in communication technology and transport created tension between established superpowers such as the UK, and France, newly established superpowers, such as the US, and emerging superpowers such as Germany and Japan. Technology made world war possible.

Why did the economy finally enter a golden age?

After the Second World War the economy, aided by economic stability and prolonged peace, found a way to take greater advantage of the innovations from an earlier age.

The Second World War brought with it social change – a sense that the elites had led us into two world wars, but that it was ordinary people, men fighting on the battlefront, women tending the fields or working in factories at home, who paid the price.

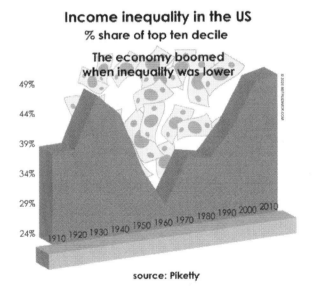

Income inequality in the US
% share of top ten decile

The economy boomed when inequality was lower

source: Piketty

In Britain especially, this created the impetus for the Welfare State, we saw the end of the Downton Abbey economy (named after the popular British television series), the rich were expected to dress themselves. Mobility of employment increased – meaning it became easier for people from a poor background to grow wealth.

After the golden age

This golden age of growth ended in the mid-1970s. Why is this? There is no mystery. The West had simply squeezed out all the economic goodness that was made possible by the second industrial revolution.

The negative jerk in technology that superseded the second industrial revolution finally began to show up in the economic statistics in the 1970s.

When an economy is geared towards creating demand to buy the goods and services that technology has created, such gearing can create a boom if the economy is learning how to make optimal use of existing innovations. When the gap with potential has been closed, such conditions of growing demand no longer create growth. Instead, they create inflation.

Robert Solow, argued that a mature economy could not grow via investment unless there is are new innovations. By the mid- 1970s, the world had become reliant on new innovation. Unfortunately, the technology wasn't, at that point, ready to create a new technology revolution. This was because the next big technology leap, the IT revolution, was not at this stage far enough advanced.

That is why the 1970s and 1980s saw much weaker economic growth and inflation became a major threat to stability. The world needed a new industrial revolution, but it had to wait.

The third industrial revolution needed time

The third industrial revolution was not as radical or far- reaching as the second, but it did give the global economy a boost.

This revolution was powered by IT. But for this revolution to occur, computers needed to be of a sufficient level of sophistication and ability.

Back in 1947, the transistor, the building block of modern computers, was invented, but advances in IT have a speed limit. Moore's Law, which describes how computers double in speed every eighteen months, meant that it took time before computers were of sufficient power to make the IT revolution, the third industrial revolution, possible.

The third industrial revolution only really became possible by the late 1980s; before then, computers were inadequate for mass business adoption. The growing adoption drove economies of scale and subsequently demand.

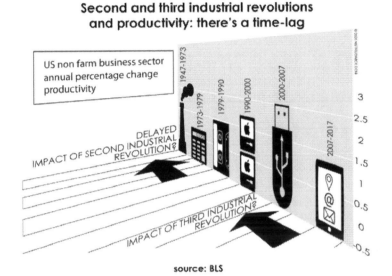

Second and third industrial revolutions and productivity: there's a time-lag

source: BLS

All the other drivers of the economy, of that period, Thatcherism, Reaganomics, neoliberalism, were like flotsam and jetsam, floating on a tide made of innovation, obeying deep forces, charged by the cycle of innovation.

The idea that the third industrial revolution could not have occurred any sooner because it took time for Moore's Law to create the necessary technological advances is important.

Moore's Law is an example of a learning rate, a process that describes advances in technology as a function of the total user base. As the total user base increases, the cost of the technology falls, and often its sophistication advances. As the cost falls, and its application increase, the size of the user base increases. This ties in with Wright's Law, described in the prologue. [27]

Such learning rates may be faster today than in the time of Theodore Wright. However, they still impose a speed limit on the time it takes for innovation to create the practical implementation of that

---

[27] Every doubling of production of US aircraft brought down prices by thirteen per cent.

39

innovation and its mass adoption. That's one of the reasons why a period of innovation does not necessarily coincide with a period of economic boom. It just takes time.

A learning rate also requires as large a potential market as possible. This is one of the reasons why a reversal of globalisation could slow down the speed with which technology advances and could ultimately hamper our attempts to use technology to defeat pandemics.

But we live in the age of the jerk, and the time interval is getting shorter.

The fourth and fifth industrial revolutions are here

And that brings us to today and then tomorrow

The early years of this century saw a curious new development. Inequality had increased during the 1980s and 1990s, as it had done during certain periods in the past. Median wages grew slowly, but ultra-low interest rates pushed up asset prices, such as house prices, encouraging a rise in household borrowing and a fall in household savings. Demand grew, but via debt, rather than higher wages. This proved unsustainable, and the 2008 crash occurred.

Today, as we still struggle with the after-effects of the 2008 crash, while the Fourth Industrial Revolution has yet to unravel fully, we risk repeating the errors of the 1930s.

Interest rates have fallen to exceptionally low levels, this has exacerbated wealth inequality, but the underlying problem of the previous decade, weak growth in wages, has not been fixed.

Dangerous social issues are building.

If the 2008 crash was analogous to the 1929 crash, maybe activities of central banks meant that the years following the 2008 crash were not as disastrous as the 1930s had been in the US. But perhaps ultra-low interest rates disguised the underlying problem, or maybe they delayed the manifestation of these problems. Despite record low- interest rates and the economic policy known as quantitative easing, we still risk repeating the errors of the 1930s, with the return of fascism, the reversal of globalisation and a more inward-looking world.

Making America great again would be an awful lot easier to achieve if the global economy could become great, too.

Now, forward wind the clock another decade. Let's say that by 2030, autonomous cars have converged with the growing sharing-economy driven by our changing lifestyles.

Assume also, that this will mean that we no longer want or need to own cars, and instead we order them on-demand. As a consequence, assume twenty per cent of the current production of cars is sufficient to meet our transport needs. Supposing the internet of things and other innovations such as AI makes more efficient use of our existing resources through better utilisation enabled by technology.

The modem economy thrives on waste – on people buying cars but only using them for five per cent of their time, on clothes that we wear once or twice before discarding, of smartphones which we upgrade every two years, of food which we buy but don't eat.

Supposing technology enables us to reduce waste. Suppose the economy can meet our needs with say half the resource we currently expect to use. That seems like a dream scenario for environmentalists, but such circumstances could lead to economic crises. We would risk an economic depression, because the macroeconomic effects of a society needing fewer cars, fewer computer upgrades and fewer clothes, generating less waste, could mean massive job losses.

It's not automation that threatens job losses. Indeed automation may make jobs more enjoyable. Rather it is the macroeconomic shocks that might come from an economy that operates more efficiently, that threatens jobs.

If the unusual circumstances of the first two decades of this century have created political turmoil, imagine the impact of the above conditions described above!

There is a fix.

If fewer resources are required to meet our needs, then the cost of providing these resources will fall. This will mean either very modest inflation or negative inflation. Interest rates are likely to stay close to zero, or even go below it. Governments could pump demand into the economy via programmes such as universal basic income, universal basic services, or tax cuts or grow employment through large infrastructure investment.

They could fund such a stimulus by borrowing at zero per cent, or by a kind of souped-up version of quantitative easing, sometimes called people's QE, funding these policies via the creation of money.

41

Alternatively, an approach known as modern monetary theory – when governments fund spending via the virtual money printing press and introduce taxes if inflation begins to emerge, may be required.

Such policies may not be appropriate today. Indeed, there is danger in implementing them too soon, but to avoid a full return of fascism at a time of rapid innovation, they may be appropriate within this decade.

It's innovation that makes such policies possible because innovation can create a gap between potential output and demand. Demand can then be stimulated without a significant risk of inflation. The unwinding of the fourth and then fifth industrial revolutions may make such policies essential. We will return to this point.

Chapter 2

The augmented ape

We are still cavemen. . . Or cavewomen. Look beyond our fashionable clothes, our bright dwellings with soft carpets, or even our smart homes with voice activation control, our central heating in the winter, our air conditioning in the summer, our TVs, our smartphones, and our increasingly autonomous cars, we have not really changed!

Our species is perfectly honed to live as hunter- gatherers, probably living in communities of around 148.[28] Evolution was not thinking[29] about houses, central heating, air conditioning, sitting at a desk, or even tending fields, eating chocolate, or potatoes, or drinking milk, or indeed using a computer, when it created us.

How many friends on Facebook, how many followers on Twitter do you have? Or contacts on LinkedIn, how many people do you meet at networking events, or parties? Evolution did not design us to be able to engage with this many people meaningfully.

It did not design us to have access to the wealth of information that nowadays exists on the internet.

Nor did evolution design us to cope with rapid technological change. It is doubtful whether evolution fully equipped us to deal with

---

[28] *According to the anthropologist Robin Dunbar this represents the cognitive limit to how many people we can meaningfully interact with. The idea that we might have several thousand friends on social media is simply not consistent with the cognitive abilities that evolution handed to Homo sapiens sapiens.*

[29] *Metaphorically speaking thinking*

the change that has occurred since we invented agriculture, let alone the extraordinarily rapid change that occurs in the age of the jerk

The critical moment in the story of our species probably occurred when we invented agriculture.[30] Ever since then, we have lived an unnatural life.

A new unit of time: great grandparents

Think in terms of great grandparents.

Approximately twelve great grandparents ago, the Battle of Hastings changed English history, the Vikings reached America, the Great Schism tore the Christian religion in half, the Crusades began. At the same time, in China the first reference to gunpowder was recorded – it was the start of the Middle Ages. Twenty-four great grandparents ago saw the Birth of Christ, and sixty to 120 great grandparents ago saw the point when we became an agricultural species.

Homo sapiens sapiens – that's us, you and I – are around 2,000 great grandparents old.

Roughly speaking, for 97 per cent of our existence, we have hunted for a living. It sounds cliched, but we also gathered from the ground or from vegetation. We lived in communities of around 148 people, and for entertainment, we probably congregated around a fire, telling, or listening to stories. We may look back with prehistoric rose-tinted glasses, but it was a form of Eden.

Before we invented agriculture, it appears we were healthier.[31] At least, the fossil records indicate less disease during this period. Our

---

[30] *Strictly speaking it was multiple event, not a single one*

[31] *The change in our lifestyle that occurred over the years since the invention of agriculture has been associated with many debilitating illnesses, such as rickets, which only shows up in the fossil record during Neolithic times, after the invention of agriculture. According to the WHO, 60 per cent of related factors to individual health and quality of life are correlated to lifestyle. Today, issues such malnutrition, unhealthy diet, smoking, alcohol consuming, drug abuse, stress and so on, are the manifestations of an unhealthy lifestyle where citizens face new challenges. For instance, emerging new technologies such as the internet and virtual communication networks, lead our world to a major challenge that threatens the physical and mental health of individuals. For example, the increasing number of hours we spend using technology is accentuating the advent of ailments such as back ache and repetitive*

backs were less likely to become bent from years of toiling in the fields. We were taller and inequality was less.[32] We also had fewer belongings and we did not own our own home. In some ways, our brains may have been more active as we had to call upon our memories to apply optimal hunting strategies, or in the gathering of foods from the ground, or in knowing what herbs treated what ailment, or how to make tools, and in recalling stories that were told to us. The myths and religious ideas of our culture not written down they were memorised instead.

It all began to end when we bit a fruit that we had grown ourselves, tempted by the serpent we call agriculture and the allure of creating plenty.

Agriculture offered one important benefit; it promoted population growth. Agricultural communities began to rise in population, the economic benefits of large families within agricultural communities encouraged this further. In this way, agrarian communities eventually became dominant, occasionally enforcing their way of life, thanks to their higher numbers, via conquest.

To put it another way, we evolved culturally into an agricultural species, but evolution does not necessarily select outcomes that are in the best interests of individuals. It selects outcomes that favour the reproduction of our selfish gene.[33] Evolution does not care about the quality of life; it only cares about quantity of life.

When accelerating technology provided us with the time to adapt

Early humans had developed the technology of creating fire, making clothes and weapons, but the invention of agriculture was an extraordinary technological leap.

Technology has been accelerating since that point when we moved from Eden to become farmers.

---

strain injuries (RSI). It also making us more sedentary driving alarming levels of obesity and subsequently diabetes.

[32] Civilization created inequality, from the Pharaohs of Ancient Egypt, Crassus from Ancient Rome, the Emperor Nero through to today's tech billionaires.

[33] Selfish Gene is the title of a book by Richard Dawkins

But although the pace of change was rapid by the standards of the past, super rapid by the standards of evolution, until recently, technological change was still slow enough for us to adjust our culture and mindset.

There were occasional episodes in history when significant change occurred over shorter periods, such as during the era of classical Greece, but this was rare. The curve that tracks the way technology is accelerating is not smooth. Occasionally it jumps, sometimes is reverses. But the trend is clear.

Of course, our physical make-up did not change as technology changed, but its pace gave us, homo sapiens sapiens, time to adapt to the changes. Our culture changed even if the physical and mental attributes nature hardwired into us didn't.

When we invented agriculture, our species expanded, but we were not necessarily better off as individuals. Take these charts; figure one shows average male height in feet and inches from 8,500 BC to today Working on the assumption that height is proxy for health and nutrition during childhood, then the inventions of agriculture meant that the average person eventually experienced a worsening diet. During the industrial revolutions of the eighteenth and nineteenth century, average height fell for a while too. That's the thing about technology, it does not always make us better -off, and when it does, there can be long time lags. [34]

---

[34] Hermanussen, Michael; Stature of early EuropeansHealth, height and history: An overview of recent developments in anthropometric history. Harris, B, Health and Nutrition in the pre-industrial era: Richard Steckel

Changing height

Average male height in centremetres in the easter Mediterranean, from the Upper Palelithic to 1980

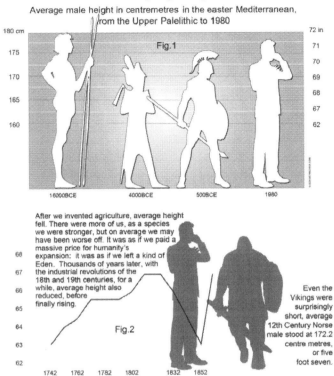

Fig.1

After we invented agriculture, average height fell. There were more of us, as a species we were stronger, but on average we may have been worse off. It was as if we paid a massive price for humanify's expansion: it was as if we left a kind of Eden. Thousands of years later, with the industrial revolutions of the 18th and 19th centuries, for a while, average height also reduced, before finally rising.

Fig.2

Even the Vikings were surprisingly short, average 12th Century Norse male stood at 172.2 centre metres, or five foot seven.

Source: Roser, Appel and Ritchie Our world in data, human heights; Michael Hermanussen, Stature of early europeans, height and history Health and wellfare during industrialization Richard H. Steckel and Roderick Floud

Inequality through the ages

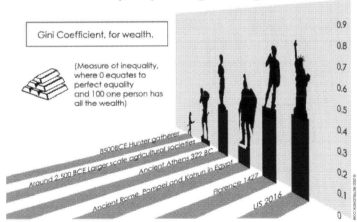

Gini Coefficient, for wealth.

(Measure of inequality, where 0 equates to perfect equality and 100 one person has all the wealth)

Source: Kohlet et al, Allianz, Global Wealth, Report 2017 and and Bitros, and Kyriazis citing Krone

Return to Eden

 Two hundred years ago, technology evolution began to create another leap; perhaps this change was as significant as the invention of agriculture. It occurred with the commencement of successive industrial revolutions – starting during the first half of the eighteenth century – of which the fifth industrial revolution and its implications, concern the subject matter of this book.

For the first time since we moved from hunting and gathering to toiling in the fields, technology began to create wealth at a speed that out-paced population growth.[35]

The full impact of the first industrial revolution did not occur immediately — as we said in the last chapter, technology creates significant change, but with time lags.

To repeat from chapter one, between the fall of the Roman Empire and 1820, average income in Europe barely changed. Within a few decades of the commencement of the first industrial revolution, growth in the western economy finally out-paced growth in the population.

Technology lies behind it all – the industrial revolutions of the eighteenth, nineteenth and twentieth century, created the economic growth and the wealth we know today.

The fourth and fifth individual revolutions

 Today, a new type of Apple is among the companies that are changing the world again. And the allure of plenty, or maybe you can call it the 'abundance of material goods', re- asserts itself.

Plenty could take the form of the temptation of knowledge. Afterall, the world's greatest knowledge library sits in our pockets.

Plenty could be in the form of meat grown in labs, from stem cells, bypassing the unfortunate business of needing methane emitting,

---

[35] Thus, apparently proving the theories of Thomas Malthus wrong. in 1798 he wrote: "Population, when unchecked, increases in a geometrical ratio, Subsistence, increases only in an arithmetical ratio," An Essay on the Principle of Population

land-hungry, resource inefficient, 'meat generating factories', we call cows, sheep, or other livestock. Plenty might take the form of clothing that is practically indestructible, and impervious to water — meaning it never remains gets dirty and can last for decades;

Or plenty might take the form of tumbling energy costs;

Or plenty may mean that living beyond 100-years-old becomes the norm;

Or instead of plenty, we may just get convenience, driving without the hassle of actually having to drive;

Or we may just get to enjoy extraordinary health benefits, thanks to significant technological advances which are about to change us in a way that has no precedent.

We recommend chapter 4 for a more extensive list of "plenties".

Some of these include synthetic biology, where the ability to create DNA, genomics, and proteomics is advancing rapidly. Consider how these technologies will be combined with others, such as cognitive computing and artificial intelligence. Our growing understanding of DNA sequencing will be at a level that will allow us to print actual human body tissue through 3D printing. The rise of a new discipline called nanotechnology is already seeing scientists and engineers developing customised white blood cells that are specifically designed for hunting down and attacking cancer cells at a molecular level. Detailed understanding of genomes now allows us to know that some drugs are more effective for some people than for others. This type of know-how will eventually mean we can treat a specific illness in a particular person. We could also get to a point where we will be able to predict and prevent future illnesses.

The end of wisdom

 Yet we are broadly the same – our great grandfather was in no significant way different from us, nor were our great grandparents ten times over, 60 times or even 2,000 times removed.

Traditionally, the elders offered wisdom. Maybe that is the reason why evolution created in us, a species which has a natural life-span significantly in excess of what is required to rear our children. Such longevity created grandparents to look after children, and people whose wisdom, of memories from long ago, was invaluable to a community's battle to survive.

Is it possible, however, that such wisdom is being superseded?

As a general rule, if we are a child during a period when a new technology emerges, we adapt pretty well. The older we are, the harder it is to adapt to or accept the change. But today, technology is increasingly defining our environment. An elder, brought up in a pre-digital era, has little relevant lifetime experiences to draw upon. We are all, every one of us, biased creatures, but in the past, our lifetime learning helped create a set of attitudes that applied to the world we knew. The world we know is now changing super-fast. As later chapters demonstrate, even human nature may be changed by technology, how relevant is the wisdom of elders in such times?.

Between the birth of the agricultural age to as recently as a few decades ago, technological change occurred sufficiently slowly for us to adjust. Even the evolution of the motor car from novelty to must-have, stretched over the duration of a great grandparent time period. This change was slow enough for it to be hard for us to imagine life without the car. Those who were brought up in an era when owning a fancy car was considered a yardstick to measure success, find it hard to imagine a time when cars are self-driving are subject to shared ownership.

The elders are among those who find it especially hard to imagine electric cars, let alone autonomous cars.

By the dawn of the 21st century, we have finally moved to that point on the curve that tracks the change in technology where the curve suddenly looks steep relative to the length of a human life.

By the end of the second decade of the 21st Century, however, the curve tracking technology changed. As the next chapter argues, it is no longer accelerating, instead, it is accelerating at an accelerating rate – $d^3T/dt^3 > 0$. (Where T = technology, t = time)

This is a problem because we are simply not designed to experience such a pace of change in our lifetime.

Yet we do experience it, at an accelerating rate. Now we look back at black and white televisions (TVs) and wonder at the primitive technology of such times, even though the time from black and white to ubiquitous colour TVs was shorter than a great grandparent in duration. Indeed, as we write these words, even the TV itself is little more than one and half great grandparents old.

PCs are barely more than half a great grandparent old; the World Wide Web is less than half great grandparent in age, (in fact it reached 30 while we penned these words), the smartphone is a quarter of a great grandparent. Over the next twenty to thirty years, the emergence of technologies which are as radical as the TV or motor car were in their time, will become ten-year events, five-year events, annual- events, six-monthly events.

That is what happens when technology accelerates at an accelerating rate.

Exponential change and the jerk

 The motor car illustrates the point. A desire to drive or own a car is not built into our genes; we were not hardwired to drive — although car designers tried to configure the vehicle so that it appealed to that which is hardwired into us.

Yet, when you read an article in the digital version of a newspaper about autonomous cars, or even electric vehicles, and then click on the comments section, you see a barrage of cynicism. The very idea, it seems, fills people with horror, "but it is so patently absurd that it will clearly never happen," or such is the gist of what they no doubt consider to be cold logic. They say words to the effect 'a self-driving-car, over my dead body.'

It's a funny thing, because, thanks to the innovation of autonomous cars, there are likely to be fewer dead bodies on roads across the world. Maybe we expect autonomous cars to apply safety standards beyond anything that could conceivably be achieved when cars are driven by humans.

Part of the problem may relate to what is sometimes called the Lake Wobegon effect – named after a US radio series; it means most of us think we are better than average especially when it comes to our driving ability. [36]

So later this decade, as technology advances, we may come to accept that for most people, autonomous cars are safer, but we may be less accepting about this when applied to ourselves.

There is, however, a deeper issue.

People are not factoring in the concept of accelerating technology, the jerk, or even exponential change – not precisely the same as the jerk, but related.

It is not in our genes, in our DNA, to grasp what exponential means. Sure, we may get it from an intellectual point of view. Take a number, and multiply it by another number, and then multiply the resulting sum, again by that same multiple. Create a graph that plots such changes, and it goes off, very quickly into infinity.

But we don't comprehend this in our soul. And we don't get it because nothing in our evolution prepared us for exponential change. As the futurist, Ray Kurzweil, points out, when we were hunter-gatherers, and a leopard was charging at us, its distance from us did not change at an exponential rate; instead, it changed at an even, steady pace. We are hardwired to think in terms of an arithmetic progression.

A good example of this is attitudes towards Covid-19. When news of the virus broke out there was a consensus, reflected in market valuations of assets, that the virus would cause little more economic or social damage in the developed world than SARS or MERS. But from very early on it was clear the virus was spreading exponentially. It took several weeks before the implications of this were widely understood.

Another example relates to estimates from the International Energy Agency on the market share of renewable energies. Over a period lasting many years, each year its projections underestimated how things would pan out.

Technology is accelerating, it is jerking, and in some cases, it is changing at an exponential rate. As a result, change in the way we live, is set to change at a pace that has no precedent.

---

[36] This is also known as the illusion of superiority, for example in one study, Svenson found that 93 per cent of US students questioned and 69 per cent of Swedish students thought they were better than average drivers.

Homo sapiens augmented

 It is clear that there is nothing in our make-up, nothing in our DNA, nothing in the evolution of a species that is designed to be a hunter-gatherer and live in a community of 148 people, to prepare us for the changes set to follow.

Indeed, whether we have truly grappled with the changes that have occurred since the invention of agriculture is a moot point.

We are a flexible species for sure, but there is no reason, no reason at all, no evidence whatsoever, to suggest we can easily adapt with the changes that will follow.

The changes will be so significant, so dramatic, so far-reaching, that we will be changed as a species. We may be enhanced and augmented by technology so much that within the lifetime of most of the readers of this book, less than half of one great grandparent in duration, we will no longer be the species we have been over the last 2,000 great grandparents. We will still be humans, but we will also be augmented homo sapiens – or the augmented ape. The changes that will be wrought upon business, the economy, our jobs, society and the way we live, will be as far-reaching as you can imagine.

And from these changes, both extraordinary opportunity but also danger lurks.

The issues described here, hinted at in the above passage, and which we will expand upon in this book, are just about the most important questions there are.

And these are way too important for us to leave it to the politicians, scientists and entrepreneurs to figure out a response and solution.

If we play this right, we could be no more than a few decades from living in a form of utopia.

We could, in effect, return to Eden, realise the advantages that were ours before agriculture changed us, but combine it with technology too, and see extra benefits.

However, if we play it wrong, dystopia beckons.

Chapter 3

Why technology is jerking

> "I invented nothing new. I simply assembled the discoveries of other men behind whom were centuries of work. Had I worked fifty or ten or even five years before, I would have failed. So, it is with every new thing. Progress happens when all the factors that make for it are ready, and then it is inevitable. To teach that a comparatively few men are responsible for the greatest forward steps of mankind is the worst sort of nonsense."
> Henry T Ford

A long time ago, something extraordinary happened. We owe our existence to this one-off, almost miraculous event.

The event is known as singular endosymbiosis.[37] It heralded the beginning of complex life, and it occurred when two entirely different, but simple organisms, living cells called prokaryotes and cousins to bacteria, came together. Each cell had its unique capabilities, its specialities, subject to around two billion years of independent evolution and they collided, one got inside the other, but carried on living.

This pivotal moment in the story of life on earth was perhaps the first real great convergence and example of cooperation.

Convergence occurs when two, or more things, come together. They can be simple organisms such as the two constituents of endosymbiosis, or they could be more human in make-up: ideas, culture, people.

---

[37] *Nick Lane, the Vital Question*

Convergence, as we will explain, is the most critical driver of innovation and change. It is the reason why we have sex, the reason why we have two sexes – despite innumerable disadvantages. It is the reason why evolution gave us the ability to love.

It is also the reason why immigration can be the most significant driver of wealth creation and a backlash against immigration, and too much reliance on small communities and nationhood, is a threat to humanity. Convergence is the single most important reason why humanity is going to see the most significant change in its history.

It is not the only reason; in fact, there are six:

They can be summed up thus: CONNEXTED
CONvergence
   Network of ideas
     EXponential technologies
      Tools
    digital **E**volution
  humans by **D**esign

Convergence

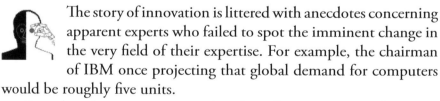

"**Virtual reality developments have slowed in recent years, and progress has not exactly been recent.**"

The story of innovation is littered with anecdotes concerning apparent experts who failed to spot the imminent change in the very field of their expertise. For example, the chairman of IBM once projecting that global demand for computers would be roughly five units.

But the above quote on virtual reality is among the most extraordinary. Those words were displayed on a website called the virtual reality forum and, in 2013, the year that the Oculus Rift virtual headset began to turn heads across the world, the year before it was sold to Facebook for over $2 billion, those comments were still there. If you had wanted to research virtual reality and began your research with a quick Google search, this website and those words would probably have been the first thing you encountered.

The jury is out on whether virtual reality will prove to be a game-changer for humanity or a passing fad but consider the reason why it may indeed be transformative. What is unique about virtual reality is that it offers a totally immersive experience. One of the more interesting characteristics of humanity is that we are great storytellers and story listeners. As we listen, we become so involved that we may feel as if we are there, we identify with the main protagonist, we may be inspired to be like them. Virtual reality has the potential to take the art of storytelling into a new dimension, engulfing us in adventures and scenarios to a degree beyond our past imagining. As with nearly all the technologies referred to in this book, it comes with dangers, too – as we shall explain.

What we can say is that virtual reality has moved from a medium that only rarely received any publicity, even in the more obscure technology publications, to one of the most widely discussed technology topics in the world. It has also become a common theme in movies. Those of you who have watched a Netflix series entitled Altered Carbon will remember the episodes where the method of psychological therapy called 'Psycho Surgery' is used to help treat and "repair" the damaged consciousness of individuals.

And it is down to convergence.

Convergence is also why virtual reality's renewed potential was not spotted at first, not even by those who ran a website charting the medium itself.

Since the idea of virtual reality was first widely discussed – back in the late 1980s – it was held back by technology – or rather lack of it. Refresh rates for screens small enough to fit into a virtual reality helmet were too slow, creating crippling time lags between a user's movement and the reaction on the screen. Graphics appeared far away as if they were being viewed from the wrong end of a pair of binoculars – and users reported a constant feeling of travel sickness.

It is changing partly due to the growing adoption of powerful smartphones. That is why its renewed potential was not spotted straight away, insiders, industry experts, were looking in the wrong direction.

For Luckey Palmer, a virtual reality enthusiast who had worked at the University of Southern California as part of a design team looking at cost-effective ways to build a virtual reality headset, the opportunity leapt into the palm of his hand, literally. The very technology needed had been developed for another purpose.

High-resolution small screens, with fast refresh rates, had become a commodity, thanks to smartphones. Smartphones also contain accelerometers, a technology that is used to sense movement and vibrations. All-of-a-sudden, the technology existed to build virtual reality headsets without the need to build the product from scratch, to invent the key components and then make them at scale.

Maybe, without the advances in smartphones, virtual reality as it is now emerging would have been impossible.

This convergence was vital – it combined technology used in an entirely different application, with the specialist knowledge that Luckey Palmer had acquired, enabling him to found Oculus Rift, which he later sold to Facebook for a vast sum.

Apple's iPod is probably one of the best examples of technological convergence. It wasn't until an Apple representative who was visiting Toshiba, a Japanese electronics manufacturer, and shown their new invention, the mini hard drive, that the concept of the iPod came to life. Apple then set about getting exclusive access to Toshiba's product to invent the iPod. And it wasn't until Apple created iTunes for Windows, a competing operating system, that the iPod was widely adopted.

Other examples of convergence are electric cars and batteries. Who would have thought that those massive batteries, so heavy it felt like you needed biceps like those of Arnold Schwarzenegger, to carry one, that sat inside mobile phones in the 1980s, would one day enable a revolution in the car industry? Mobile phones were clunky, the batteries only lasted long enough for a few short phone calls and were way too expensive for most people to buy. At first, mobile phones were so heavy that most usages were as car-phones.

Over time, they fell in cost, slowly the batteries got lighter, and longer-lasting until eventually they were also used inside computers making laptops possible. Then they made the tiny MP3 music player, the iPod, possible and then in 2007 the iPhone. During this process, by around the beginning of the 21st century, lithium-ion batteries began to dominate.

It was in 2008 that the first Tesla electric car, using a lithium-ion battery, the Tesla Roadstar, like the model that is currently in orbit around the earth, contained a lithium- ion battery. Convergence made the electric car revolution possible.

And from electric cars to cutting edge technology that really does feel like science fiction brought to life. The remarkable and emerging field of optogenetics makes it possible to stimulate targeted neurons in the brain, which produce all of our thoughts and behaviours, turning them on or off by shining light on specific areas of the brain. This technology provides the potential to study neurological diseases such as Parkinson's or epilepsy. Optogenetics is only possible thanks to convergence. The technology involves implanting specific proteins found in algae to inject into neurons, making them sensitive to light. But the key light source is supplied by embedded fibre optic cables.

In short, fibre optics, a vital part of computing and networking, a technology that is fast becoming the backbone of the internet, could be used to fight and even defeat some of the terrifying diseases which many of us suffer from or may develop. The technology also has far-reaching consequences – both exciting, such as augmenting our brain but also has pervasive potential such as mind control. Convergence, whether for good or bad, is making this possible.

But to fully appreciate the story of convergence, and why it can be such a force for innovation, consider a myth and then the reality concerning one of the great inventions of the twentieth century: rock and roll.

According to mythology, rock and roll was invented when Robert Johnson, a travelling musician, met the Devil on the crossroads of highway forty-nine and sixty-one, Clarksdale Mississippi. The story goes that the Devil offered to make Johnson the greatest guitarist that there would ever be in return for his soul. And Johnson did the deal. The rest, as they say, is history. The link between the Devil and rock and roll is there for all to hear – the genre is littered with references to the Devil and indeed crossroads.

The real story is as inspiring as the myth is terrifying, rock and roll was created by convergence. It came about as two cultures, just like the prokaryotes that converged to form complex life-forms, that had developed separately from each other, subject to their own evolution, came together. In the case of rock and roll, the two constituent parts were European music, with an emphasis on mathematical precision, which had evolved over several hundred years, and African music, with a focus on rhythm. It took the slave trade descendants to bring those cultures together, and rock and roll emerged via Baptist-music and jazz.

That's what happens when people with different cultural backgrounds come together. The result of convergence is unpredictable, but you can predict that the end result will be something exceptional. This is the crucial point that critics of immigration overlook – in fact immigration may be one of the most critical drivers of innovation. You only need to look at the great US tech companies, such as Google, co-founded by a Russian migrant, or Apple, whose most famous co-founder was the son of a migrant from Syria, to see this. Indeed, the US is built on immigration, and that fact alone may be enough to explain its economic and technological success to date.

The story of convergence and rock and roll does not finish there. Another round of innovation occurred via the cauldron of British and American culture, converging through the medium of TV, radio and cinema. This happened when working-class English kids in Liverpool and middle-class kids from Dartford, took the rock and roll that evolved in America, sold to them in the form of Elvis, Little Richard and co and gave it an English spin, creating a new phase in the evolution of the medium via the Beatles and the Rolling Stones.

The only devil in convergence is in the detail.

Convergence is a crucial driver of innovation, and right now we see convergence, made possible in part by the internet, breaking down the knowledge barriers, amongst others, once created by geography and cultural differences, to bring ideas together like never seen before in the history of humanity.

But other technologies, such as Augmented Reality may yet prove to have an even more significant effect. These technologies enable people from all over the world, who all speak different languages, to come together, meet up in a kind of half virtual space (virtual space superimposed over their local environment) communicating fluently via real- time language translation tools.

As a tool for supporting convergence, one of the great drivers of innovation, modern technology has no equal.

CONNEXTED

Are you convinced? Do you agree that we are indeed amidst the most significant technological revolution humanity has ever seen? Do you accept that this revolution will be so significant, that we may be less than a lifetime away from artificially mutating into a new species?

To convince you, let us begin with why this is so, why it is that technology is changing so fast.

We begun this explanation with convergence. Now we tell the story of the five other drivers, which together make CONNEXTED.

Connected, they create a compelling reason why technology is indeed accelerating.

The network of ideas — the adjacent possible

> *Nanos gigantum humeris insidentes (We are like dwarfs sitting on the shoulders of giants) - Bernard of Chartres 12th Century*
> *"If I have seen further it is by standing on the shoulders of Giants" Isaac Newton in 1675*
> *"Creativity comes from without, not within" Kirby Ferguson, Ted, 10th August, 2012*

Ideas don't jump into the world, fully formed, like a Greek goddess from the head of her father. Just as is the idea of Athena being introduced to the world, in full armour, complete with all her wisdom from the head of Zeus, it is absurd to assume ideas are developed in isolation.

No one person is the father or mother of invention, necessity might be a godmother, but collaboration is the more important.

Every idea that has ever been worth having has grown from an existing design or innovation. That is why originality is practically a non-existent concept.

An excellent example of this is the movie franchise Star Wars. While the original movie was acclaimed for its originality at launch in 1977, in many ways, it was derivative of older films. For example, the famous scrolling letters at the beginning were a quite deliberate homage to the 1936 Flash Gordon movie. The movie also drew inspiration from the 1958 Japanese classic movie Hidden Fortress, directed by Akira Kurosawa. The similarity with the film Hidden Fortress, down to two comic characters who gave the apparent inspiration to the C3P0 and R2D2 droids from the franchise, and the famous bar fight in the first Star Wars movie, is no coincidence. For that matter, George Lucas, the creator of Star Wars, was not shy to admit it.

Lucas was, in fact, a student of the cinema, and a great fan of Kurosawa who he introduced to Hollywood.

But Star Wars is just one famous example among many – look at the evolution of scientific ideas, and over and over again, you find different people, sometimes not even living in the same continent, independently coming up with similar or practically identical ideas.[38]

Edison patented his lamp in the US in 1879, a year after Joseph Swan demonstrated an incandescent light bulb in Britain. Darwin discovered evolution, but before he finally got around to publishing an account of his theory, Alfred Russell quite independently stumbled upon a similar idea. Sunspots were discovered by four different scientists, each living in a different country in 1611.

This list of apparent coincidences goes on and on. But they are not coincidences at all, neither are they evidence of plagiarism – as cynics might suggest – not usually, anyway. It is just that ideas build upon ideas, creating a network of ideas, and apply similar technologies. So the network of ideas and technology percolating in the early 1600s, made the discovery of sunspots inevitable. You could say ditto for the discovery of evolution in the mid- years of the 19th century, and the light bulb in the late 1870s. Ideas build upon ideas, forming a network,

---

[38] *Watch Kirby Fergusson's superb documentary, 'Everything is a Remix' for more detail on this idea. It's one of those videos you can watch several times. Steven Johnson also explains this well in his book, Where good ideas come from.*

and once this network reaches an appropriate level of advancement, and the market conditions are right, it's a case of whoosh – innovation follows as inevitably as sunrise follows sunset.

As the industrialist, AJ Mundella said: "Every invention we have made and patented, and some have created almost a revolution in the trade, has been the invention of onlookers, or ordinary working men, or skilled mechanics, in every instance."[39]

Or to return to the story of rock and roll, the four men who formed the Beatles were indeed enormously talented. Nonetheless, it is stretching credibility to say that Paul McCartney and George Harrison, who knew each other from school, and the slightly older John Lennon who McCartney met at a fete, would have been as brilliant if they had not known each other.

Indeed, though Lennon and McCartney are widely acknowledged as among the very greatest songwriters of all time, Harrison was the talent behind some of the Beatles' most beautiful music – 'While my guitar gently weeps', and 'Something', for example. Even Ringo Starr is credited with having written 'The Octopuses' Garden', not the greatest Beatles song for sure, but a good deal better than many of the most talented of musicians ever manage.

Were these four men independently geniuses? They were individually talented, of that, there is no doubt, but their sublime musical achievements became possible because they fed off each other's creativity. The 10,000 hours plus of work they did together turned talented individuals into four of the most influential musicians ever.[40]

That's the point about innovation and indeed the creation of genius. It's down to collaboration and relentless iteration, forming a network of ideas.

This is the essence of our species.

---

[39] *Quoted in Sex, Science and Profits by Terence Kaeley*
[40] *As described by Malcolm Gladwell in Outliers. Gladwell described how the Beatles, performing in Hamburg, notched up thousands of hours of experience, and were transformed from a talented band with potential to an outstanding band. It is not that the individuals who made up the Beatles weren't naturally gifted, probably more naturally gifted than the member of other bands who performed in Hamburg at this time, but it was Gladwell's 10,000 hours that transformed them, or so he suggested.*

In the tale of our species, there have been four key breakthroughs that have supported the spread of ideas, thereby making the network of ideas more potent. Another breakthrough is currently being formed.

The creation of language helped us work together and collectively out-innovate other animals, always with the application of technology.

The innovation we call writing helped spur a new age of innovation, the significant advances of the ancient world, the architecture, works of philosophers, poets that we marvel at, were sparked off by the invention of writing around 3,500BC and helped create the great civilizations of the Ancient World.

The printing press, first introduced to Europe around 1440, helped create a new era – the reformation, renaissance and eventually the industrial revolutions. Printing helped support the rise of new religious thinking and helped provide the fuel that underpinned the English Civil War, the French Revolution and then the Russian revolution.

Although many of the pioneers of the industrial revolution, such as George Stephenson, a key figure in the advancement of the steam train, were illiterate during their youth, the pool of innovations that created steam power was immense. The ripples from ideas created by print were vital, and without print spreading ideas, the industrial revolution may never have happened or if it had, would have happened much more slowly.

Writing and print were the key drivers of human innovation in history.

And each of these breakthroughs was accompanied by an acceleration in innovation. The fossil record shows a dramatic pick-up in the pace of innovation as early humans mastered the art of language. But this pace went up several notches with the invention of writing – for two hundred thousand years Homo sapiens sapiens technology changed slowly. Within three millennia of the invention of writing, the world saw the wonders of classical Greece. We can measure the time lag from the invention of the printing press to the industrial revolution, the use of electricity, the motor car and aeroplane in just a handful of centuries.

But the latter half of the twentieth century saw another great innovation – the internet. 1987 saw the birth of the World Wide Web. And with these advances, coupled with accelerating internet bandwidth speeds, created a new medium – one that stands alongside writing and printing as one of the most significant technologies for spreading ideas and knowledge.

To reiterate, four significant breakthroughs have been vital in supporting innovation. After each breakthrough, the pace of change accelerated from a rate that was already accelerating – it jerked. These four significant breakthroughs were the evolution of language, the invention of writing, the printing press and then the internet.

Technology cynics who pour scorn on the internet, something they see as frivolous, providing modest advances in entertainment, miss the point. Innovations that create wealth – whether these innovations relate to the production of food, clothing, warmth, shelter or transport – require the spreading of ideas, a network of ideas and convergence. Nothing in history can come close to the power of the internet in providing the means for achieving that.

That is why technology innovation is accelerating.

But the internet itself may give way to an even more powerful force for spreading ideas – virtual and augmented reality will bring people together, from across the world, like no medium in history has done before. It will create a network linking the nodes (that's us) in that network more closely than ever. Although such technology will be enabled by the internet, it will represent such a leap in supporting communication and the spread of ideas, that it will in effect be another medium. AI will enhance this effect, supporting us in our interactions, giving us timely reminders and making connections for us that we may not have otherwise encountered.

The idea of the network of ideas also relates to the advancement of open source. Open source projects, such as Wikipedia or Linux, illustrate the power of people pooling their ideas. On occasions, intellectual property can hinder this process, as it provides barriers in the very process of sharing ideas. Supporters of patents say they are essential to incentivise companies to invest in innovation, but maybe, instead, patents can act against the sharing of ideas.

The fight against Coronaviruses is an excellent example of this. The best way to develop cures and vaccines for new viruses, such as the succession of coronaviruses that have emerged in the 21st Century (SARS, MERS and Covid-19) is by supporting the network of ideas with access to open source innovation and technology to share vital data, reduce duplication of effort and fast track breakthroughs.

Accelerating change was a constant theme from the emergence of speech, but with each jump in medium, to writing, print, internet and then in time to augmented and virtual reality supported by AI, there was, is and will be a jerk.

Date	Medium	Rate of change
1.75 million years ago	Speech	At first, change measured in tens of thousands of years, later in millennia
3000 BC	Writing	Change accelerated, peaking in classical times in the west, then experienced a temporary hiatus after the fall of the Roman Empire
15th Century in Europe, earlier in China	Printing Press	Supported spread of new religious ideas, first, second and third industrial revolutions, led to English Civil War, French Revolution and the Russian revolution, initially change measured in units of several decades in length, later in single decades
1990s	The internet	A unit of a few years became a relevant measure for change, by the time of the fourth industrial revolution, this was shortened to periods of less than a year
2020s	Augmented and virtual reality with AI	Months, then weeks then days relevant units for measuring change

Exponential technologies, or Metaphorical Moore's Law, or learning rate

 If the average family saloon had seen its top speed rise at a trajectory consistent with Moore's Law, and we take 1965 as the starting point, then today it would be able to reach speeds approaching the speed of light.

Jerk refers to acceleration accelerating. Sometimes though, change is even more rapid than that. It can occur at an exponential rate, for example, doubling every few years. Exponential and jerk are not identical, but they do refer to a similar concept. This section looks at exponential change, something we return to in chapter five, where we look at sudden change.

Let's begin with Moore's Law.

To explain further, we begin the story in 1965.

In that year, the Rolling Stones lamented that they "can't get no satisfaction", the Beatles asked for "help", and Sonny and Cher said: "I've got you, babe." In that year, Gordon Moore, who went onto to become a co-founder of Intel, said that "the number of transistors on an integrated circuit doubles every two years." At first, he said that he expected this phenomenon to last for ten years, later he extended the time frame indefinitely. Today this is known as Moore's Law - it refers to computers doubling in power every 18 months to two years.

If something doubles in power every two years, within sixty years, it becomes roughly one billion times more powerful. And who can say what will become possible when specific applications become a thousand times more powerful, let alone a billion times.

In 1949, Popular Mechanics, a respected publication still running today, stated: "Where a calculator like ENIAC today is equipped with 18,000 vacuum tubes and weighs 30 tons, computers in the future may have 1,000 vacuum tubes and perhaps weigh only 1½ tones."

The hint that this was going to change was already there when Popular Mechanics made its infamous prediction. In 1948 Bell Laboratories announced the invention of the transistor. Presumably, people did not grasp the importance of the invention – the possible convergence with computers was not understood.

What vacuum tubes and transistors have in common is that they provide digital information, either on or off, one or zero. Transistors are tiny switches – one switch or transistor is the equivalent of a vacuum tube.

What we can say is that by 1974 there were around 8,000 transistors on an integrated circuit. The iPhone X has four billion transistors.

An exciting, incredibly important, and enlightening optimistic point arises from this story. The advance of Moore's Law was a democratising process. Its advancement was made possible by economies of scale, which, in turn, was made possible by the creation of a mass market. Moore's Law has made smartphones a reality in some of the poorest places on earth. Cynics and pessimists immediately react to the news of some technology breakthrough by saying that it will only ever benefit the rich. But the tale of Moore's Law suggests the opposite.

See it in terms of James Bond. In the latest James Bond movies, whizzy technology is no longer so popular – the reason: no intelligence service can match the mass market for creating an invention.

The celebrated economist Brad De Long once estimated that if someone had tried to build a computer with similar processing power to the iPhone X in 1957, then it would have cost 150 trillion of today's dollars. The device would have taken up a hundred-story building, 300 meters high, and three kilometres long and wide and draw 150 terawatts of power – 30 times the world's generating capacity at that time.

But forward wind. Let's say the world committed 150 trillion dollars, allocated space the size of a small city, and 300 meters high, and was to create 150 terawatts of power somehow, imagine what computer could be built using today's state of the art.

Imagine what a computer could do in twenty-years-time if it is a thousand times more powerful than an iPhone X. Or for that matter, a computer in sixty-years-time that is one billion times more powerful.

If your mind does not boggle at such a thought, then there is something wrong with your mind's ability to boggle. As it happens, as we explain in the next chapter, Moore's Law, as defined by Gordon Moore, has come to an end. Packing ever more transistors into a computer requires th integrated circuits to get smaller and smaller, and we may be reaching the point when it is a physical impossibility for silicon-based integrated circuits to get smaller, without creating excess overheating.

But this does not mean computers will stop getting faster. Just as silicon integrated circuits replaced vacuum tubes, creating a new and much faster trajectory for computer evolution, there are plenty of possible technologies that could take up the baton of computer advancement from silicon integrated circuits. Graphene, the apparently miraculous super-material, first isolated in 2004, may prove to be a far superior alternative to silicon. Some papers suggest a graphene-based computer could be 1,000 times faster. As we shall see in Chapter four, an Age of Plenty, there are other examples.

Quantum computers, when used for specific applications, maybe in conjunction with graphene, also represent the potential of a massive acceleration in the rate at which computers become more powerful. Back in the early 2000s, Geordie Rose, former CEO of D-Wave, said that the number of qubits in a scalable quantum computing architecture should double every year.[41] But this leads to something extraordinary. In quantum computers, each additional qubit leads to the perceived doubling in processing ability. We are effectively getting an exponential of an exponential. The number of qubits doubles every year (exponential), each qubit represents a doubling of processing (exponential of the exponential). If you like you could say the exponential function will jerk.[42]

Consider that. During the age of vacuum tube computers, processing power increased, but slowly. Then followed the era of silicon-based integrated circuits, where processing power doubled every 18-months. In the age of quantum computers, processing power could double every six months. At that rate of change, computers could increase one trillion-fold in processing power in just twenty years.

Every switch in the computer technology, from vacuum tubes to Moore's Law to quantum, sees an acceleration in the rate at which

---

[41] *Computing Quantum computing Rose's Law is Moore's Law on steroids*

[42] *The computing power of a quantum computer is more related to the algorithm, than the number of qubits. People are looking from quantum algorithms that scale differently, or more efficiently, with the number of additional qubits. So, the number of qubits determines the complexity of the quantum wave function/states.*

computer power is accelerating – technology accelerating at an accelerating rate.

Another possible technology relates to photonic chips – traditional computer chips operate via electrical signals, meaning the movement of electrons. Photonic chips work by light signals, and since electrons in computer chips move at around five per cent of the speed of light, photonic chips could be twenty times faster. But if a photonic chip were three dimensional, the increase in speed would not merely be twenty-fold. It would be twenty times, twenty times, twenty times faster. Or 8,000 times faster.

So, while you could say the original meaning of Moore's Law is dead, you should add to its epitaph, long live Moore's Law.

The speed and power of computers is only part of the story. If instead, you see Moore's Law as a metaphor for describing any form of technology that increases at an exponential rate, then things get truly exciting. Alternatively, instead of saying metaphorical Moore's Law, you can say exponential change.

Question: how much does it cost to sequence a human genome? And how long does it take? Answer: it depends on the date. If you had begun the process in 1990, it would have taken thirteen years and 2.7 billion dollars. By 2008 it cost around ten million dollars. By 2015, press reports talked about the cost falling to $1,000. At the time of writing one company claims to have got the price down to $100.[43]

But actually, you can trace the story of genome sequencing back further. In 1955, Fred Sanger at Cambridge University[44] determined the sequence of the protein insulin. In 1976 and 1977 the first two viral genomes were decoded.

In 1995 the genome of Haemophilus influenzas, complete with one point eight million letters of genetic code was sequenced. Five years later it was the genome of the fruit fly – 180 million letters of genetic code. And then we saw the sequencing of the three billion base pair haploid human genome – this is exponential change writ large.

The energy industries have multiple examples of exponential change – the cost of energy generated by a solar panel today is roughly

---

[43] Meg Tirrell, Unlocking my genome: Was it worth it?

[44] As Craig Venter once described when he gave the 32nd Richard Dimbleby Lecture.

one per cent of what it was forty years earlier. And there is no sign of this trajectory slowing.

There is another way of describing the exponential change in this context – a learning rate. In the case of wind and solar power, the cost per unit of energy falls by a specific amount, with each and every doubling in the installed user base.

Another example is lithium-ion batteries – the cost per kilowatt-hour has fallen from $1.000 in 2010 to $227 in 2016, to $140 in 2017, primarily driven by higher adoption and usage.

But actually, the phrase could be used to describe Moore's Law. There are many critics of the ideas of using Moore's Law to describe the falling cost of renewables, but they miss the point. If you use the phrase learning rate to describe the falling cost of computers per unit of processing power and learning rate to describe the falling cost of renewables, then the comparison is apt. There is nothing wrong, with using a sexier phrase, metaphorical Moore's Law, or exponential technologies to describe this process.

As we mentioned in the prologue, the idea of a learning rate can be traced back to the 1930s, when Theodore Wright. An aeronautical engineer back in the 1930s, Wright "observed that every doubling of production of US aircraft brought down prices by 13%." (Ramez Naam)

Henry VIII, one of the richest men in the world of his time, could not have afforded to have his genome sequenced – not so long ago, all the money in the world would have been insufficient. Today it costs no more than a few hours work for an average worker in the developed world. Not so long ago, smartphones that could fit in your pocket, but which double up as powerful cameras would have been impossible. Because technology advances following a learning rate, technology can be democratising – providing mass-market access to technologies that a few years earlier were impossible.

That's why globalisation is essential. It gives the learning rate more scope by increasing the size of the potential customer base of a product. A reversal of globalisation, perhaps in reaction to the spread of Covid-19, could reduce the potential of learning rates, and among other things, reduce our ability to fight disease Inequality can also work against the learning rate. If you are super-rich and want technology that enables you to live until you are 200, then you are most likely to see your dream realised if there is a mass market for life-extending technology.

Tools

 It is a strange thing, but often, when cynics look at modern technology, they can be quite dismissive of computers. Or indeed other technologies of the last few decades.

We will be returning to the topic of technology cynicism. For now, it suffices to say that critics and cynics argue that computers and the internet are not what they are cracked up to be.

You hear it over and over again. 'I prefer using a pen and paper'. 'Computer games are great and all, but they are not exactly life-changing'. Others cite the way antibiotics are losing their effectiveness. The discovery of penicillin saved millions of lives. Scientists fear that overuse of antibiotics, especially in agriculture, could lead to them ceasing to work. Maybe then, in that respect, technological progress has been in reverse until now as new technologies emerge.

Arch technology critic Robert Gordon, from Northwestern University, Chicago, sums up the issues by arguing that flushable toilets have been far more critical than the innovations of recent years, ergo technological change is slowing down.

Flushable toilet or iPhone, what would you choose? The professor surely misses the point.

Computers, the internet, artificial intelligence, blockchain, augmented reality, and many of the great technologies that are evolving, are enablers.

Flushable toilets make one of those most natural of all our activities more comfortable and hygienic. Modern technologies will create new activities.

The technologies themselves are not what will improve humanity's lot. Instead, what matters is how we use these technologies and the innovations that they facilitate.

It's not just through the way they support convergence or the creation of a network of ideas.

Many of the innovations that really will change the world, innovations that will help us cure diseases, increase longevity, or create more food and energy, require data and computer modelling.

Technology crunching numbers and processing data on a scale that humans could not begin to manage, and then simulating different ideas, testing them safely at speeds once thought impossible, will create remarkable new products that could extend our lives and make us healthier.[45]

Digital Evolution

It is like a miracle worker: evolution has created wonders which science can only marvel.

You name it. The strength of a spider's web, the stunning accuracy of a bat's or dolphin's sonar, the human brain and consciousness, show how the natural world reduces us, for all our supposed ingenuity, to wonder.

But natural evolution is also incredibly slow. And unpredictable.

What is unusual, not totally unique, but for all practical purposes, uniquely important about humans is that we pass on our learning via storytelling and then writing, our memories passed on to future generations.

Evolution, as described by Darwin, requires chance mutations that happen to promote survival long enough for us to reproduce.

Once a particular ape learned how to communicate via speech, we saw a new type of evolution develop — cultural evolution. With speech, we could more easily pass ideas on from one generation to the next.

Ideas evolve. What we learned in our lifetime suddenly has long-term meaning. Before this, with every generation, we saw a reset. With Darwinian evolution, all that is learnt in a lifetime is forgotten.

You could say that with Darwinian evolution, a functional unit of measurement of significant evolutionary change is a million years, [46]with cultural evolution, centuries, even decades, and of late, a single year is an appropriate unit of measurement

---

[45] Google The Wild New Materials of the Future Will Be Discovered With AI, by Marc Prosser, for a good explanation

[46] *although this has accelerated over time, following the evolutionary jerk*

73

In short, we had Darwinian evolution, then cultural/ technological evolution, when the change was no longer subject to chance mutations in DNA.

But we are on the verge of seeing a third form of evolution: digital.

Returning to the topic of antibiotics, one of the reasons that we are struggling to win the arms race against superbugs is that the bacteria which antibiotics compete against can reproduce so rapidly. The E. coli bacterium can divide in two as quickly as twenty minutes. While Darwinian evolution usually only sees change occur over millions of years, bacteria, which also reproduce asexually, meaning convergence does not apply, are an exception.

In a digital environment, the change could occur in seconds – maybe even fractions of seconds, after-all, the iPhone X can perform up to 600 billion instructions per second. [47]

An excellent example of digital evolution is genetic algorithms. Traditionally, a computer algorithm, designed for a specific task is developed by a creator – a computer programmer. Supposing, instead, it evolves. It would work thus: to begin with; there is a large population of members (say bits of code). A fitness score is assigned to each member based on how close it is to achieving a pre-defined goal. The members of the population with the highest ratings are selected and divided into twos which are combined – bred.

Other members are killed off. The resulting members are then multiplied, but with random mutation built-in.

And the process is then repeated.

An area which has seen considerable research into applying the techniques of evolution is neuro-evolution. An essential area in the field of artificial intelligence is neural networks – a computer system that mirrors the way the brain works, with artificial neurons forming links (akin to synapses in the brain) with other artificial neurons. Neural networks are crucial in such fields as image recognition and language translation – for example, they are a key technology on the advancement of self-driving cars.

Professor Kenneth O. Stanley, from the University of Central Florida and the Uber AI Labs is an expert in this field. He, along with

---

[47] *Let's evolve a neural network with a genetic algorithm – code include, Matt Harvey, 7 April 2017, Coastline automation*

Risto Miikkulainen, from the Department of Computer Sciences, The University of Texas, Austin, published a paper looking into Evolving Neural Networks in 2002.

They showed how it is "possible for evolution to both optimise and complexify solutions simultaneously, offering the possibility of evolving increasingly complex solutions over generations, and strengthening the analogy with biological evolution." Today, that paper is something of a classic in this field.

In an interview with Quartz, Professor Stanley talked about the beginning of applying evolutionary processes in artificial intelligence: "There was a small community of people who thought about how brains, which are really the only proof of concept of intelligence in nature, get into the world," Stanley says. "Some people thought maybe the most straightforward way to do this would be to create an evolutionary, Darwinian-like process in a computer that acts as little artificial brains."

You can see demonstrations of genetic algorithms on YouTube. In one example, a video demonstrates the evolution of a simple animation for walking, another for jumping over a ball. [48]

As computers become more powerful, and computer models more accurate, we can only guess at what solutions genetic algorithms may evolve. Take as an example, simulation of the human body and how it ages or can be weakened and then killed by disease. Digital evolution may, and indeed probably will come up with solutions we may never have developed otherwise.

Three stages of evolution

Some might say that innovation, and hence the potential for economic growth, is slowing. But here's an alternative contention: it is not merely growing, it is not even only accelerating, it is – or maybe it is about to – accelerate at an accelerating rate. This is why:

In his book 'The meaning of the 21st Century', James Martin[49] suggests there are three stages of evolution. Stage one is primary evolution: the evolutionary process described by Darwin. It relates to

---

[48] *Dollar Akshay Genetic Algorithm. Learning to walk - OpenAI Gym*
[49] *The meaning of the 21st Century, James Martin*

the evolution of living species by natural selection. This stage is slow: it requires mutation to DNA to introduce change; this is the product of chance. Stage two is secondary evolution, which relates to cultural evolution and of ideas themselves, culminating perhaps in the ability to manipulate DNA. This second stage is faster than the first because it builds on what we have already learned. It works by selecting and favouring ideas developed through deliberation. The third stage is what Martin calls tertiary evolution. This type of evolution occurs when intelligent beings learn how to automate evolution itself.

Stage two in Martin's three stages has already accelerated. It has accelerated thanks to convergence, or ideas creating new ideas, Moore's Law and new tools created via technology.

This all begs the question: what about stage three?

Thanks to nanotechnology and the way nanotechnology may well be able to create advanced versions of itself, which can then create even more advanced forms, we may be close indeed very close – to tertiary evolution.

Economists and governments are ill-equipped to deal with this, and economists seem to be unaware that within the lifetime of most readers of this book, tertiary evolution may turn known boundaries of technology evolution on its head.

Humans by Design: The augmented ape

There is an even greater force that is about to be set loose. It is not hard to appreciate that if scientists, inventors and researchers suddenly became more intelligent, there would be an increase in the pace of innovation.

As we consider later, this is precisely what is going to happen.

Whether these super-intelligent creators are us, or artificial intelligence of some sort, is one of the most important questions we can ask.

In one possible scenario, computers continue to develop over the next twenty years at the pace they have evolved over the last twenty years, such that by say 2038, computers are around 10,000 times more powerful than they are today. During this period, AI algorithms are also allowed to evolve.

In this scenario, AI does most of the thinking for us. We are passive observers, more to follow on this theme.

In the other possible scenario, we become enhanced by computers – augmented, such that we become a new version of humanity, an augmented ape, or Homo sapiens augmented.

This is a topic that will be explored in more depth as this book continues and the full implications of accelerating technology begin to unravel.

For the time being, it may suffice to say that this process has already begun. Most of us carry around with us, in our pockets or handbags, a device that gives us access to the biggest library that has ever existed.

Imagine that. It is science fiction becoming a cultural reality. Nearly all of us can now find out just about anything we want within seconds. We can, for example, confirm or disprove a claim made by a politician, a friend on social media or in a newspaper within seconds.

It is undoubtedly one of the great mysteries of the world that as such technology becomes ubiquitous, fake news becomes a threat to democracy.

Some see the solution as being with the established media, handing back to them more control, eroding the influence of user-generated content and the plethora of news and editorial outlets that have emerged, not subject to the exacting standards of the more traditional media.

But such a view takes a dim perspective on humanity, castigating us as little more than well-dressed apes, who need the benevolent protection of editors who filter the noise of news and public opinion through their good sense and responsibility. AI may eventually fulfil such roles. But we have to be more than that. Just abdicating the responsibility of telling fake news from the truth, cold comfort for change,[50] is a step on the route to the scenario in which technology makes us slothful.

We don't and should not need kindly newspaper editors or uncles Joe, Jinping and Donald or even Big Brother, deciding what is best for us.

We just need, by the process of education, to learn how to turn the powers of computers to our advantage, embracing them, letting

---

[50] *Hard to resist a Pink Floyd quote.*

them enhance us, augment us. If we do that, then humanity's ability to innovate will be like something no one had hitherto imagined.

Accelerating at an accelerating rate

 Moore's Law and Wright's Law illustrate how some technology is changing exponentially. But Quantum Computing offers the prospect of the exponential rate accelerating.

The internet is enabling the convergence of ideas and knowledge, as never experienced before. The internet is supporting the growth of the network of ideas. Evolution itself is about to enter a new phase when we see digital evolution. We are also set to become augmented by computers.

As a result of these factors, technology is no longer accelerating. It is accelerating at an accelerating rate. Once computers are running at that pace, the potential for digital evolution becomes, well, if your mind does not feel like it is about to explode at that thought, there is something wrong with your mind's ability to explode.

If computer power were to double in processing every six months, it would take just ten years to see a million-fold increase in computer power, and after twenty years that increase will be by a factor of a trillion.[51] With quantum computing, this could happen.

---

[51] *That is an American quintillion, ten to the power of eighteen, or a British trillion*

Chapter 4

An age of plenty

Introduction

In 1958, von Neumann, a Hungarian-American mathematician and computer scientist, noted the accelerating progress of technology and constant changes to human life. He felt that this tendency was giving the appearance of our approaching some *essential singularity* beyond which human affairs, as we know them, could not continue.

> **"We wanted flying cars; instead, we got 140 characters."**

In 2013, Peter Thiel, an American entrepreneur, venture capitalist, philanthropist, political activist, and author, said: "We wanted flying cars; instead, we got 140 characters." If the post-war era gave us fabulous inventions like the washing machine, the refrigerator, the space shuttle, and the pill, lately it has merely been improved iterations of the same phone we bought a couple of years ago.

So, is technological and scientific innovation decelerating? Or are we in a period of reorganisation before the major acceleration?

Mr Thiel argues that the rate of technological innovation is decelerating, (Something you could call a negative jerk) despite our collective belief that there are brilliant scientists in labs, somewhere, working to solve our problems. Like most US Republicans, he believes that government regulation is to blame and that inventive minds are too focused on the internet and too neglectful of the world beyond it.

This point of view does seem to ignore the premise that the Internet is as much a tool which facilitates innovation as it is one for everyday consumption. As we argued in chapter three, the internet supports convergence and the spreading of ideas, fundamental building blocks in the story of innovation.

The economists Robert Gordon and Tyler Cohen articulate similar negative views about technology change. Robert Gordon, in particular, argues that we have picked the low hanging fruit of technology and that from now on technological change will be slow. We look at these arguments in more depth in Chapter five.

We are not aligned with Mr Thiel's point of view, as innovations are aplenty, but we will not attempt an exhaustive study of these. Unlike the authors' previous, this book is not a study of the many technological advances which define the fourth and fifth industrial revolutions. We would be remiss if we did not consider these primary technological building blocks and consider their applicability to humans, our environment and our ecosystem.

There is much coverage and debate as to how the fourth industrial revolution shaping our future. We would, therefore, encourage you to consider the fifth industrial revolution to be the era of full adoption and real disruption, building on the fourth's innovation.

To begin, we set the scope of our focus as that of Deep Tech, which refers to technologies based on genuine scientific breakthroughs or innovations that can profoundly change entire industries and people's lives.

We will thus endeavour to pinpoint and explore the core deep tech drivers of innovation and significant impact on the economy and society. We will focus on those technology innovations which will trigger the acceleration leading to the fifth industrial revolution.

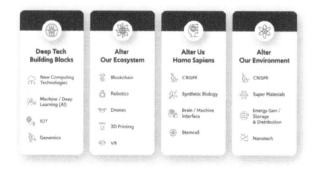

The Deep Tech Building Block

New computing technologies: quantum, neural network, biological data storage

In 1965, Gordon Moore, one of the founders of Intel, a major computer chip manufacturer, observed that the number of transistors on an integrated circuit was doubling every 24 months. The first integrated circuits in 1960 had almost ten transistors. Today the most complex silicon chips have ten billion.

But Moore's Law ended a decade ago. The rest of us didn't get the memo! So, is this the beginning of the end of innovation as Mr Thiel would argue hence his claim of deceleration or have we humans, been able to overcome this rate-limiting step? In other words, are we, in fact, at the stage of the end of the beginning? Arguably one of the most disruptive fourth Industrial Revolution innovations in this field is quantum computing. Here we say goodbye to transistors, where we rely on the binary one or zero, and we say hello to qubits which can operate in multiple states at a time, i.e. be both a one and a zero at the same time!

First mooted in 1982 by Richard Feynman, quantum computing is still only a laboratory phenomenon as quantum computers remain very difficult to engineer. For example, achieving stable qubits requires the machine to operate at absolute zero temperatures.

Things are changing, though. Google now claims to have built the first quantum computer that can carry out calculations beyond the ability of today's most powerful supercomputers, a landmark moment that has been hotly anticipated by researchers. Google researchers claim that their processor was able to perform a calculation in three minutes and twenty seconds that would take today's most advanced classical computer approximately 10,000 years.[52]

The researchers' proud boast is that we have reached the 'quantum supremacy' stage when quantum computers are capable of carrying out calculations that had been impossible.[53]

---

[52] *According to a paper by Google's researchers, published in Nature*

[53] *An important consideration here is the unit of quantum computers, the so-called qubit. Each increase in the number of qubits on a quantum computer leads to a*

Quantum computers cannot yet do many of the tasks that conventional machines can do. However, they can do specific tasks, such as simulating protein folding, which would be beyond the capability of traditional computers.

The potential for quantum computing lies in combination with traditional computers, and eventually in conjunction with humans, too.

The contribution to the acceleration of innovation through quantum computing is genuinely mind-boggling and highly disruptive.

Machine learning often referred to as Artificial Intelligence needs to be able to consume large data sets of images, video and text. Powerful computers are required to process the petabytes of all the unanalysed data. Quantum computers could empower machine learning by enabling machine learning programs to search through these gigantic data sets to the advantage of medical research, not to mention consumer behaviour analysis and the financial markets. The potential benefits to medical science, in particular, are remarkable.

Quantum computers also come with a downside. They are dream technology for computer hackers. So great is the potential for quantum computers in this respect that cybersecurity experts sometimes talk about an impending quantum apocalypse.[54]

---

doubling in the volume of information it can process. Also, of relevance here, is Rose's Law, see chapter three. Named after Geordie Rose, former CTO and CEO of D-WAVE Systems, this suggests that the number of qubits on a quantum computer doubles every year. Consider the implications of the above two sentences for a moment, that are truly extraordinary. If a quantum computing sees a doubling in the number of qubits every year, and the processing capability of a quantum computer doubles with each additional qubit, this means, for example that if you start with one qubit, after ten years you will have 1,000 qubits, with a 10 to the power of 999 processing capability. However, there could be a catch. D-WAVE Quantum computers use a different technique and one less powerful that the quantum computer developed by Google. A 1,000-qubit quantum computer of the type recently developed by Google is probably many years off.

[54] Quantum computers create grave security risks for data that has long been safely guarded by the premise that certain math problems are simply too complex for computers to solve. Potentially even rendering blockchain redundant! Much of the world's digital data is currently protected by public key cryptography, *an encryption method that relies on a code based partly in factoring large numbers.*

Machine Learning aka Artificial Intelligence (AI)

> *"AI is probably the most important thing humanity has ever worked on. I think of it as something more profound than electricity or fire."*
> *Sundar Pichai, CEO, Google*

Artificial Intelligence, or AI, concerns the building of smart machines capable of performing tasks that typically require human intelligence. AI is an interdisciplinary science with multiple approaches, but advancements in Machine Learning, the computer code methodology behind AI, is creating a paradigm shift.

Machine learning makes it possible for machines to learn from experience, adjust to new inputs and perform human-like tasks. Most examples that you hear about today

from chess-playing computers to self-driving cars – rely heavily on deep learning and natural language processing.

By using these technologies, computers are trained to accomplish specific tasks by processing large amounts of data and recognizing patterns in the data.

The term artificial intelligence was initially coined in 1956, but the science has become more popular today thanks to increased data volumes, advanced algorithms, and improvements in computing power and storage. Much has been said about AI over the past few years, so much so that it has become a buzzword, a marketing tool, a black box of future wonders with no real shape or understanding to it.

There is a 50 per cent chance that machines will outperform humans in all tasks within 45 years, according to a survey by the University of Oxford and Yale University of more than 350 artificial intelligence researchers. Respondents assessed that machines are predicted to be better than humans at translating languages by 2024, writing high-school essays by 2026, driving a truck by 2027, working in retail by

---

Computers have traditionally struggled to do the calculations based on factoring, so data transferred in this way remains secure. Though a functional quantum computer of the necessary size to crack RSA encryption is still far off in the future, the threat that such a computer poses still resonates among digital security experts.

2031, writing a bestselling book by 2049 and perform surgery by 2053. In fact, all human jobs will be automated within the next 120 years, say respondents.

In 2017, Google DeepMind's AI software AlphaGo defeated Ke Jie, the world's number one player at the hugely complex Chinese game of Go, in the first of three games played in China. The AI won by half a point – the smallest possible margin of victory – in a match that lasted over four hours. Though the score-line looks close, AlphaGo was in the lead from early on in the game. We should bear in mind that AI favours moves that are more likely to guarantee victory, so it doesn't usually trounce its opponents. A later DeepMind program called AlphaZero, defeated AlphaGo within three days of being turned on, learning its moves solely from playing itself.

AI applicability is wide-ranging and will have a significant evolution and disruptive effect on our environment, ecosystem and, on we humans.

Our top three (in no ranking order) would include:

Self-driving Vehicles

Companies building these types of driver-assistance services, as well as full-blown self- driving vehicles, need to teach a computer how to take over essential parts (or all) of driving using digital sensor systems instead of a human's senses. To do that companies generally start by training algorithms using a large amount of data. A million sets of data are fed to a system to build a model, to train the machines to learn, and then test the results in a safe environment. The primary concern for autonomous car developers is handling unprecedented scenarios. A regular cycle of testing and implementation typical to deep learning algorithms is ensuring safe driving with more and more exposure to millions of scenarios. Data from cameras, sensors, and geo-mapping is helping create succinct and sophisticated models to navigate through traffic, identify paths, signage, pedestrian-only routes, and real-time elements like traffic volume and road blockages.

Healthcare and Medicine

From diagnosis to disease management and from drug research to population health management in a pandemic, AI is completely reshaping the life sciences sector, medicine and its practitioners, and the healthcare ecosystem.

Some of the Deep Learning projects picking up speed in the healthcare domain include:

- Helping early, accurate and speedy diagnosis of diseases
- Augmented clinicians addressing the shortage of specialist physicians
- Pathology results and treatment course standardization
- And understanding genetics to predict future risk

Re-admissions are a massive problem for the healthcare sector as it costs tens of millions of dollars. But with the use of deep learning and neural networks, healthcare is mitigating health risks associated with re-admissions while bringing down the costs.

In drug discovery, the machine-learning algorithm improves the models that predict how molecules will work, in the hope of accelerating the expensive and cumbersome drug discovery process. By using a secure blockchain- based system, these algorithms can trawl competing pharmaceutical companies' data with full traceability and importantly without revealing commercial secrets to rivals, resulting in significant efficiency gains and potentially a new pipeline of life-saving drugs. This is a welcome outcome bearing in mind the average drug costs up to two billion dollars and over ten years to bring to the patient.

Infrastructure Management

Most of us are familiar with the ability of software on our smartphones to do image recognition, such as identifying people in our photographs. More advanced applications, enhanced by deep learning networks, are enabling machines to identify individuals in a crowd and generate insights on the behaviour of people, cars, and potentially other objects.

This provides unique insights to better manage security, safety, counter-terrorism and emergency services.

For example, governments have made increasing usage of these capabilities to more effectively track and trace populations to control the spread of the novel coronavirus pandemic.

Other applications include fraud detection in both financial and news/information, energy consumption and forecasting, to name a few.

It's all doom and gloom for humans! But is it?

There is also a debate concerning whether AI represents the most significant risk factor for the human workforce. Will machines and computers develop the capability of taking on cognitive tasks and activities formerly considered the preserve of humans?

In contrast, Google's CEO, Sundar Pichai, claims that artificial intelligence will save us not destroy us. He said that the technology could eliminate many of the constraints we now face, helping us significantly to improve our environmental record by making "clean, cheap, reliable energy" a reality.

The Internet of Things

The Internet of Things, (IoT) refers to what is approximately seventy-five billion physical devices around the world that are now connected to the internet, collecting and sharing data.

Thanks to the convergence of cheaper and smaller processors, improving battery lives and wireless networks, it is now possible to turn anything, from a pill to an aeroplane, into being an element of the IoT. This adds a level of digital intelligence to devices that would be otherwise dumb, enabling them to communicate without a human involved, and merging the digital and physical worlds.

Four building blocks are required to make uo this gigantic web of devices:

- A device capable of sensing, communicating and taking action
- A communication infrastructure to connect all the devices, e.g. 5G
- A data management distribution system that is secure
- Applications to interpret the data and make appropriate recommendations. The most valuable element. IoT will facilitate key evolutions in our ecosystem and environment, such as:
- The creation of smart-interactive devices providing humans with new ways to engage with machines and thus bring about further societal value such as continuous human biological vitals monitoring
- The generation of rich contextual data directly relevant to the analysis. For example, a smartwatch reading a user's heart rate will give their physician highly pertinent information on the individual's lifestyle, and heart behaviour.
- The ability for devices to communicate and coordinate between them (D2D) to improve efficiency and productivity such as proximity-based services where devices detect their proximity and trigger different services (advertisements, local exchange of information, smart communication between vehicles, etcetera..

Akin to electrification in the early 20th century

Most coverage of IoT tends to revolve around the application to consumer products such as smart fridges. Still, we are underestimating the profound transformation of all industries which IoT will trigger. This is akin to electrification in the early twentieth century. For example, the impact on manufacturing, more specifically its operational efficiency such as better asset utilisation and productivity, will be worth as much as 11 per cent of the value of the global economy, according to McKinsey, a global consultancy.

It is therefore highly likely that IoT will fundamentally transform all known business models across all industry verticals. We should also expect new models to take shape. We will, for example, be able to buy by the hour. Just as airlines no longer buy their engines but lease them, we are unlikely to own a car but will pay for its use per kilometre driven or per hour used. The same for insurance products.

A question which remains unanswered will be the need for businesses, employees and consumers alike to develop new ways to trade their data for value. This will also transform the manner in which value creation and capture occur along the value chain. This is because greater visibility will exist concerning who owns each data point and who profits from it.

This, in turn, may force value distribution/allocation in a fairer more representative manner.

The current lack of standards around interoperability, privacy and security will need addressing.

IoT key enablers: Mesh and Edge Computing

Mesh computing enables data from IoT devices such as thermostats, appliances, and connected devices in the home to be shared with each other without internet connectivity. Since there is no cloud involved to store the data, the security concern is also reduced multi-fold.

Mesh computing will mean that devices can be completely automated, prioritising human comfort and safety.

Another technology related to Mesh computing is Edge computing. This describes computing that's done at or near the source of the data, instead of relying on the cloud. Such capability will improve issues of latency, privacy and security (e.g. our data is stored securely on our smartphones providing safer access than if it were all on a third-party server or cloud). In addition to these advantages, local/in-built AI capabilities will mean significantly improving the potential of IoT.

Self-driving cars are currently the most comprehensive form of Edge computing as they require onboard/ autonomous capabilities to function wherever they are.

Genomics

Genome sequencing or DNA sequencing is the process of determining the complete DNA sequence of an organism's genome at a single time.[55]

Sequencing DNA means determining the order of the four chemical building blocks – called "bases" – that make up the DNA molecule. This sequence tells scientists the kind of genetic information that is held in a particular DNA segment. For example, scientists can use sequence information to determine changes in a gene that may cause disease.

Since the completion of the Human Genome Project, technological improvements and automation have increased speed and lowered costs to the point where individual genes can be sequenced routinely. Some labs can sequence well over 100,000 billion bases per year, and an entire genome is sequenced for a few thousand US dollars.

Researchers are now able to compare vast stretches of DNA – one million bases or more – from different individuals quickly and cheaply. Such comparisons can yield an enormous amount of information about the role of inheritance in susceptibility to disease and in response to environmental influences. The ability to sequence the genome more rapidly and cost-effectively also creates a vast potential for diagnostics and therapies.

Although routine DNA sequencing in the doctor's office is probably more likely towards the end of this decade, some large medical centres have begun to use sequencing to detect and treat some diseases. In cancer, for example, physicians are increasingly able to apply sequence data to identify the particular type of cancer a patient has. This enables the physician to make better treatment choices.

Genome sequencing provides the highest resolution information about an organism's genome and has the potential to transform infectious disease management. By analysing differences in the genetic code of viruses such as Covid-19 from different patients, we can map

---

[55] *This entails sequencing all of an organism's chromosomal DNA as well as DNA contained in the mitochondria and, for plants, in the chloroplast. In other words, understanding the full code of the program that drives the existence of the organism. In practice, genome sequences that are nearly complete are also called whole genome sequences.*

the spread of the virus in real-time, tracking new mutations to identify if unconventional strains are emerging. A better understanding of the genetic makeup of the virus could save lives by facilitating the design of therapies and vaccines to combat the virus.

In the future of 'personalized medicine', genome sequence data will be an essential tool to guide therapeutic intervention spelling the end of one size fits all medication and clinical trials. The mechanism of gene sequencing is also used to pinpoint functional variants and improve the knowledge available to researchers, and hence lay the foundation for predicting disease susceptibility and drug response.

On a related note, human DNA has been identified as having remarkable data storage properties assessed to approximate 100,000 times what is achievable in modern- day laptops[56] and is exceptionally resistant to the elements.

DNA could replace hard drives, tape and other storage mediums one day. It's not as far-fetched as it sounds, and significant progress is being made, including new, zero- error individual-file data retrieval. Such storage capability presents the opportunity to reduce our reliance on energy- intensive storage. The exponential growth in data volume will place significant loads on the energy sources available, not to mention the vast space that is taken up by server farms.

Ray Kurzweil, who is a well-known futurist and a director of engineering at Google, believes that clinical applications of biotechnology will profoundly transform health and medicine:

"Biotechnology is not just another type of medicine. It's a whole profound methodology for reprogramming the outdate software in our bodies. We have software in the form of our DNA. They're actually linear forms of data, and they control our lives. But they evolved in a period when it wasn't in the interest of the human species to live past the age of twenty because there were limited food and resources." Ray Kurzweil said.

If this sounds too far-fetched, consider the alteration and improvement of DNA which will soon become commonplace in hospitals through techniques such as immunotherapy.

Immunotherapy is an emerging way to fight autoimmune diseases, which are conditions caused by a weird response from the immune

---

[56] *SSD memory also presents the advantage of being used in any condition and its microscopic size offers numerous options for flexible and localised solutions*

system. For this type of treatment, medical specialists bolster the immune system by providing it with artificial proteins and stimulating it to work harder in fighting the ailment.

CAR T-cell is short for chimeric antigen receptor T-cell therapy. With CAR-T-cell therapy, doctors are 'reprogramming' a human's T cells to attack cancer cells. CAR-T is now a reality, with pharmaceutical company Novartis receiving regulatory approval for its CART-T cell therapy for leukaemia in 2018.

The potential to alter our ecosystem

Blockchain & Distributed ledgers

 In 2008 an anonymous paper[57] detailed the building blocks of a new distributed ledger technology called bitcoin. Today while bitcoin itself[58] is controversial, the technology behind it, known as blockchain or distributed ledger technology, or even DLT, is creating an entirely new mechanism for the storage and exchange of information/data.

Bringing this transformation to reality means overcoming challenges such as agreeing on the structure of blockchain networks, having common standards, and national data transmission regulations (such as GDPR).

Distributed ledger technology involves the creation and exchange of unique digital records without a centralised trusted party, principally achieved through advanced cryptography and peer2peer networking. The combination of secure cryptography with the ability to tag any physical product with a digital attribute allows blockchain to create a unique identification effectively and unchangeable record rendering the transaction between supplier and customer to be simpler, cheaper and trusted. This method for facilitating exchange is called a smart contract.

---

[57] *Paper was named as being by Satoshi Nakamoto, but no one knows who he/she is (except for 'Nakamoto' himself, herself or Itself*

[58] *But not bitcoin itself, another version of blockchain now exist and may prove more disruptive than bitcoin itself*

This technology has the potential to revolutionise many industries for the following reasons:

- It enables the creation and transfer of unique digital objects which are verifiable and eliminates the risk of false copies
- It enables transparency, verification and unchangeable objects without the need to trust a central third party.
- It enables smart contracts entailing programmable transactions (execution, tracing & verification) which are stored on the ledger and requires no human involvement. These smart contracts can transfer any piece of information under any set of specific circumstances
- It requires little software, storage and connectivity, thus democratising any exchange/market right down to the individual and eliminates the current centralised and rent-seeking intermediaries
- It finally provides an opportunity for the individual to realise the value of their personal digital data and the security in its usage

Studies suggest that the human data marketplace represents an estimated $150B to $200B per annum. Our inherent human data is regularly bought and sold without our consent, authorisation, consideration, or compensation.[59]

If we look beyond the bitcoin and other cryptocurrency hubris, blockchain technology represents enormous potential to create new secure marketplaces or exchanges. For example, blockchain could mean overcoming the lack of interoperability within vast data pools such as medical data (e.g. electronic health records) which is an essential step in discovering new cures for diseases such as cancer.[60]

The convergence between distributed ledger creating trust transactions and other technologies, such as the Internet of Things,

---

[59] *According to hu-manity.co, a new venture which wants to change the way we share data by giving people legal ownership with contractual enforcement handled on the blockchain.*
[60] *Blockchain technology for improving clinical research quality, Mehdi Benchoufi & Philippe Ravaud*

will transform entire ecosystems. An example of an application could be a reformed voting system.

Risks exist including the misuse of data by anyone with keys to the blockchain security.

Regulators will need to tread carefully not to thwart the innovation built around blockchain while preventing the creation of systemic risk.

The future of flight

Air travel is set to be transformed. New materials are making planes lighter and, we are promised, more comfortable to travel in. Better engines are making them quieter and cheaper to run. And better avionics are making them safer.

We also approach a day when most aircraft will no longer need pilot(s). Airlines and their passengers and regulators will take a while to come to terms with this, so it is likely that pilots will sit in the cockpit long after they are needed with the simple task of providing reassurance to the public. But we mustn't forget that armed forces are already embracing this pilotless future. Surveillance and missile-carrying drones have been around for a couple of decades. The 2020s will see robot military helicopters introduced and pilotless fighter jets starting to emerge even though these jets will, at least, to begin with, be parts of squadrons that have a human leader in control.

Cargo aircraft, probably military and civilian, will be robotised as well.

New technology is also extending the concept of civil aviation. The idea of supersonic transport for civilians is now a reality again, some two decades after Concorde's last flight. Another age-old fantasy is flying cars which seem likely to become a reality in the next few years, as manufacturers both new and old rush to build electrically- propelled small aircraft. Some of these will also serve as remotely controlled taxis. Its owners will pilot the private car version.

Indeed, technology cynics often refer to TV shows from the past, such as the Jetsons, which featured flying cars, illustrating how disappointing technology is compared to predictions from three of four decades ago. Yet, flying cars are now being developed by several companies. This is being made possible thanks to convergence, in particular convergence with drone technology. Drones were initially developed by the military for spying and then as weapons, before being adopted as toys and used by industry.

Now the technology is sufficiently advanced that the dream of flying cars may be realisable within a short timeframe. Advances in lithium-ion batteries and lighter, durable materials, are also helping advance flying cars, as carbon fibre manufacturing, for example, benefits from a learning rate. GPS (think Sat Nav) technology, in combination with 5G, sensors and AI, will be used to help ensure air crashes between flying cars are all but eliminated.

3D Printing/additive manufacturing

3D printing, also referred to as additive manufacturing, is a manufacturing process through which three-dimensional (3D) solid objects are made. It enables the creation of physical 3D models of objects using a series of additive or layers laid down in succession to create a complete 3D object.

Whereas the first industrial revolution led to the mass production of goods, transforming the global economy, 3D printing technology could enable humans to create single items as cheaply as it is to produce thousands. This could reverse the fundamentals of global manufacturing. 3D printing could have as profound an impact on the world as the birth of the factory did in the eighteenth century.[61]

3D printing can be the perfect technology for creating prototypes, supporting the innovation process, and for creating shapes that might be quite difficult to create using traditional manufacturing techniques. Surgeons are employing such technology to familiarise themselves with complex surgery procedures by printing precise models of the organs in-question based on precise MRI scan imagery.

3D printing could have a profound impact on humanity

---

[61] *In 2014, when researching for iDisrupted, experts we spoke to at the time were sceptical that it would be possible to ever 3D print a motor car. Some five years on, such a car exists! We have also witnessed the printing of dwellings, musical instruments and food!*

in one respect. As we age, the wear and tear on our bodies will become an ever-growing challenge. This problem will become more pervasive as more of us live beyond 100.[62]

3D Printing presents humankind with a unique opportunity to print body parts bespoke to our specific dimensions. The introduction of bioprinters is already being used to create organelles for scientific research, and there have been some impressive proof of concept for full organs.

The combination of the 3D Printing technological and automation will rewrite centuries of well-established manufacturing rules and probably decentralise businesses completely, reducing the need to transport manufactured goods or components over long distances, such as by lorry or via shipping lanes. This would fundamentally change logistics and transport requirements, reducing shipping and road traffic, perhaps helping to reduce the emission of global warming gases, but simultaneously destroying millions of jobs in some industries, while possibly creating jobs in others.

Virtual Reality or VR

Virtual reality describes a three-dimensional, computer-generated environment which can be explored and interacted with by a person. That person becomes part of this virtual world or immersed within this environment and while there, is able to manipulate objects or perform a series of actions. This is more difficult than it sounds since our senses and brains provide us with a finely synchronised and mediated experience. If anything is even a little off, we can tell. The issues that divide convincing or enjoyable virtual reality experiences from jarring or unpleasant ones are partly technical and partly conceptual.

VR's application in video games, movies or in adult entertainment is obvious.

---

[62] *Also relates to significant number of people already on the organ transplant waitlist across the world*

It also has applications beyond the field of entertainment, for example as an aide for training humans. It can be applied to:

- Military personnel preparing for the battlefield
- Special forces practising the rescue of hostages
- For bringing greater experiential near-reality to classrooms and lecture halls
- And for architects and civil engineers, it can be used to prototype a complex construction within a near-real context.

But one very practical application which stands out is in the field of Mental health. One in four of us will experience mental health issues at some point in our life. Virtual Reality-enabled therapy is the use of technology for psychological therapy, for example, treating Post Traumatic Stress Disorder.

Patients navigate through digitally created environments and complete specially designed tasks tailored to treat a specific ailment. This is potentially an opportunity for us to treat mental health illnesses without necessarily resorting to the use of chemicals which will invariably have side effects.

We should also be mindful that it would not be difficult to weaponise these medical advances and find them used in the field of torture.

The potential to alter us Homo sapiens

An entirely new range of biotechnologies will soon be available, which will have the potential to change us as humans.

At its simplest, biotechnology is technology based on biology – biotechnology harnesses cellular and biomolecular processes to develop technologies and products that help improve our lives and the health of our planet. We have used the biological processes of micro- organisms for more than 6,000 years to make useful food products, including bread and cheese, and to preserve dairy products.

Significant biotech advances in the pipeline include:

- Heal or cure by harnessing nature's own toolbox and using our own genetic makeup
- Use biological processes such as fermentation to harness biocatalysts such as enzymes, yeast, and other microbes to become microscopic manufacturing plants
- Improve crop insect resistance, enhance crop herbicide tolerance and facilitate the use of more environmentally sustainable farming practices.

Both academia and corporates are already engineering DNA to produce new or modified species, and Chinese scientists are using a DNA editing tool called CRISPR/Cas 9 to treat cancer patients.

The ability to edit our DNA ties in with genome sequencing. Ever since 2000, when Bill Clinton, at the time president of the USA, launched the Human Genome Project, we have seen the cost of sequencing the human genome drop and its application to medical research grow significantly.

This future will challenge our understanding of what it will mean to be human, from both a biological and a social perspective. Will we achieve longer lives, enhance our physical and mental capabilities? How will we ensure that us humans' benefit? How will we manage the ethics of the application of such technologies? See chapter 8 on morals and sloth to see the implications of technologies used to augmented us so much that it could be argued we have become a different species of humans.

Editing our DNA

One of the most important breakthroughs of this century so far is the discovery of CRISPR/cas9 – a method of editing DNA already used by nature.

Up until now, the fledgeling field of genome engineering has offered researchers only a few options with a great deal of limitations attached to them. It is not therefore surprising that the discovery of the simple, and affordable, CRISPR/ Cas 9 (CRISPR) mechanism is completely changing the face of genomic engineering.

CRISPR technology is creating a biological revolution. What was an unknown technique a few years ago is quickly becoming a standard laboratory tool, and it is on its way to touching all aspects of our lives.

Researchers are deploying CRISPR across a wide range of life science disciplines, from agriculture, medicine to industrial fermentation.

The discovery of CRISPR technology can be traced back to 1993. It wasn't until 2007 that researchers concluded that CRISPR's function was related to microbial cellular immunity. It wasn't long before researchers realised that CRISPR could be repurposed to make specific alterations in the genomes of not only microbes, but plant, animal, and other varieties of cells. In 2012, CRISPR was eventually utilised in this manner. CRISPR's is the most powerful genome-editing technology ever. Its adoption and application are growing exponentially.

Applications of Genome editing

In the USA, some 100,000 people suffer from sickle-cell disease. This is a genetic disorder caused by mutations in the genes that make haemoglobin, an important protein in red blood cells.

Typically, both parents must pass on an abnormal gene in order for a child to develop this disease. CRISPR Therapeutics and Stanford are taking different approaches using CRISPR. Both groups are extracting stem cells from patients' bone marrow and then altering them with CRISPR. One is trying to fix the defective gene in sickle- cell, but CRISPR Therapeutics is using the editing tool to make cells produce another protein, an infant version of haemoglobin. The modified cells will then be returned back into the patients.

Cheaper and far more precise than previously available gene-editing processes, the CRISPR toolkit will continue to see new applications. We share a few promising areas to give you an idea of the scale.

Enabling transplant organs

There is a shortage of organs for transplant for those who desperately need them. Until we can grow new ones from our stem cells, another technological advance which we cover later in this chapter, we will need to consider some alternatives; some made more plausible through CRISPR.

The medical community is exploring using pigs for their kidneys instead of their bacon. The risk of catching a common porcine virus is a huge stumbling block, one that CRISPR could solve by taking a molecular chainsaw to the pathogens' genes.

Simplifying insulin therapy for diabetics

For people with type 1 diabetes, topping up their body with much-needed insulin is an invasive, onerous and uncomfortable process which impacts their quality of life.

Researchers are designing a skin graft that contains a CRISPR-modified version of a protein that helps insulin regulate blood glucose levels and could potentially help make the needle history.

Erase killer heart conditions

Scientists have successfully edited a gene responsible for a heart condition in a human embryo resulting in the cells being discouraged from developing further. Although the embryos were only allowed to grow for a few days and were not implanted, the researchers will continue to move forward.

Destroying superbugs

MRSA and other superbugs represent a grave threat to human health, particularly as the overuse of antibiotics, is creating bugs with greater resistance. The threat posed by so-called superbugs could be far greater than the threat posed by Coronaviruses.

One potential way to combat these superbugs could be to modify viruses with a payload that forces a bacteria to go rogue and chew up its own genes – in other words; the superbug commits suicide.

Without a doubt, CRISPR is not only paving the way for us to solve the most difficult of problems in the life sciences, but also enabling the scientific community to explore dimensions of the genome that we've been unable to study up until this point.

The Experiment – Testing CRISPR ethics

On November 26th, 2018, He Jiankui, a DNA-sequencing expert at the Southern University of Science and Technology, in Shenzhen, China, claimed he had orchestrated the birth of the world's first gene-edited babies: twin girls. They arrived in early October that year. His claim triggered the fury of the world.

What Dr He achieved has been called into question. He says he used CRISPR to disable, in one of the twins, called Nana, both parental copies of a gene called CCR5. This gene encodes a protein used by HIV to enter cells. If Dr He's claim is true, he may have conferred on Nana immunity to infection by HIV, thus protecting her from Aids. Moreover, by editing the genes of a fertilised egg – from which all body tissues, including the ovaries, are derived – he has done this in a way that can be passed down to future generations.

Nana's sister Lulu, Dr He says, has also had her genome modified, but with only partial success. Only one parental copy of CCR5 was disabled, and so she remains unprotected. However, an independent assessment of Dr He's data by several gene-editing experts, including Kiran Musunuru of the University of Pennsylvania, suggests the experiment achieved only partial success in both twins.

Stem Cell Technologies

Stem-cell research studies the properties of stem cells and their potential use in medicine. As stem cells are the source of all tissues, understanding their properties will help our understanding of the healthy and diseased body's development and homeostasis.

As you read this book, your body's stem cells are working hard to replace your skin, create red and white blood cells and complete thousands of other tasks essential to you being alive.

One theory of ageing suggests that between the ages of thirty and fifty, our stem cells reach a turning point and start to decline in number and function, so we age.

Scientists generally agree that a stem cell is capable of:

- Self-renewal by dividing into another stem cell, and so making an identical copy of itself; and
- Differentiate, meaning to change into a variety of other cell types.
  These properties offer unique applications.

Stem cells have the ability to replace damaged cells and treat disease. This is already being used in the treatment of burns, and to restore the blood system in patients with leukaemia and other blood disorders.

Stem cells may also hold the key to replacing cells lost in many other devastating diseases for which there are currently no sustainable cures. Today, donated tissues and organs are often used to replace damaged tissue, but the demand far outweighs the available supply. If stem cells can be directed to differentiate into specific cell types, offer the possibility of a renewable source of replacement cells and tissues to treat diseases including Parkinson's, stroke, heart disease and diabetes. This prospect is an exciting one, but significant technical hurdles remain that will be overcome through years of intensive research.

Studying diseases

It is difficult to obtain the cells that are damaged in a disease and to study them in detail. Stem cells, either carrying the disease gene or engineered to contain the disease genes, offer a viable alternative. Scientists are exploring the use of stem cells to model disease processes in the laboratory, and therefore better understand what triggers the disease.

Testing new medical treatments

New medications could be tested for safety on specialised cells generated in large numbers from stem cell lines and reducing the need for animal testing and potentially, the cost of developing new drugs. Cancer cell lines, for example, are used to screen potential anti-tumour drugs.

Synthetic Biology

Synthetic biology involves redesigning organisms for useful purposes by engineering them to have new abilities. Synthetic biology researchers and companies around the world are harnessing the power of nature to solve problems in medicine, manufacturing and agriculture.

The potential to significantly improve the sustainability of many industries could be realised, such as the development of crops which will grow in seawater. We will consider these technological advances later in this chapter as we investigate innovations that have the potential to alter our environment.

We should be aware that synthetic biology is also driving significant advances in biomedicine, which will lead to transformational improvements in healthcare. We have already described how patients are benefiting from so-called CAR (for chimeric antigen receptor) technology, which engineers the immune cells (T-cells) of the patient to recognize and attack cancer cells.

The ability to re-programme somatic cells from patients into induced pluripotent stem cells is furthering our understanding of their disease, reducing the use of animals in research, and paving the way for the development of personalized medicines and cell therapies. In principle at least, a patient's cells can be engineered to multiply, differentiate into different cell types and even self-assemble into new tissues, or even organs, to repair those damaged through disease or injury.

Work on new vectors that can deliver large genetic loads to target tissues is helping to produce more efficient therapeutics and vaccines that will have fewer side effects and a smaller risk of resistance. Furthermore, optimizing antibody or vaccine production so that they are in an edible format (plant-based), could greatly reduce the cost and increase the speed of vaccine production in a pandemic.

The convergence of molecular biology, materials engineering, computational approaches and predictive mathematical modelling will positively impact our society, industrial landscape and global environment. With such potential power at our fingertips, we must carefully consider the consequences of our actions as we progress towards this biotechnological future.

Brain/Machine interfaces

A brain-computer interface (BCI), sometimes called neural lace, is a wireless brain-computer system that would add a digital layer of intelligence to our brain.

The stuff of many science fiction movies such as the popular 1999 movie The Matrix, which saw Keanu Reeves enter an artificial reality, it's a concept nanotechnologist have been developing.

Such technology represents an untested and incredible opportunity to seriously augment us humans and, as Elon Musk put it, give us a fighting chance in a world of Artificial Intelligence.

Neural Lace

At its most basic form, neural lace is an ultra-thin mesh that can be implanted in the skull, forming a collection of electrodes capable of monitoring brain function. It creates an interface between the brain and the machine.

To be able to insert neural lace, a tiny needle containing the rolled-up mesh is placed inside the skull, and the mesh is injected. As the mesh leaves the needle, it unravels, spanning the brain. Gradually, the lace will be accepted as part of the brain and will even move with it as it grows or very slightly changes size.

It's thought that neural lace could treat neurodegenerative disorders such as Parkinson's disease and other life-altering brain disorders.

Elon Musk, whose numerous companies include a company called Neuralink, says his neural lace technology will eventually be able to seamlessly combine humans with computers, giving us a shot at becoming "symbiotic" with artificial intelligence.

The potential to alter our environment

 We are all aware of the environmental and ecological debate sparked off by the Swedish activist Greta Thunberg. Much of the debate is centred on the near-term actions which humans could and should be taking to mitigate the impact we have on our habitat and environment.

Her arguments are important, but we should not ignore the opportunity we have to correct and undo the damage humans have inflicted on the planet through the appropriate use of technological innovation.

Could the CRISPR technology helps us overcome climate change?

According to the Intergovernmental Panel on Climate Change (IPCC), feeding the world's population now employs almost three-quarters of the world's ice-free surface, while contributing twenty-two per cent of global greenhouse gas emissions. Put simply; there is not enough land to produce enough calories for all our hungry human mouths, without negatively impacting the Earth.

This, in turn, creates a further problem. Insufficient land to feed a growing population has put pressure on farmers to make increasing use of antibiotics expediting the point at which they are no longer effective. As the kingdom of humanity continues to encroaches on the kingdom of nature, the risk of pandemics such as Coronaviruses increase.

By 2050, eating less meat and throwing less food in landfills could keep several gigatons of CO_2 out of the atmosphere and free up millions of square miles of land to return to carbon-sucking forests, according to the IPCC. But that's not as sexy, or as controversial, as CRISPR'ing crops to thrive amid the coming onslaught of severe droughts, massive heatwaves, mega-floods, and rising seas.

And though not a silver bullet solution, the potential for gene editing to make every acre of land yield yet more is capturing the imagination of plant scientists, AgTech, climate change activists and governments alike.

The trick is knowing which genes to target and which edits to make. Enter CRISPR. Because it's best at cutting DNA, CRISPR allows plant scientists to knock out genes one at a time and observe what happens to the plant without them. It's more a case of reverse-engineering each plant's genetic code.

Could the discovery or creation of super- materials change our world?

A super material is any material with remarkable physical properties. Those of you familiar with the Superman films will think of Kryptonite.

Graphene is the king of super materials. Research indicates that it is stronger than steel, thinner than paper and the future of technology advancement.

But what is graphene? The simplest way to describe graphene is that it is a single, thin layer of graphite. Graphite is an allotrope of the element carbon, meaning it possesses the same atoms, but they are arranged in a different way, giving the material different properties. Both diamond and graphite are forms of carbon, yet they very different.

Diamonds are incredibly strong, while graphite is brittle. Despite its incredible thinness (merely one atom thick), graphene is one of the strongest materials known. It is more than 100 times stronger than steel. If it's incredible strength is not already enough to make it amazing, its unique properties don't stop there. It is also flexible, transparent, highly conductive, and seemingly impermeable to most gases and liquids.

Scientists are developing a wide range of uses for this material in fields as varied as consumer technology and environmental science. In addition to applications in flexible electronics, solar cells, semiconductors, it is its applicability in water filtration and desalination, which holds further huge potential.

Because graphene consists of tight atomic bonds, it is impermeable to nearly all liquids. Curiously, water molecules are an exception. Because water can evaporate through graphene, whilst most gases and liquids cannot, graphene could be exceptional for filtration. Researchers at the University of Manchester in the United Kingdom tested graphene permeability with alcohol and were able to distil very strong samples of spirits.

These properties could make graphene also immensely helpful in purifying water of toxins. With overpopulation continuing to be one of the world's most pressing environmental concerns, maintaining a clean water supply will become more important.

Water scarcity afflicts more than one billion people worldwide, a number that will continue to rise given current trends. Graphene-based filters will have the potential to improve water purification, increasing the amount of freshwater available while requiring far less energy to produce. For countries such as Jordan, which will run out of freshwater in the next few decades, this will be welcome news.

But graphene isn't the only game-changing material to come out of the laboratory. Here are six super materials (not exhaustive) that have the potential to transform our world and future.

Self-healing materials

The human body is very good at fixing itself. The artificial environment is not. The University of Illinois has been engineering bio-inspired plastics that can self-heal. Last year they created a new polymer that oozes to repair a visible hole. The polymer is embedded with a vascular system of liquids which, when broken and combined, clot just like blood. While all the materials have been able to heal microscopic cracks, this new one repaired a hole four millimeters wide with cracks radiating all around it. Engineers have also been envisioning concrete, asphalt, and metal that can heal itself. Imagine a city with no more potholes!

Thermoelectric Materials

If you ever had a laptop burn your lap or you have touched the hot engine cover of a car, then you have experienced waste. Waste heat is the inevitable effect of running any device that uses power. We waste, through heat, as much as two-thirds of all energy used. But what if there was a way to capture all that wasted energy? We may have the answer in thermo-electric materials, which make electricity from heat.

Perovskites

Solar power is getting even cheaper but making a plant of solar cells from silicon is still an expensive, energy-intensive process. There is now an alternative material called perovskites.

Perovskites are a class of materials defined by a particular crystalline structure. They can contain any number of elements, usually lead and tin. These raw materials are cheap compare to crystalline silicon, and they can be sprayed onto glass rather than assembled in clean rooms.

Aerogels

Aerogels sound too good to be real. They can withstand the heat of a blowtorch and the weight of a car. The material is almost exactly what the name implies: gels where the liquid has been replaced entirely by air. Sometimes also referred to as frozen smoke or blue smoke, aerogel can take the form of any number of substances, including silica, metal oxides, and graphene.

Meta-materials

If you've read about meta-materials, you likely have read about it in a sentence that also mentioned Harry Potter and an invisible cloak.

Indeed, meta-materials, whose nanostructures are designed to scatter light in specific ways, could one day be used to render objects invisible.

What's more interesting about metamaterials is that they don't just redirect visible light. Depending on how and what a particular meta-material is made of, they can also scatter microwaves, radio-waves, and other types of rays. These are highly attractive properties to the military.

Stanene

Stanene is also made of a single layer of atoms. But instead of carbon, stanene is composed of tin which allows it to do what even wonder material graphene cannot conduct electricity with 100 per cent efficiency.

If the predictions about stanene bear out, it could revolutionise the microchip industry. Namely, the chip could get a lot more powerful as heat limitations dissipate. Silicon chips are limited by the heat created by electrons moving.

Its adoption in the energy storage and distribution sector could be its most revolutionary application.

Or will convergence be the saviour of our environment?

The inevitable convergence of data, analytics and super- materials such as graphene will be applications that no one had considered. This provides a unique opportunity for us to use technology to reduce and even reverse the damager we have inflicted on the environment, defeat hunger, while handing humans a potential final victory over disease.

But for these technologies to develop fully, we need to allow the learning rate described in the previously to come in to play, meaning the creation of global markets. We need a network of ideas to be freely available. This means that the whole of humanity can be enlisted in making these opportunities happen. If instead, we retreat behind borders, emphasis self-sufficiency, and reverse the trends of globalisation, these opportunities will be lost.

Consider the likelihood of a world where the generation of electricity from renewables is more efficient (thus reducing the dependence on fossil fuels), where the storage and distribution are almost loss-less, and where the consumption is highly efficient. Overlay this with management systems governed by machine learning to ensure near-perfect resource management and allocation, and we can all begin to conceptualise that we could realistically reduce humankind's impact on the environment.

The burning of fossil fuels for energy and animal agriculture are among the biggest contributors to global warming, along with deforestation. Globally, fossil fuel-based energy contributes to about sixty-four per cent of human greenhouse gas emissions, with deforestation at about eighteen per cent, and animal agriculture between thirteen per cent and eighteen per cent.

One of the main ways in which the livestock sector contributes to global warming is through deforestation caused by the expansion of pastureland and arable land used to grow feed crops for the animals. Overall, animal agriculture is accountable for about nine per cent of human-caused carbon dioxide emissions globally.

Animal agriculture is also a significant source of greenhouse gases. For example, ruminant animals like cattle produce methane, which is a greenhouse gas about 20 times more potent than carbon dioxide. The livestock sector is responsible for about 37 per cent of human-caused methane emissions, and about sixty-five per cent of human nitrous oxide emissions (mainly from manure), globally.

With the debate raging on whether humans should consume less meat in order to reduce the impact on the climate, it is an appropriate point to explore whether lab-grown meat, related to the stem cell technological advances, could also have a positive impact on our environment.

Unlike the trendy Impossible Foods and Beyond Meat burger brands which use plants to try and recreate the taste of meat, lab-grown meat takes a different approach. It takes the stem cells from an animal and places them in a bioreactor, encouraging the growth of more cells that can be used to create a new cut of meat.

However, some researchers speculate that depending on the efficiency of the production process, the rise of the cultured meat industry could actually make climate change worse than traditional beef production. One issue is the long-lasting impact of carbon pollution versus methane gas pollution.

Lab meat doesn't currently solve anything from an environmental perspective since the energy emissions to manufacture it are high. The product still has a carbon footprint that is roughly five times the carbon footprint of chicken and ten times higher than plant-based processed meats.

This could all change. The suggestion that cultured meat has a high carbon footprint has come under some criticism as studies looking at the costs of this technology assumed that the energy provided to produce cultured meat will be generated in exactly the same way in the future as it is today.

But renewable energy costs are steadily falling, driven by economies of scale through the growing adoption and the introduction of technologies such as the super materials discussed previously. Furthermore, cultured meat production requires temperatures to be kept at certain levels, but creating either hot or cool air are both examples of exactly the kind of applications that make optimal use of renewables. Warmth can be stored in storage heaters, and the process of creating cool air can be supported by creating ice at times when energy is more plentiful.

The critique of cultured meat also overlooks a key point. When the meat is created in factory conditions, it requires much less land and water than either meat created by rearing livestock or even imitation meat created from plants. Since de-forestation to make room for land used for farming is a major contribution to climate change, a reversal in the process, planting trees freed up by developments in cultured meat, could be a crucial step in winning the war against climate change.

It cost two point seven billion dollars to sequence the human genome for the first time; now it costs around $1,000. If cultured meat can develop at a comparable rate, then within one or two decades, meat created from this source could be cheaper, and cleaner on the environment, making less use of the most important resource of all, freshwater.

But all these promises and challenges could be upset by insects!

Imagine that you are in a restaurant. On the menu, you can choose between the classic beef steak, but also, a cricket steak. What would be the advantages of choosing crickets rather than beef?

While red meat is often known to be a significant source of protein in our diet, it is interesting to note that crickets have a protein content of about two to three times higher.

Crickets, just like beef, are an excellent source of complete protein, namely up to sixty-five per cent versus beef's maximum of twenty-six per cent. In addition to their higher protein content, crickets also provide more essential amino acids than beef on the same weight basis. Thus, the cricket steak would be much more profitable in terms of proteins offered.

And crickets are bred in very large numbers in smaller spaces, reaching adulthood in less than six weeks. By way of example, a 60,000 square foot building hosts approximately one hundred million crickets, only requiring very small quantities of food and water greenhouse gas emission.

Many Asian nations already include insects within their diet but are Westerners ready to switch our perceptions and diets?

Did You Say, "So What"?

We should not, however, assume that humanity's technology advances will automatically lead to substantial improvement. A prime example would be the supposition that more efficient lighting leads to diminished consumption. The very contrary is the truth!

LEDs (Light Emitting Diodes) use a lot less energy per lumen produced. We are generally advised that LED lighting uses an average of forty per cent less power than fluorescents, and eighty per cent less than incandescent lighting, to produce the same amount of light.

A few years ago, there had been predictions that the use of LEDs to illuminate buildings and outdoor spaces would reducee the total carbon dioxide (CO_2) emissions of lighting by an estimated 570 million tons in 2017. This reduction is roughly equivalent to shutting down 162 coal-fired power plants.

The industry went as far as saying that LED conversion is unlike other measures, which require people to reduce consumption or make lifestyle changes.

But we humans didn't.

In its claims, the industry assumed that we would replace inefficient lighting with LEDs. In fact, we are using more energy than ever as we keep finding ingenious ways to use LEDs, including in places that we hadn't before.

Lighting has now become so cheap to run, thanks to the low cost of energy and the efficiency of the technology, that we have adopted new lighting technologies wholeheartedly. We are using far more of it, particularly in developing countries where standards of living are improving dramatically.

And much of this is happening in parts of the world that generate most of their electricity with coal.

So, we must remember that the many lauded benefits of our technological advancement will only be to our true advantage if we adapt, change, shape and own its implementation.

But here is the real opportunity

On the other hand, ever since we invented agriculture, our species has engaged in practices that threatened the environment, perhaps made us less healthy and maybe less happy.

We can't reverse, ever!

Agriculture led to a rising population. We would have no hope of feeding and clothing the world if we returned to hunter-gathering. Indeed, we would have no hope of feeding and clothing the world without technology and if we reverse globalisation.

But new technologies, subject to convergence, provide us with an opportunity to enjoy plenty – all the material needs we need. Back in 1798, Thomas Malthus speculated that as technology advances, and output increases, the population also increases, thereby cancelling out the benefits of increased production on a per person basis. It is the gloomiest theory in economics, the reason why economics is sometimes called the dismal science.

Although the global population is increasing today, there is reason to think that this increase will peak this century. Indeed, throughout much of the world, the fertility rate is lower than what is called the replacement rate. Very soon, the number of deaths will be greater than the number of births across much of the world. Japan's population will decrease by around thirty million by 2049. Europe, North America and then China will follow. In fact, China may experience an especially rapid fall in its population because of the disproportionately high male to female ratio. Even in Africa, where the population is still increasing fast, we expect a peak.

This means a so-called Malthusian trap can be avoided. Instead, we can at last look forward to a time when technology enriches us all, making material goods affordable for everyone. This will, in turn, allow us to focus our attention on that very thing that makes us human our social skills, our empathy our interaction with others.

It will be as if we can return to a kind of Eden.

By fighting against technology, failing to see the opportunity it creates and focusing on the wrong dangers, thereby losing sight of the real threats created by technology, we risk turning humanity's greatest triumph into disaster.

If we react to challenges created by pandemics by retreating behind our borders, pulling up national drawbridges, reversing globalisation, we risk repeating the errors of history

Let's not mess this one up.

Chapter 5

Technology cynicism and sudden change

"You can always fool yourself into seeing a decline if you compare rose-tinted images of the past with bleeding headlines of the present."
Steven Pinker

 Darwin taught us that evolution is a super slow process. In fact, the famous evolutionary biologist Richard Dawkins once said that Darwinian evolution has three speeds: slow, dead slow and stop.

Maybe this view of evolution serves as a metaphor for how people think and expect the world to change, how society changes, how technology develops. Change is slow, and to say otherwise is to ignore the lesson of history, even ignore the rules of evolution itself, or so some might say. And further, to argue technology is accelerating, or even accelerating at an accelerating rate, as this book suggests, is to say 'this time it is different', which history tells us, it never is.

It is just that if you look at the story of life on Earth, you find it changes in fits and starts, and on occasions, extraordinarily rapid change has occurred.

And the most crucial moment – singular endosymbiosis, which created all complex life, may have taken place over a few minutes.

The Bible says God created the world in seven days. It seems that the moment that complex life emerged was even more rapid than that.

Later on, in the story of life, the Cambrian explosion led to an incredible period of change. It may have occurred over several million years, a good deal slower than endosymbiosis, but in evolutionary terms, this is the blink of an eye.

Indeed, look at natural evolution and then cultural evolution, and you will find it is punctuated with moments of rapid change. [63]

So, consider these events:

- Singular endosymbiosis
- The Cambrian explosion
- The meteorite wiping out the dinosaurs creating a gap in the market of life which mammals filled
- The formation of the East African Rift Valley, leading to the evolution of a bipedal ape
- The evolution of an ape that could speak leading to the rapid acceleration of evolution creating Homo sapiens sapiens
- The discovery of agriculture enabling the formation of cities — hubs for supporting the spread of ideas.
- The invention of writing
- The invention of the printing press
- The internet
- And now, we are at the early stage, the development of augmented and virtual reality supported by AI.

These moments mark points when the curve tracking change, got steeper. More recently, they marked stages when the curve got steeper at an accelerating rate — an acceleration in acceleration. This time it is no different; this time, we are merely seeing the tale of accelerating change continue inexorably to its conclusion.

To argue that technological innovation is not likely to accelerate is to ignore the lesson of history.

---

[63] This is a deliberate reference to the work of the late great Stephen J Gould advanced a theory of punctuated equilibrium.

The danger of denial

Sometimes denial can be motivated by the most nefarious of reasons. Sometimes it is simply based on a misunderstanding. We all have our biases – our preconceived ideas that we hold dear and then we interpret the evidence of the real world through the filter of such preconceived notions. It is called confirmation bias. We only consider the evidence that supports our beliefs, ignore evidence that contradicts them and become convinced we are right – after all, in such circumstances, the evidence is overwhelming.

Why do people deny anthropogenic climate change? A case for saying 'I am not sure' may be reasonable. A case for denial can only be presented by ignoring a massive weight of evidence. Climate change denial requires a preconceived notion that humanity can't change the climate, but why does such an idea exist? Is it based on religious grounds? Or maybe there is too much money in burning fossil fuels to consider the possibility that it is poisoning the environment such that an existential threat to humanity is created.

Given the way that renewable energies are falling in cost, the price to be paid for fighting climate change does not need to be high. Indeed, by forcing us to adopt sustainable practices, the price may, in fact, be negative in the long run.

Suppose the idea of human-made climate change proves to be based on a false belief, then so what, the cost of this error will be small.

Consider, however, the risk that we are understating the reality. Maybe we risk creating a horrendous positive feedback loop, as the Arctic and permafrost in the tundra melts, causing the release of even more greenhouse gases into the atmosphere, accelerating climate change. If that is correct, then we could be creating the worst disaster to occur on this planet since the meteorite that wiped out the dinosaurs.

Given the balance sheet; on the one extreme, not that bad, on the other, total annihilation, with catastrophe somewhere in the middle, what is the motivation for denial?

It is not an objective appraisal of facts, because, frankly, Homo sapiens sapiens rarely do that. If you assume a belief, whatever the belief, is founded on a lack of objectivity, then you are usually right.

Compare the motivation behind climate change denial with the motivation behind 'accelerating technology denial', and the

115

comparison seems lame. But actually, the dangers are just as serious. It is just that the opportunities are more significant.

Within the academic world, especially in the field of economics, 'accelerating technology denial' is rife. The whole essence of this book, its warnings and recommendations are meaningless if you do not accept the idea of accelerating technology.

Such denial is well-meaning. It is not like climate change denial. It is merely academics trying to be objective, scientific if you will.

All the same, it is fantastically dangerous, and it's a view that needs to be debunked and urgently.

This academic view that suggests that the golden age of innovation is behind us, that we have picked the low hanging fruit of progress and that from here on innovation will be slow, ponderous and nearly always disappointing, is wrong. And it is wrong because the people who hold on to it are missing the point.

Technology creates the possibility of new technology and innovation. It builds on existing ideas. And on occasions, such as happened with singular endosymbiosis and the Cambrian explosion in the distant past, we see a sudden acceleration. When the conditions for this acceleration are being created, not much changes. When they are created, we see extraordinary change.

This is the lesson of both natural and human history.

The high priest of technology cynicism, of accelerating technology denial, the American economist Robert Gordon is only looking at the build-up. He is looking at the phase that creates the conditions for change, noting that not much evidence is yet available and concluding from this that it never will be.

It is like watching the building of a house. First of all, the foundations are built. The progress seems slow. During this critical and lengthy phase, there is no sign of any doors, windows or roofs being installed. Instead, there is lots of digging and laying down of concrete and steel deep down such that, to the untrained eye, there is not so much as a hint as to what the final outcome will be.

A cynic might note that with each day's labour nothing much seems to change. The door is not slowly being revealed. Instead, it feels like it is just 'never-ending' digging.

But of course, the door is not built up layer by layer with the house. It is transported there as a finished article when the time is right. One day there is no door, the next there is. The change feels instantaneous.

Such cynicism would be foolish. Houses are always built that way.[64]

But 'accelerating technology denial' is akin to looking at the early stages of a construction project and saying that because there are not yet any windows or doors, the project is not progressing.

 As Bill Gates said: "We always overestimate the change that will occur in the next two years and underestimate the change that will occur in the next ten. Don't let yourself be lulled into inaction."

The rest of this chapter will focus on four areas:

- Look more closely at technology cynicism
- Consider the story of Apple
- Consider why we tend to underestimate the significance of new technology
- And then consider what this means.
- So, first, we need to understand a little more about such cynicism.

The high priests

 The story starts with Tyler Cohen. In 011, this incredibly talented and eloquent economist published a book entitled The Great Stagnation.

In the book, he states: "Apart from the seemingly magical internet, life in broad material terms isn't so different from what it was in 1953...The wonders portrayed in The Jetsons, the space-age television cartoon from the 1960s, have not come to pass...Life is better, and we have more stuff, but the pace of change has slowed down compared to what people saw two or three generations ago."[65]

---

[64] Or at least nearly always, they can be mass produced off-site in a factory, and erected within a day.

[65] *The Great Stagnation: How America Ate All The Low Hanging Fruit of Modern History, Got Sick, and Will (Eventually) Feel Better:*

Robert Gordon, an economics professor from North Western University, in Chicago, takes the idea further.

He says: "If the automobile had followed the same development as the computer, a Rolls Royce would today cost $100 and get a million miles per gallon and explode once a year killing everyone inside."

He also says: "Advances since 1970 have tended to be channeled into a narrow sphere of human activity having to do with entertainment, communications, and the collection and processing of information. For the rest of what humans care about – food, clothing, shelter, transportation, health, and working conditions both inside and outside the home – progress slowed down after 1970."66

A paper by economists Nicholas Bloom, Charles I Jones, John Van Reenen and Michael Webb, entitled 'Are Ideas Getting Harder to Find?' takes the concept of accelerating technology cynicism further.

They argue that the volume of research required to advance new ideas is increasing – to put it another way, innovation is becoming more labour intensive.

Then, to add salt to the wound, they suggest that not only is it becoming harder to innovate, the resulting innovations are less significant too.

---

66 *Robert Gordon's New Yorker Game iDisrupted looked at Robert Gordon's theory. Quoting from that book: "Gordon] calls it the New Yorker game, after an experiment carried out by the New Yorker publication. It commissioned someone to watch TV for a week and then write about it. The commissioned writer said: 'I was so struck by situation comedies of the 1950s, the reruns, how similar their lives seemed to today." Gordon asks us to imagine what life was like 30 years ago, and then to imagine it 30 years before that and keep going back in 30-year intervals. He says the changes between now and the early 1980s are not that great. The changes between the 1950s and 1980s, he says were modest too. But between the 1920s and 1950s lifestyles were transformed. The transformation was even more radical, he says, between the 1890s and 1920s.*

Or consider it another way, he suggests. Imagine you have two choices. In one option you have technology circa 2002, complete with Windows '98 PCs. In the other you have iPhones, and tablets, and Facebook, but you lose indoor toilets and hot and cold running water. Which option will you select?

Evidence for and against

The evidence to support such theories comes in the form of hard economic statistics on growth in productivity.

Productivity growth isn't what it used to be.

If you look at output per hour, across the mature world, it grew at a brisk pace during the 23 years or so after World War 2. It then slowed, but ever since the financial crisis of 2008, this growth has virtually ground to a standstill.

'Ergo', say the cynics, innovation is slowing.

Some react to this and suggest that the problem is that economic statistics do not accurately reflect the real benefits from technology – such as social media, which is free but surely offers excellent levels of customer satisfaction.

But according to research from Chad Syverson, even this predominance of free benefits that don't show up in the economic data is insufficient to make much difference.

They miss the point

There is another way of looking at it.

Thanks to innovation, older couples, via the magic of Viagra, can enjoy an active sex life.

Thanks to prosthetics, before his career came to an ignominious end, Oscar Pistorious, the South African Olympic athlete, could run the 400 metres in 45.44 seconds, despite having no legs.

Stem cell technology creates the possibility of the manufacturing of human organs enabling drug testing, thus eliminating the impact on animals and potentially rethinking clinical trials, and addressing the shortage of organs, perhaps using 3D printing.

Cures for diseases once thought incurable beckons. (For that matter, a vaccine for Covid-19 looks likely to be developed in record time. Maybe when you read this, you will know if that did indeed turn out to be the case.)

Real-time language translation devices promise to transform the way we communicate with people.

The augmentation of Homo sapiens sapiens into a new species, with an incredible memory, is possibly around the corner.

3D printing, the Internet of Things and AI create extraordinary new ways for companies to manufacture goods or achieve greater efficiency.

Extended longevity is approaching, who knows how long people recently born will live – until they are 120? 150? 200? Maybe their consciences will also be loaded into virtual reality, where perhaps they can live forever or until they are bored.

The ideas of technology cynicism, when seen in such a context, no longer make sense.

But, with a few exceptions, most of the above technologies are evolving, are being created. Consider this list:

- Computers
- The internet
- Ever-increasing network speeds
- The sequencing of the human genome
- The discovery of the genetic editing technology CRISPR/Cas 9
- The isolation of graphene
- The falling cost of renewable energy
- Stem cell research
- AI
- Technologies that will augment us

These technologies are creating the possibility of rapid change; at the moment, we are merely seeing the foundations. And just as it can take time to build the foundations, but once complete, a house can emerge rapidly, the foundations for the age that is coming are now mostly laid.

The change that is coming is looming close, and it will be extraordinary.

The story of Apple and Kodak

There are those who love their smartphone. They gently caress it, they hold it lovingly in their hand, it is precious to them, like Gollum's ring.

It's a device that provides access to the sum total of humanity's knowledge. It tells us what our friends are doing. It is a superb camera, a photo album, even a tool for storing ideas as if it were an extension of ourselves.

At some point in a not very distant future, we may look back and ask: "When did our species cease to be Homo sapiens sapiens, but Homo sapiens augmented?" That point in 2007, when the Apple boss revealed the iPhone to the world, in one of the most memorable of all business presentations, might be it. And largely thanks to this device, Apple became the first company in the world to be valued at one trillion dollars.

But rewind the clock to the late 1990s. Back then, the company was on its knees. Had you suggested that one day it would be the world's biggest, you would have been laughed at.

The magical days seemed over; the company limped from one sorry attempt at an earth-shattering product to another. The Newton, for example, an electronic organiser, or the Pippin, a kind of edutainment console. It felt like a company, desperately trying new ideas.

In fact things got so bad for the company, that in 1997, it had to appeal to Bill Gates, the arch-enemy, for help.

But that same event also saw the return of Steve Jobs to the company, the prodigal son.

But not even Jobs could seemingly save the company. In October 2002, the share price was down to $1, a quarter of the price two years earlier. The company was worth around $5 billion.

Contrast that with a company like Eastman Kodak, which saw a peak market cap of around £30 billion in the 1990s.

But things happened at the turn of the millennium. Moore's Law meant computers had the power to offer certain functions at a price that would have been impossible a few years earlier. The homogenisation of specific components meant it was possible to make consumer-friendly devices, such as the iPod, that a few years earlier would have seemed like a pipedream.

Wireless access to the internet created a new opportunity for consumer devices.

Apple did not invent the technologies, but when they emerged, they made the iPhone possible.

The Apple share price rose from $1 in 2002 to $24 in 2007, to $120 in 2015, and $349 on June 21, 2019.

Kodak, by contrast, went bust in 2012.

And that is the lesson of Apple and Kodak. When the conditions aren't right, things can seem disappointing, stagnant, even in reverse. But when the conditions are right, change can follow the trajectory of a rocket. There is no trend, no pattern. It is human nature to look for gradual change, but it isn't there.

This was a David vs Goliath moment. Apple was David with everything to win, Kodak was Goliath with everything to lose and so buried its invention of the digital camera

We should, therefore, not be complacent!

Exponential change reveals the reason

 If Bill Gates is right that we overestimate the change that will occur in the next two years and underestimate the change that will happen in the next ten, then therein lies the dilemma.

If you have been around for a while, you may have witnessed it firsthand. During the last tech boom, what we used to refer to as dotcoms, was hot.

The internet was going to change the world, we were told, but no one seemed quite sure how.

Bold predictions, business plans that promised the earth wonder products were dominating the media. But there was something missing. Behind the hype of the internet, there was little more than ether. Investors ploughed money in, but no one was sure why.

Some very wise old owls talked about the South Sea bubble – an investment craze in the eighteenth century in which the great and the good, including Sir Isaac Newton, invested money and got burned, badly.

During the South Sea Bubble period, one company released a prospectus for fundraising with the title: "For carrying out a venture of great advantage, but no one to know what it is."

When the dotcom boom turned to bust, money was lost by many – including one of the authors.

Yet, the aftermath was just as impressive.

After the dotcom bust, the words 'don't touch', 'with' and 'barge pole' often appeared in the same sentence when talking about the internet's investment potential. 'Caveat emptor' became the new watchword.

Just as they did during the boom, the markets also overreacted, but in the other direction, during the bust.

Such technology cynicism from investors was wrong, of course. Just over ten years later, tech companies which applied business models that hinged upon the internet, became the biggest companies in the world.

But if you are a keen observer of new technologies, you see such a pattern over and over again.

Gartner, the research and advisory company, has a name for it: the hype cycle. It divides the lifecycle of new technologies into five stages:

- Technology trigger
- Peak of inflated expectations
- Trough of disillusionment
- Slope of enlightenment
- And plateau of productivity

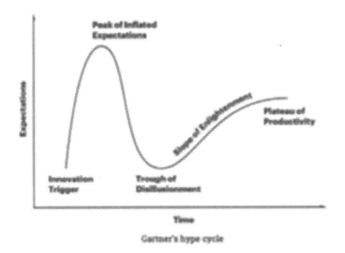

Gartner's hype cycle

Perhaps it over elaborates.

The story of the dotcom boom, crash and subsequent realisation of potential, when the world's largest companies were all techs, could also be summed up as follows:

- The hype phase
- Sceptical phase
- Transformational phase

There is a good reason for this, and it lies with the difference between arithmetic and geometric change.

Technology is accelerating at an accelerating rate. But some technologies are not so much jerking as changing at an exponential rate. Moore's Law is an example of exponential change, as are quantum computers obeying Rose's Law. Genome sequencing falling at a cost that makes Moore's Law look sedentary, renewables and lithium-ion batteries falling at a pace described by a learning rate, are all examples of exponential change.

But we don't expect change to accelerate, we don't expect it to accelerate at an accelerating rate, and we most certainly don't expect change to occur at an exponential rate. Instead, we expect change to occur at an arithmetical rate.

Maybe this mistake was made during the build-up to the Covid-19 crisis. Too many people shrugged their shoulders when the infections were in single digits, they failed to take notice of the fact that this is how exponential works. Numbers start small and seem to change only slowly. Then the pace of change becomes terrifying.

In the short run, arithmetical change is often quicker than exponential change.

Take these two examples: Take arithmetical and exponential change. In case one, you start with the number one, say \$1. And keep adding \$20. In example two, you start with the number one and keep doubling.

The end result looks like this:

Exponential change is often slower at first but gets much, much quicker.

First phase	Arithmetical change, keep adding 20	Exponential change, keep doubling
Step 1	$1	$1
Step 2	$21	$2
Step 3	$41	$4
Step 4	$61	$8
Step 5	$81	$16
Step 6	$101	$32
Step 7	$121	$64

Arithmetic versus exponential change, phase 1

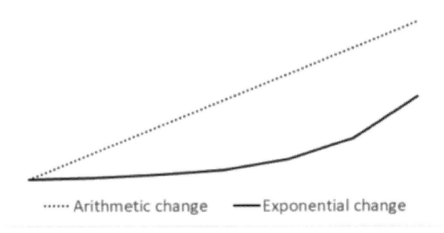

······ Arithmetic change   ——Exponential change

Second phase	Arithmetic change, keep adding 20	Exponential change, keep doubling
Step 8	$141	$128
Step 9	$161	$256
Step 10	$181	$512
Step 11	$201	$1,024
Step 12	$221	$2,056
Step 13	$241	$4,096
Step 14	$261	$8,152
Step 24	$461	Approx: $8,000,000
Step 34	$661	Approx: $8,000,000,000

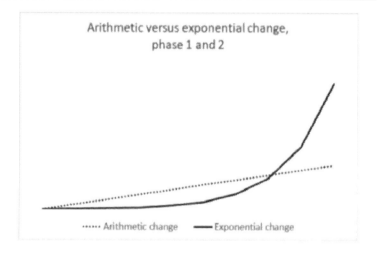

Arithmetic versus exponential change, phase 1 and 2

······ Arithmetic change   ——— Exponential change

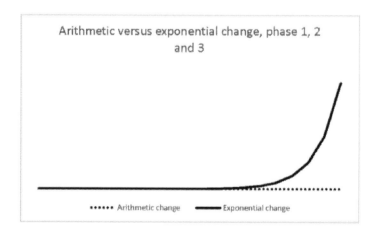

Arithmetic versus exponential change, phase 1, 2 and 3

······ Arithmetic change   ——— Exponential change

If you expect change to occur at an arithmetic rate, when in fact it occurs exponentially, an inevitable consequence of this is that you will overestimate the speed of change in the short run but underestimate it in the long term, just as Bill Gates said. It's simple mathematics.

It is possible, maybe even likely, that technology has been accelerating right from day one, when we learned how to fashion tools in the hearth of a fire that we had created. It is just that, up until very recently, we have been on that part of the curve tracking change in acceleration where it's too slow to notice, especially when memories are only ever a lifetime in length.

Accelerating change, jerking change, and exponential change is not new. We just happen to be on that part of the curve when it changes at a rate measured in years, months or even days, whereas, until recently, with occasional spurts, such as the period of ancient Greece, change was measured in decades, centuries and millennia. [67] [68]

No wonder some have likened technology change to singularity, a point at the centre of a black hole, where gravitational fields of a celestial body are thought to become infinite.

Time to prepare

Kodak didn't notice. There was no memo saying, 'we have got to explore a new business model, or we will be disrupted to the point of collapse.' By the time the threat to its continued solvency became apparent, it was too late. The same happened to RIM Blackberry.

That's exponential change for you.

Bertrand Russell once told the story of a chicken living on a farm, in blissful happiness. Nassim Taleb, in his books 'Fooled by Randomness' and 'The Black Swan,' re-told the tale, but in his story, it was a turkey.

The turkey was looked after well by the farmer. The bird got fatter and happier. How lucky it was. It laughed off doubts cast by

---

67 As Ramez Naam points out, the model T Ford had a learning rate of sixteen per cent. So that means that the cost fell by sixteen per cent for every doubling in user base.

68 So, this idea of falling costs with output is not new. So why do cynics respond to the idea of falling energy costs, storage and electric cars by sarcastically proclaiming: "This time it is different!" History tells us that this is normal:

other turkeys that the farmer could not be trusted. Then one day, the turkey blissfully allowed the hands of the farmer to grip it by the neck, unaware that the next day was Thanksgiving.

The change that is coming, just like climate change, does not follow a dress rehearsal. It does not happen slowly, giving us time to adjust.

Exponential change means that soon after major shifts occur every year, they will occur every month, and in an even shorter time interval, every week, then day, then an hour. The time to think about the meaning and the impact and draw up plans is now.

See it in terms of the super-cooling of water.

Most of us assume that water freezes at zero degrees. This is not true. If water is pure and undisturbed, it can be cooled to temperatures of minus 40c. What happens at 0C is that ice melts. There is a difference.

But when a pool of water is supercooled, it may be possible to cool the water to minus 20C, 30C or 40C, but once a part of that pool freezes, the entire pool of water freezes over immediately. It is not a gradual process. It is instantaneous.

Examine the super-cooling of water in the context of the Thanksgiving turkey.

One water molecule says to the next: "I don't believe this turning to ice nonsense. They said that as temperatures turn to zero, we will turn to ice. But it hasn't happened. It's minus ten degrees, but I am still free."

However, once super-cooled water begins to freeze, it freezes immediately. So, the water molecule might have spoken thus: "Fears that we will freeze are exaggerated. All the evidence suggests that we will be." Alas, the molecule didn't quite get to finish its sentence.

Or the turkey may think: "I love this farmer. This place is great. I didn't know I was entitled to a Shiatsu…"

So, that is why technology critics miss the point. But we don't have much time to make the correct choices. When technology is on the trajectory of the jerk, you have to consider the implications and draw up plans as soon as possible. If you leave it until the changes start occurring, it may be too late to do anything about it.

If the Covid-19 crisis taught us anything, it is that very point.

So, will technology create utopia or dystopia? And what kind? The next part of this book is entitled Techopia, and it considers eight scenarios.

Part 2
Techopia

Chapter 6

The end of nationhood, the rise of the global citizen and the future of work in an age of plenty

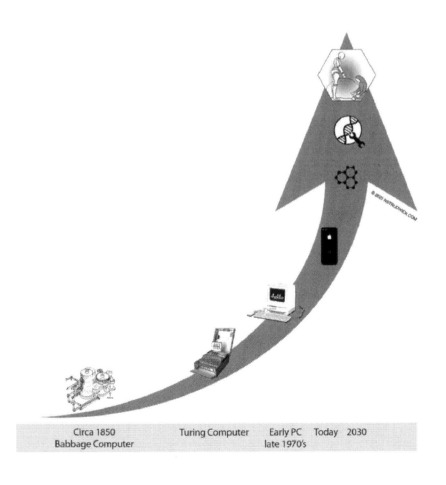

Circa 1850   Turing Computer   Early PC   Today   2030
Babbage Computer   late 1970's

"I am a citizen of the world." – Diogenes

"I am not an Athenian or a Greek, but a citizen of the world." – Socrates

"We are citizens of the world. The tragedy of our times is that we do not know this." – Woodrow Wilson

"The people of the future will not say, 'I belong to the nation of England, France or Persia'; for all of them will be citizens of a universal nationality – the one family, the one country, the one world of humanity – and then these wars, hatreds and strifes will pass away." – Abdu'l-Baha, The Promulgation of Universal Peace, p. 18.

"Imagine there's no country, It isn't hard to do Nothing to kill or die for"– John Lennon

"There is no global anthem, no global currency, no certificate of global citizenship. We pledge allegiance to one flag, and that flag is the American flag." – Donald Trump

"If you believe you are a citizen of the world, you are a citizen of nowhere. You don't understand what citizenship means." – Theresa May.

"We will rock you," sang Jessie J in a trio with Roger Taylor and Brian May from the band Queen, during the closing ceremony of the London 2012 Olympic games. This two- week festival of sport was viewed worldwide by no less than 3.6 billion people – meaning that over half the human population of planet earth saw at least some of the event.

They were no doubt rocked in their seats, and Jessie J's popularity worldwide was not harmed either.

Five and half years later, the singer saw another boost to her popularity. This time she sang in China. One billion people watched a talent show enabling established musical stars to connect with the Chinese audience and which the singer from London won, becoming one of the biggest stars in China.

The world, as they say, has become a smaller place. There was a time when a talented musician's fame spread no more than a few valleys. TV and radio have introduced a global audience. People living in a region of China, which to the western mind may seem remote, are listening to the same music that music lovers in Surrey, England or Boston, Massachusetts might be enjoying.

This convergence in musical tastes illustrates how cultural differences are merging. Maybe that is why no less than six per cent of the visitors to the Beatles Story, a tourist attraction in Liverpool, are Chinese.

Talking of Liverpool, you are more likely to support the city's eponymous football team if you come from Uruguay than if you are English. As a proportion of the population, Denmark, Ireland, Thailand and Norway have more Liverpool supporters than the UK.

Of course, Manchester United's fan base is as global as you can imagine – sure it counts Usain Bolt as its most famous supporter, but in addition to the Jamaican sprinter, Manchester United has 659 million fans scattered around the world. According to a poll conducted by the club in 2013, 325 million people from the Asia Pacific region, 173 million in the Middle East and Africa, 90 million in Europe and 71 million in the Americas all have one big thing in common. They support Manchester United.

The world really does seem like it's a smaller place.

We can also drink a coffee or eat a burger in one of a handful of restaurant/coffee shop chains around the world, and wherever we are, have a near-identical experience to someone on the other side of the planet. Whether it is for the good or ill, the world not only feels smaller, it feels less different.

Technology, whether it is print media, TV, radio or modern transport, is the reason.

But, "wait a minute" to quote from the 1927 movie, the Jazz Singer, "wait a minute, you haven't heard anything yet."

Those words marked a crucial moment in globalisation and the process of bringing the world closer together. Sure, they marked the first moment when movies were also 'talkies', pictures and sound blending, in the process changing the world in so many ways. But there was an often- overlooked side-effect of the movie industry. The movie helped to export cultural values. You could, of course, say it promoted cultural imperialism – Superman standing for 'truth, justice and the American way'. Few people would disagree that truth and justice are valuable values — not everyone would agree that abiding by them is solely the preserve of America.

What Hollywood has done is show to the world that deep down, we are all very similar. It matters not whether you are a cowboy protecting his 19th-century ranch, a servant at Downton Abbey, or a character from a Bollywood movie, across the world we have more in common than we have differences.

Considering how closely related every human being is on this planet – how few great grandparents separate a star from a Swedish detective series to an Australian Aboriginal – surely no more than 1,000 great grandparents — it should come as no surprise. We all have similar attitudes, similar hopes and fears, even humour, because the family of humanity is genetically, for all intents and purposes, the same.

Global citizen

In the original version of the TV series Star Trek, the principal characters consisted of a Russian, an Asian (possibly Japanese), a black female, a Scottish engineer, an American doctor and American captain and a Vulcan.

At the time, this was quite a radical idea. Such diversity was exceedingly unusual. (Indeed, even in modern society, it remains rare for Vulcans to mingle with humanity, although there might be the odd individual who mixes with others who does think they are Vulcan). The ambiguity over the nationality of the Starship Enterprise – did USS stand for United States Ship or United Star Ship – meant the programme was able to gently introduce the viewer to this concept of a united planet.

If you have to criticise the attempt by the show's creator, Gene Roddenberry, to present diversity, you could draw attention to the lack of significant female characters. This oversight was corrected later, until eventually a series of the franchise aired in which not only was the main character female (and black), but she had a man's name — Michael.

Star Trek could be said to symbolise the idea of the global citizen.

There is a misunderstanding as to what this means. Some think of a global citizen as a member of an elite group, extraordinarily wealthy, maybe a child of Silicon Valley, who flips from working in say San Francisco one week, to London the next, to perhaps working with a team of software developers in Lithuania the week after.

But that is not what we mean here.

By global citizen, we simply refer to an individual who feels loyalty to a group, or idea that stretches beyond the borders of their country.

It may be love of a football team, or they may be united with other nationalities by a group on Facebook that promotes discussion on a topic for which they are passionate.

Being a global citizen is not mutually exclusive from having a national identity and feeling pride in your nationality — a sense of patriotism. Feeling an attachment with global issues, caring about topics that draw you together with people from other countries, maybe in disagreement with people from your own, does not make you a traitor.

In 2017, the then British Prime Minister, Theresa May, described a global citizen as "a citizen of nowhere" — she completely missed the point.

Today, people from across the world have no choice but to care about global issues. The evil side of technology is creating dangers that don't recognise international borders: climate change, over-use of plastic polluting the oceans, overfishing, nuclear proliferation, cybercrime, and the potential threat posed by AI. And now, to add to that list, we also know that new diseases also threaten to go global. International collaboration on a scale once considered unthinkable is required just to grapple with these challenges.

Nations are new

One of the odd characteristics of the 20th and 21st century is our attachment to nationhood. It is as if we think that feeling a sense of belonging to our country is natural — in our genes.

In fact, the countries we know today are new.

No more than two or three great grandparents ago, most of us had never travelled more than a few hours walk from where we were born. The people in the next valley seemed a bit strange and not at all 'like us.'

In most cases, nations are no more than a few great grandparents old. Even countries where borders are clearly defined by geographical barriers, such as Britain, Italy or Japan, have existed for a short time. The nation we call England was established during the last few centuries of the first millennium – from the time of King Alfred to King Athelstan, around 927 AD, or approximately 15 to 20 great grandparents ago. The state we call Italy was founded in 1861, less than two great grandparents ago. The first record of a united Japan dates back to around 25 great grandparents ago, to the middle of the first millennium during the period of the Yamato Court. However, there have been periods of disunity since.

Returning to England, the nation that gave the world its most commonly spoken second language, was only united by a common tongue during the last few hundred years. Old Norse, Cornish, Cumbric, Anglo-Norman and Medieval Latin competed with English to be the standard form of communication in different regions during the early centuries of the second millennium. Even today, there can be a communications problem. To the ears of many English people, the language spoken in other parts of what is a small country, seem so strange that they are barely recognisable as English.

But, 'summatsupeer', as they say in Yorkshire, something is going on.

Technology destroys barriers

Technology will make the barriers that separate us all but disappear.

The internet lowered these barriers, when all of a sudden email and the World Wide Web transformed the way we communicated, sourced new products – or if you prefer to see it in consumer terms, the way we shopped – and the way we were sold-to, was transformed.

Buying or selling a product to someone on the other side of the world became an order of magnitude easier.

Social media has created communities that recognise no geographical barriers.

Multiplayer video games has thrown people together from around the world to achieve a common aim.

Commerce and social interaction, making money and having fun together — they became global things.

Now we see a backlash against globalisation. A sense of social disquiet over rising inequality, fears over decimated labour markets have put globalisation in the dock, amplified by opportunistic politicians and tried by the court of public opinion.

Add to the dialogue the belief that globalisation created a worldwide pandemic from Covid-19. In fact, pandemics predate modern globalisation, perhaps by several millennia.

It is very doubtful that globalisation is the leading cause of economic ills – indeed, across the world, billions of people have been lifted out of abject poverty thanks to it, but truth counts for little when politicians find an easy target for the electorate's ire.

At the point when the first draft of this chapter was being written, a furious row had broken out between the US and Canada over trade. The US accused Canada of ripping it off by running a substantial surplus in trade in goods. Yet, in 2017, when services were added to the balance of trade equation, it was the US that was in surplus.

In 2019, a similar dispute came to a head between the USA and China with the eventual introduction of punitive tariffs impacting businesses on each side. Covid-19 has exacerbated the issue.

But in many ways, the backlash against globalisation is running against the grain of technology. Voters with a more traditional mindset, often rooted in older industries, are recoiling against globalisation and immigration. Traditional well-paid jobs that conferred on the individuals doing them a sense of pride, in doing the work, have been devastated. In part, they have been replaced by less well-paid work in warehouses or the gig economy.

Technology may create jobs as well as destroy them, but such a process is not smooth. Neither is it equitable. The individuals who have lost out in this way look for someone or something to blame and their wrath often falls upon foreigners – whether that is other countries or migratory workers.

Simultaneously, others react in horror to the way society has changed, and long for a return to older values.

Others benefit from the technology shift. They secure well-paid sources of income, often doing the kind of work that didn't even exist a few years ago. They flourish in the emerging collaborative way of doing things and seamlessly interact, with the internet as the tool of their trade, with others across the world.

The result is a polarised society, creating two very distinct sets of beliefs. The echo chamber created by social media then magnifies these differences. The result is that we see nations divided in a way that we have not witnessed for a very long time. Class conflict is not unusual, but the emerging divide runs across social classes, the two distinct factions united by people of very different backgrounds.

The economic effects of Covid-19 may serve to exacerbate such a divide. Fourth and fifth industrial technologies will have an even more dramatic impact.

As a consequence, we risk seeing the kind of divide in the US not seen since the US Civil War. In the UK, as we explain later in the book, we see a scenario emerge, which in some ways has similarities with the conditions in England during the time of its Civil War.

This difference may be exacerbated by technology in more direct ways.

Virtual and augmented reality – could be transformative, leaving those who don't like the technologies feeling disenfranchised.

Virtual reality will promote more closely intertwined communities stretching across the globe, as we communicate in virtual space: avatar to avatar.

Language translation tools, which, within a decade or so, will be able to translate spoken language in real-time, with near-perfect accuracy, will transform how people from different backgrounds from all over the world communicate with each other.

Armed with earpieces connected to a computer linked to the internet and AI systems, we will be able to have a fluent conversation with anyone in the world, whatever language they speak, providing that they are also connected to a language translation device. It's the dream of science fiction – from Douglas Adams, Star Trek and Doctor Who – the problem of communicating with different species was overcome via technology. AI communication devices may not use physhic readings of brain waves — unlike Douglas Adams' Babel Fish – but for promoting understanding between people of different cultures, they will feel just as miraculous.

Augmented reality superimposes images over reality. And it could transform the way we communicate with people over a long distance. Augmented reality glasses or contact lenses, will mean we will be able to look at people, see the whites of their eyes, as if they are in the room with us.

Business meetings in which people appear to be sitting around a board table can take place, even if the people in the conference are in different locations.

You can imagine a predominance of green screens. We sit at a table in front of the screen. AI will apply chroma key technology to copy and paste a live video of us and superimpose it in front of any background selected. When viewed from our augmented reality device, such as contact lenses, we appear to be sitting in the same room as others, who are in fact also in front of a green screen in some distant location.

We will see virtual meetings, where all your colleagues are sat around the large table either in person or superimposed from an image taken from where they are physically-based, maybe from many miles away, may emerge – like a traditional boardroom meeting – just not physically so. [69]

Such communications will not be restricted to business use. Couples will be able to meet up, perhaps for a romantic meal, at a restaurant chain with green screens. We may select food from an identical menu and gaze at each other, even though we are separated by a thousand miles.

We may even date and get to know someone without ever meeting them in the flesh.

Talking of flesh, we may also be able to kiss our partner via a membrane simulating our partners' lips, moving in synchronisation. We may even have sex at a distance. These ideas are explored later.

---

[69] Not like a Zoom call, it will be as if you are sitting at a table alongside others, but the table will be a simulation, the image of others will be holograms.

You may find some of these possibilities scary; they may not all come to life as described. But it is clear that augmented and virtual reality has the potential to transform the way we communicate. For social interaction, these technologies could reduce barriers created by distance to a minor inconvenience, making the world seem smaller than ever, cultural differences squashed from being like hurdles to no more than a gentle step.

With such technology, the feeling of a global citizen will become powerful – national loyalties increasingly relegated to trivial concerns.

"I'm Human, I don't have any money," said Nog, a character from the TV series Deep Space Nine, a part of the Star Trek franchise.

Gene Roddenberry, had an idealistic view of the future. As described above, one manifestation of this idealistic view involved breaking down the national barriers that separate us. He also envisaged the end of money.[70]

In an earlier series, Captain Jean Luc Picard said: "A lot has changed in three hundred years. People are no longer obsessed with the accumulation of 'things.' We have eliminated hunger, want, the need for possessions." [71]

Money exists as a mechanism for allocating scarce resources. Everything has a cost: everything takes time and Jresource to create. Oil carries a price because it requires human labour, and capital to drill and turn into fuel. It has a cost because its supply is limited.

Economists may well argue it should carry an additional cost, one that reflects the environmental damage that results from its consumption. Price is the means by which consumers of a product can determine whether its consumption is worth its cost.

But there is an inaccuracy in the paragraph above – not everything carries a cost. Air is free, at least it is free at the point of consumption. It's not that the creation of oxygen is cost-free, photosynthesis requires resource, all be it one that nature provides without our input. Nonetheless, the marginal cost of oxygen is zero. [72]

---

[70] *Deep Space Nine: (In the Cards*
[71] *Star Trek the Next Generation, the neutral zone.*
[72] *Trees are one of the great creators of oxygen, they turn carbon dioxide in the air into carbon, oxygen becomes a biproduct. But because air is free, we humans take it for granted so we should remind ourselves that it is erroneous to believe oxygen does*

The question is, could technology, at a time when it is accelerating at an accelerating rate, following the trajectory of a jerk, create other examples of abundance? Maybe we are some way from realising Roddenberry's dream of a world without money, but a world where certain things are exceedingly cheap, might not be so far off.

Exponential change provides part of the explanation. We know that computers are roughly one billion times more powerful than they were at around the time of the moon landings. It is likely they will be a billion times more powerful than they are at present within the lifetime of most readers of this book.

But supposing other technologies either grow in power or fall in price at a similar trajectory. Genome sequencing is another example.

The unit cost of production of energy generated from renewables has not entirely fallen at the same pace as of computers or genome sequencing, but it has declined rapidly, all the same. The cost of one unit of energy generated from solar power today is roughly one percent of the cost it was in 1980. According to a report from Irena,[73] the cost of electricity generated from onshore wind fell by 13 per cent between 2017 and 2018. Energy from solar photovoltaics fell by a similar amount. "In most parts of the world today, renewables are the lowest-cost source of new power generation," or so it was stated in the report.

If the cost of energy from wind and solar is already comparable to the cost of energy generated from fossil fuels, consider how low the price will be if the cost continues to fall at the trajectory seen either over the last year, the last decade or the last half a century.

Critics say that renewables are not effective when it is neither sunny nor windy. Their critique overlooks so many points. For one thing, if we only have to use fossil fuels when renewables are ineffective, then our consumption of these rare and environmentally damaging resources will still be much lower than at present. For another thing, they overlook the falling cost of energy storage.

And they overlook convergence.

---

carry a cost. If we leave deforestation of the Amazon rainforest unchecked perhaps because one of the products of this region, oxygen, will become something we must pay for.
[73] *Renewable power generation costs in 2018, Irena*

Technologies such as AI, the Internet of Things, resulting in the creation of data, will be able to match the demand and supply of energy more efficiently. Energy which is captured at times of high supply, such as when it is windy, or there is full sunshine, can, after meeting regular demand, be channelled into areas where the use of energy is less time-sensitive. So surplus energy could be used to warm up storage heaters, charge-up electric cars, freeze water in air conditioning systems, and be used by energy-intensive 3D printers.

At the moment, there are occasions of optimal renewable energy conditions, when some energy generated is not used. Imagine the opportunities that open if this otherwise unused energy suddenly does find uses – not exactly an age of plenty, but certainly more plentiful.

Other technologies that might support plenty include CRISPR/cas 9 editing the DNA of plants to create food and other materials more efficiently, reducing price.

Stem cell technology could be applied to create meat if the cost can fall at a Moore's Law trajectory, between ten and twenty years from now, the cost will be at a level that is lower than the current cost of meat created from more conventional sources. Between 20 and 30 years from now, lab-grown meat would be so cheap that it would be effectively free. [74]

Even dwellings could fall in cost. By mass-producing the shell of houses off-site in factories, maybe using 3D printing technologies, the cost of construction could fall sharply. (3D printing is typically energy-intensive, but this drawback could be overcome by only running the 3D printing press at times of high energy output from wind and solar energy and when normal demand for energy is less than supply.)

Engineering at the molecular level, supported by quantum computers, may also create new super-efficient building materials.

The problem with free

Economic theory says that price is the means for matchingdemand with supply. If something is subsidised by the government, in other words, the taxpayers, so that consumers can obtain it for free, demand

---

[74] This would require massive government support, as the markets are unlikely to fund projects that won't cover the initial investment for twenty years.

will invariably exceed supply. Economic theory has already been put to the test in the UK, via its system of providing universal healthcare at the point of consumption for free – otherwise called the National Health Service (NHS).

According to economic theory, the NHS should have collapsed at the point of its creation; it would never be able to meet demand.

Yet, something extraordinary has emerged. The NHS might be almost-free at the point of consumption, but many of its users feel a sense of identity with it. Many refer to it in a possessive manner "our NHS" – unlike the US, UK citizens see free healthcare at the point of use as a right for all.

The Covid-19 pandemic has brought home for most of us how valuable this health safety net is and how undervalued its staff are.

In the US, where healthcare is tied to employment, it is not uncommon to sue health providers, because the relationship between customer and provider is defined by money. In the UK, this is much more unusual – there is a sense that suing the NHS is like suing yourself.

In short, there is a sense of a greater good.

This takes us back to the idea of Star Trek. "The acquisition of wealth is no longer the driving force in our lives. We work to better ourselves and the rest of humanity," said Captain Picard.[75]

Working for the greater good is perhaps a much more realistic aim when technology has created abundance.

Working week

The day when we have eliminated money is a long way off— far outside the timeframe considered here.

But there is a fall-back position.

We may not be able to eliminate money, we may be some way off living in an age of abundance, but maybe we are not so far away from living in an age when we do not need to work so many hours to earn sufficient money to fund our needs.

Roddenberry foresaw the end of money, John Maynard Keynes, one of the finest minds the UK has ever produced, had a similar vision.

---

[75] (Star Trek Movie: First Contact.)

In 1930 he said: "For many ages to come the old Adam will be so strong in us that everybody will need to do some work if he is to be contented. We shall do more things for ourselves than is usual with the rich to-day, only too glad to have small duties and tasks and routines. But beyond this, we shall endeavour to spread the bread thin on the butter- to make what work there is still to be done to be as widely shared as possible. Three-hour shifts or a fifteen-hour week may put off the problem for a great while. For three hours a day is quite enough to satisfy the old Adam in most of us!"

Keynes wrote those words in a paper called Economic Possibilities for our Grandchildren, in which he was looking ahead to a period which he said would not dawn "for at least 100 years."

Keynes' critics argue that the great man has been proven wrong – that the 15-hour week remains elusive, but somehow, they have confused the phrase 'for at least 100 years', with the timeframe 'end of the 20th Century'. A narrative has emerged that Keynes, an economist whose views were often quite right-wing, is a symbol of the left', was wrong about his utopian dream and therefore, we assume we should not take him seriously. In fact, at least 100 years from when he wrote those words takes us to around 2030 — but the phrase 'at least' means that 2040 or even 2050 could fall within his timeframe.

In short, Keynes was considering a time which coincides with the fifth industrial revolution.

Part of the problem in creating more leisure time is that we have become obsessed with material goods that meet superficial needs. So many of us end up in jobs, working incredibly long hours, providing limited service to society. [76]

We also live in a wasteful society. Fourth and fifth industrial revolution technologies will, in part, help eliminate waste – car sharing for example, or the Internet of Things and AI in combination, being used to more accurately match
demand with supply.

---

[76] *As Lord Adair Turner, former cairn at the UK Financial Services Authority said after the 2008 crash, "Some financial activities which proliferated over the last ten years were 'socially useless.'"*

It is also possible that the lockdown measures that accompanied the Covid-19 crisis will lead us to re-assess our priorities and focus on things that matter.

Take Maslow' hierarchy of need.s

It seems that in mature countries, modern-day society has become so accustomed to having Basic Needs that it has taken them for granted and has therefore led to an increasingly superficial mindset. There are early signs of a reality check as most people experience their Covid-19 pandemic 'new normal' lifestyles.

It is also expected that the fourth and fifth industrial revolution technologies will easily generate enough global output capacity to meet the basic needs listed in the hierarchy. [77]

Is a 15-hour week by 2040 possible? Is a 15-hour week by 2030 plausible? The answer to both questions is maybe, but a 28-hour week, seven hours a day, four days a week by 2030 is achievable, providing we (that's the human race) get our act together.

---

[77] *The only obvious basic need to have changed related to healthcare, but technology has created the opportunity to create health and support greater longevity that was previously not possible*

Jack Ma, the founder of Alibaba, has argued in favour of what he calls 996 — working from 9 am to 9 pm six days a week, he says workers will reap the "rewards of hard work."

Maybe, if we only work a few hours a week, we will become lazy, slothful creatures, like snowflakes – delicate and easily melted. These ideas are discussed later.

But not many people would agree that working 72-hours a week is an appealing aspiration.

In the age of smartphones, we are never entirely switched off from work. The sad writer of this passage often checks his email in the middle of the night.

But consider what is natural, consider how hard we worked before the industrial revolution and before that, the invention of agriculture. Studies of modern-day hunter- gatherer societies suggest we worked as little as three hours a day. Sure, our needs were fewer, but is that not the point. Many of our needs in the twenty-first century are superficial.

As Juliet B. Schor[78] writes: "All told, holiday leisure time in medieval England took up probably about one-third of the year. And the English were apparently working harder than their neighbours. The Ancien Règime in France is reported to have guaranteed fifty-two Sundays, ninety rest days, and thirty-eight holidays. In Spain, travellers noted that holidays totalled five months per year." [79]

The Chinese version of the European peasant may have worked longer hours — rice farming does after-all tend to see output more closely correlated with labour input. Maybe Jack Ma was reflecting a more Chinese mindset — forged by a tradition of rice farming.

In Europe, it changed with the industrial revolutions of the eighteenth and nineteenth centuries. By 1800, the average farm

---

[78] *Science Daily, Farmers have less leisure time than hunter-gatherers, Pre-industrial workers had a shorter workweek than today's from The Overworked American: The Unexpected Decline of Leisure, by Juliet B. Schor*

[79] *http://groups.csail.mit.edu/mac/users/rauch/worktime/hours_ Shor draws this information from Edith Rodgers, Discussion of Holidays in the Later Middle Ages (New York: Columbia University Press, 1940), 10-11. See also C.R. Cheney, "Rules for the observance of feast-days in medieval England", Bulletin of the Institute of Historical Research 34, 90, 117-29 (1961).*
The Next Generation of the Penn World Table†
By Robert C. Feenstra, Robert Inklaar, and Marcel P. Timmer*

labourer worked 8.2 hours a day. One hundred years ago, the average working week in Belgium was just over 70 hours.

There is good news, however. In the twentieth century, things got better. Today, the average working week in Belgium is 35 hours, in short, the working week in Belgium has halved in 150 years. It is a similar story in Switzerland, Italy and France.

In the UK, the average length of the working week fell from around thirty-three hours in 1992 to about thirty-one and half hours in 2005.

But with the financial crisis of 2008, things went into reverse. By 2016, the average working week was back to thirty-two hours.

Source Our World in Data

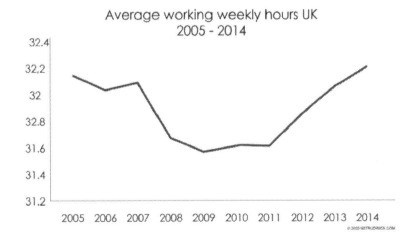

Source Our World in Data

As Torsten Bell, director of the Resolution Foundation thinktank, said: "The economic fundamentals are going against the grain of the politics of hour reductions."

Although the recent increase in the average working week is modest, the reversal of the trend is quite stark – no wonder there is so much social discontent. As will be discussed in the chapter on conflict, if a period of rising living standards is followed by one of either flat or falling living standards, civil war and revolution often follows.

But as the fourth and then fifth industrial revolutions unwind, there are multiple reasons to believe an ever-falling working week is possible.

Technologies creating abundance is one driver. AI, combined with the Internet of Things making more efficient use of rare resource, is another. If, in the age of autonomous cars, we share cars, if the dream of car ownership becomes less of an imperative, then less resource will be required to meet our needs.

Another driver could be automation – technologies such as robotics process automation, automating tedious processes that used to require hours and hours of mind- numbing human labour.

In an interview, Neeti Mehta, SVP, Brand and Culture Architect, at Robotics Process Automation company, Automation Anywhere said: "We think we have automated ten to twenty per cent of processes using traditional technologies, with that we have increased life spans by twenty-five to thirty years, we have been to the moon. With RPA and AI, we think we can automate another forty to fifty per cent, think what you can do for humankind if we can free them up from that repetition."[80]

What will we do with the benefits from such automation? Mehta, said that this is something that society needs to determine, but she suggested the creation of a four-day week would be one option.

As these words are written, various studies are occurring around the world, looking at cutting working weeks without reducing wages. Supporters of the idea say that there is no discernible reduction in output.

---

[80] *Will technology really destroy jobs? Amber Rudd reckons automation is driving the decline of banal, Information Age, article by Michael Baxter*

But if the result of the fifth industrial revolution is that people are forced to work longer hours, as happened after the first and second industrial revolutions, people are entitled to ask: 'what's the point?'

If you love your work – and let's face it, some work is more enjoyable than others — it may not matter. (Writing a book, for example, is an enormous amount of work, but it is also enjoyable and gratifying — with or without financial reward, although direct or indirect financial reward commensurate with the hours it takes to research and write, would be nice.)

If you work more than thirty-five hours a week, but these hours include time researching while using your smartphone, checking emails while on a train journey, or whilst something dull is on TV, or attending networking events, then your time investment may not feel too onerous.

But there is more to life than earning money. If technology can create more free time, with which we can do what we want, including working for the greater good such as voluntary work, this would surely be a good thing, and must be an aspiration for humankind.

An age of such abundance where we no longer need money, where we work for higher motives than earning money, might still be some way off, but working four days a week by the year 2030, seems to be a reasonable target we should set for us all.

Then again, when technology changes at an exponential rate, or when it is accelerating at an accelerating rate, the dreams of Roddenberry and Keynes could be within reach. It is hard to think of a more positive ambition.

Chapter 7:

Totalitarianism and inequality

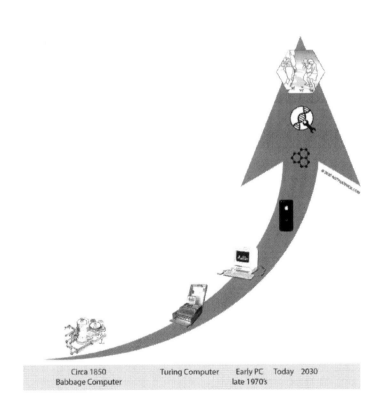

Circa 1850   Turing Computer   Early PC   Today 2030
Babbage Computer   late 1970's

In March 2011, a shoal of sardines was navigating through the Pacific Ocean just south of Los Angeles. They swam in tight formation, moving as one. To the observer, the shoal seemed to possess a collective intelligence. This particular group took refuge in Redondo Beach, King Harbor, California from a so-called red tide; an algae bloom that can often occur after a storm, and can be harmful to sea creatures.[81]

Packed into such a tight and contained water space, they sucked the oxygen out of the water. Starved of oxygen, each fish copying the actions of other fish in their immediate vicinity, they became victims of self-destructive group behaviour. They were unable to find the collective intelligence to navigate to a safer area, so they died en masse, suffocated in what had appeared to be a safe harbour, leaving the local authorities with the unpleasant job of cleaning up. Such events are not unusual in the natural world. Swarms, shoals, flocks or even crowds gather, work apparently in unison, but can sometimes meet a tragic end of their own doing or indeed undoing.

It is not deliberate. The individuals that makeup such a group, we could call them nodes for short and the group, a network, find it hard to understand the consequences of their individual activity when it is multiplied out across a group.

In that sense, people are no different from the shoal of sardines that met its fate in a watery grave of their own making. As the Victorian author Charles Mackay wrote: "Men, it has been well said, think in herds...they go mad in herds, while they only recover their senses slowly, and one by one."[82]

He wrote those words in 1841. Almost 200 years later, we have not learned that lesson.

---

[81] See Blindfolded Masochist, by Michael Baxter
[82] Extraordinary Popular Delusions and The Madness of Crowds by Charles MacKay

The more extreme the circumstances, the higher the risk to crowds and their madness. Mackay was writing about financial bubbles, in which an investment craze become so pervasive, that otherwise wise souls lose all sense of reality, jumping on a bandwagon, perhaps motived by greed. Sir Isaac Newton himself, is an example of such an individual, who lost a small fortune in an investment craze of the eighteenth century known as the South Sea Bubble. He is reported to have said, "I can calculate the movement of the stars, but not the madness of men".

In 2020, another type of crisis emerged to envelop the world. It was not the worst crisis to beset humanity, mild in mortality terms when compared to the Black Death, even Spanish Flu of the early twentieth century, but for most people living in the more affluent part of the word, it was the biggest crisis of their lifetime. There are occasions, when a crisis, such as Covid-19, can bring out the very best in people, creating a kind of common purpose. But the risk of overreaction, of a sort of self-defeating madness of crowds, analogous to the behaviour of our sardines which led them to a watery grave is real.

In one respect, however, Mackay was wrong. Sometimes, men and indeed women, don't recover at all, like in the case of the Californian sardines, their madness eventually proves fatal.

Times when the madness of crowds is more likely to exert itself come on occasions of significant change and insecurity.

Technology is creating such uncertainty today. The danger is becoming apparent and is exposed in newspapers almost every day, as politicians of the Far-right, advocating extreme sets of beliefs, come to power. They opportunistically surf a wave of popular support, charged in part by the so-called echo chamber, and in part by the way changes to a traditional way of life are being enforced. The challenge of pandemics, such as Covid-19, exaggerates the danger. It is almost sure that humanity' reaction to Covid-19 will lead to behaviours that do not help, for example, the spread of xenophobic views, fuelling a growing anti-Chinese sentiment. [83]

---

[83] *It may have been that xenophobic views that meant that the crisis became more serious in the West, where China seemed so distance and so different. "It wouldn't happen here," mentality.*

A backlash against the very forces that help us win future battles against pandemics is an example of a risk created by the Covid-19 crisis.[84]

The Echo Chamber

Nothing is surprising about the way social media has amplified the very worst of humanity; those who studied human nature and the behaviour of the crowd predicted it; the biggest surprise might be that someone as well-read and as obviously intelligent as Mark Zuckerberg, the CEO and co-founder of Facebook, didn't see it coming.

Crowds exaggerate – a group of people sharing a common concern, can become like a rabid beast, howling for blood.

Crowds exaggerate the tendency of those who make them up. A group of people who, on an individual basis, tend to be mild risk-takers, can, when they collaborate, become reckless in the extreme. A group of people who, on an individual basis, tend to be mildly risk-averse, can become paralysed by indecision.

This is not a new insight. Psychologists have understood the phenomenon for some time – it is called group polarisation.[85] Anyone who has observed the behaviour of a group of kids would already be aware of this type of effect. The book Lord of The Flies, published in 1954, described the dangers of groupthink and the consequences of group polarisation, even if the author, William Goldstein, didn't use those terms.

The rise of Nazi Germany and the atrocities committed by an otherwise decent people illustrates the point. The massacre of Rwanda, when neighbour turned upon neighbour, people they had known all their lives –reiterates the danger.

Sometimes, the media and technologies such as, in the case of Rwanda, the radio, can spread a message of hate.

---

[84] *For example, the USA's decision to suspend its contribution to the World Health Organisation funding.*
[85] *H Lamm and D Myers, were the pioneers in studying group polarization. Forsyth summed it up well in Group Dynamics*

But our fear of diverging from the group, our desire and our need to be part of some kind of collective, tribe, group, or nation, can overwhelm our rational, moral selves and make demons of any of us.

Such is the evil face of man and woman. Although groups of men and women, each sex held in equal esteem, maybe a partial proof against such madness.

But no medium in history, absolutely none, can come close to the internet in magnifying the worst excesses of human nature.

Divorced from direct human contact, otherwise, mild- mannered, apparently considerate people, can return from a day spent mingling with others, a day in which politeness is their default form of behaviour, please, thank you and excuse me the currency of their face to face interactions, and release their venom, fingers gliding across their computer keyboard, expressing their rage like warriors engaged in a war dance.

And when like-minded people meet in e-space, upon the diatribes of Facebook and other social media networks, their views become more polarised than ever. Their views are reaffirmed by like-minded individuals.

The risk in the post-Covid-19 era is even more acute, as people look to cast blame.

Fascism

As we all know, fascism emerged before there was an internet. Germany, wilting under the poverty forced upon it in the 1918 Treaty of Versailles, the humiliation still raw, was a breeding ground. "A fascist," said the former US Secretary of State, Madeleine Albright "is someone, who claims to speak for a whole nation or group, is utterly unconcerned with the rights of others, and is willing to use violence and whatever other means are necessary to achieve the goals he or she might have."

Or, as Robert Paxton, a guru on fascism says, it is "a form of political practice...that arouses popular enthusiasm by sophisticated propaganda techniques for an anti-liberal, anti-socialist, anti-socialist, violently exclusionary, expansionist agenda."[86]

The authors have their own more straightforward definition – fascism can occur when a majority enforce their views ruthlessly upon minorities.

But by these definitions, fascism is not what we are in danger of getting.

Instead of sophisticated propaganda, we are instead risking the rise of a kind of people's fascism. The propaganda is not fashioned by clever men and women, cunningly planning to rule us; instead, it is the creation of the crowd although this may be fed by clever men and women who try to turn it to their advantage.

It is a bit like blockchain in that respect. Blockchain is a way by which the crowd can transfer and record the ownership of an asset without the involvement of a central hub. For example, it could be a currency that does not require a central bank to oversee it, a means of buying and selling an asset, such as ownership of a house, or a share certificate without the need of a central body to keep records or facilitate transactions.

Just like blockchain, the internet as a means for spreading ideas can also cut out the intermediary.

In the era of the internet, views can be formed, cemented and become aggressively supported by the crowd, perhaps with an occasional hub in the social media networks acting as a conduit – enabling, reaffirming and helping to define the message of the crowd.

The economist Keynes once said: "Economists and political philosophers are more important than is generally realised. Practical men who believe themselves to be quite exempt from any intellectual influence, are usually the slaves of some defunct economist. Madmen in authority, who hear voices in the air, are distilling their frenzy from some academic scribbler of a few years back."

Keynes may have been right, but in the era of social media, ideas, the frenzy of madmen in authority, are no longer slaves of defunct economists. Instead, the prevailing views of our time have been

---

[86] *Fascism: A Warning by Madeleine Albright The Anatomy of Fascism, Robert Paxton*

crowdsourced. Populist leaders try to discern voices from the ether, rather than the air.

Today's political extremism

Political leaders who come to power on the back of a wave of populism, and advance views that have similarities with fascists from yesteryear, differ in that vital point. They don't set the agenda, they merely turn an agenda created by crowds, and fashioned in the cauldron of tribal loyalty, to their benefit.

Joseph Goebbels, a German Nazi politician and Reich Minister of Propaganda of Nazi Germany, argued that the German state in 1933 had become "a higher form of democracy in which, by virtue of the people's mandate, the government has authority while there is no possibility of parliamentary interference to obliterate and render ineffective the execution of the nation's will."

But the form of populism that is in the ascendency at the time of writing is one in which there is not so much propaganda, which is deliberate and produced to gain calculated effect. (Although there is propaganda, sometimes funded by foreign powers) Instead, views and 'prevailing wisdom' are fashioned in the maelstrom of social media discussion. Traditional media, lobbying groups, politicians act as mirrors – maybe magnifying mirrors – in which the views of a self-enraged crowd are reflected, exaggerated, a little, and feed an ever greater popular frenzy. Occasional engagement from the magnifying mirror of the press and politicians, and indeed powerful lobbying groups, forms part of this downward spiraling vortex. Some organizations such as foreign powers may take advantage of this, but are not instigators.

In such circumstances, Parliament, just as Goebbels suggested eighty-five or so years ago, is seen as the enemy of the people. When the British High Court agreed that the implementation of the results of the 2016 EU referendum was to be subject to parliamentary ratification, the judges who made that decision were called 'enemies of the people.' But the term 'will of the people' is a confusing term. A partial danger lies where the majority hold views that are counter to the needs of minorities. These days, populism implies anti-political correctness, but such correctness can serve the interests of minority groups. Ethnic minorities, followers of minority religions, people whose gender might not be shared by the more vociferous members of a crowd, are put at risk from the tyranny of the majority, potentially condemning minorities to ill-treatment. Unfortunately, sometimes we even see the tyranny of a small majority or even a tyranny of a minority which by quirks, deliberate or otherwise, of electoral boundaries, exert authority.

Given the risks of bubble filters, and the internet rapidly magnifying misguided crowd actions, it is tempting to impose rules to avoid irresponsible behaviours and extremism.

As the philosopher, Karl Popper,[87] argued, maybe we should be intolerant of intolerance. It is called the paradox of freedom.

The end of moderate politics

Not so long ago, before the financial crisis of 2008, the political debate had become bland.

In the UK, for example, little more than the width of cigarette paper separated the views of the UK's leading political parties. Mainstream political parties hogged the centre of the political spectrum offering little to differentiate them.

Just before the 2008 crash, government finances across the developed world – with only a handful of exceptions, namely in Italy, Japan and Greece -- were in good shape. In the US, UK, Spain, France, Germany and many other OECD countries, public sector debt to GDP was modest.

The economy seemed healthy: inflation was low, but so was unemployment – the times appeared to be good. Political debate had become dull: as politicians seemed to look for reasons to row.

Some called it NICE – non-inflationary continually expansionary. Others called it the Great Moderation.

The 2008 financial crisis changed this. The economy moved sharply into reverse gear – and even more worrying for the baby boomer generation, house prices crashed.

---

[87] Popper, Karl, The Open Society and Its Enemies, volume 1, The Spell of Plato, 1945 (Routledge, United Kingdom); ISBN 0-415- 29063-5 978-0-691-15813-6 (1 volume 2013 Princeton ed.)

No one came up with an acronym to describe this period, but if they had, it would have had to encompass the words: correction, recessions and payback. If only there were a good acronym we could draw from those words.

Bankers were blamed. But while many households had their homes repossessed, a tragedy for a vast number of families on a gigantic scale, no bankers went to jail – or at least hardly any of them did. They were not forced to sell their mansions or yachts, or second and third homes in tropical paradises. Banks were bailed out. Central bankers cut interest rates and tried to enforce low-interest rates via the policy of quantitative easing, and governments-imposed austerity. They tried to cut borrowing at a time when they could borrow money at near-zero interest rates.

These policies eventually sowed discontent. While there were sound macro-economic reasons for the 2008 and 2009 banking bailouts, these reasons were not explained to a bemused public.

In the era after Covid-19, which has created a whole new set of economic challenges, the risk for social discontent rises.

With companies bailed out again, and millions of individuals made unemployed, how might they react? If the 2008 crash, and the tools used to fix it, eventually led to social disquiet and polarisation, imagine the long term ramifications of Covid-19! Imagine the consequences if, in the aftermath of Covid-19, authorities are seen to have botched their response, or to have favoured the rich, corporates and their shareholders, while leaving millions of people to manage the best they can? Can they simultaneously betray capitalist ideals by bailing out the corporate sector, but say to ordinary people who were disadvantaged by the Covid-19 crisis "that's capitalism it will make you better off in the long run?"

In fact, Quantitative Easing and banking bailouts were an attempt to ensure we did not repeat the lessons of the 1929 crash and Great Depression, a period which the chair of the US Federal Reserve in 2008, was an expert.

But the net result was to help incubate popular discontent.

QE helped drive up inequality between the baby boomer and younger generations by exacerbating further wealth distribution.

Austerity, a policy that ignored the lessons of the 1930s, has exacerbated inequality.

Before the Covid-19 crisis, the prevalent economic conditions were nothing like the conditions in Europe in the 1930s. Yet, even though economic conditions were much more benign than in the 1930s, there were plenty of signs of a return of fascism.

William Paxton said: "The United States is in significantly better shape than Germany or Italy were after World War I. However, some opportunistic politicians have convinced many Americans that the situation is similarly dire."

He may not have been precisely right. It is not a group of conniving politicians who have sold a narrative of dire economic conditions — instead the bubble filter has created and propelled it.

But there had to be something there first. There had to be a reason why social media discussion should throw up such intolerance.

And while the policies of austerity, combined with the seeming hypocrisy of the banking bailout didn't help, something bigger is going on, an undercurrent was building. The world seems to be experiencing a global Cnut moment. Legend has it that King Cnut, vainly tried and failed to hold back the tide. This legend appears to be resonating with elements of today's society who strive to prevent the inevitable and preserve a culture and a way of life which have already become obsolescent.

If fascism can peep through, like the weeds in a reasonably well-tended garden, imagine what might happen in times of change.

The economic consequences of the Covid-19 crisis have created new dangers, real dangers that compound issues that were already leading to social discontent.

And the tech revolution will indeed create conditions that are ripe for political extremism.

The generational divide

The baby boomer generation calls the millennial generation names — snowflakes, for example. The generation that gave the world the summer of love, hippies and prog rock, worry that their children have become too precious.

A generation divide is emerging. There is nothing new in this. The elders have always frowned upon the 'youth of today' and wondered what the world was coming to. The big difference partly lies with demographics. The baby boomer generation is unique in history because of its numerousness relative to the younger generation. This is creating a kind of tyranny of the baby boomers, partly reflected in electoral decisions that would have been enough to make John Lennon and Jimi Hendrix, the stars of the baby boomer generation, turn in their graves.

But it is also about technology.

Technology is creating a divide between digital natives. Typically, younger generations are at home with technology, and older generations more frequently see technology as a threat.

Part of the problem lies in biology. As we age, our ideas, beliefs and way of living become set — as if the links between the neurons in our brain become hard-wired. Whereas, younger people tend to be more open-minded and adept at dealing with change and more open to new ideas. This is not new: it has always been thus.

And so, the older generation fret about technology destroying jobs; fret about how the internet is breaking down attention spans; fret about immigrants ruining their culture and worry about the morals of the youth.

The youth, by contrast, take on a more international collaboration mindset, as illustrated by different voting choices at the ballot box and are more likely to embrace technology.

Technology is terrifyingly

The unknown is terrifying. Hollywood has made billions of dollars thanks to that inevitable truth.

And in the world of finance, if there is one thing the markets hate more than bad news, it is the unknown — or to use the parlance: uncertainty. Yet, technology is driving us to an uncertain world.

Take jobs. Will technology destroy jobs? The precise answer to that question is uncertain.

Back in 2013, academics from Oxford University looked into the question of how many jobs will be destroyed by technology. Their conclusion: up to forty-seven per cent of the workforce were vulnerable to job losses. [88]

They say that jobs that involve a high level of social intelligence are less likely to be disrupted. Occupations that are likely to be safe include those which include developing ideas, originality, negotiation, social perceptiveness, and assisting or caring for others. In contrast, top of the list of jobs that are likely to be replaced by technology are insurance appraisers, insurance underwriters and tax preparers. By contrast, occupational therapists, mental health counsellors, healthcare social workers and teachers seem quite safe from disruption. At least that's for the next two decades.

The Frey and Osborne Report garnered no shortage of headlines and a long list of critics. The critique rests on two arguments:

Firstly, Frey and Osborne paid insufficient attention to the different tasks that a single job entails. Without doubt, some of the daily tasks carried out by workers engaged in occupations they identified as vulnerable to automation, but many of the functions are much harder to automate. Maybe, then, instead of destroying jobs, technology will change them, free workers up to spend more time practising social skills.

Doctors will not be eliminated, but up to eighty per cent of what they currently do will be automated. Their role will be transformed, and they will change from reactive to proactive practitioners of medicine, but the doctors' clinic receptionists are perhaps doomed.

The case for the defence

Others say that technology doesn't destroy jobs; it frees up people to focus on less routine tasks. It will render us more productive.

Take robotics process automation company UiPath. In an interview with Guy Kirkwood, Chief Evangelist at UiPath, said[89] : "One of the big myths of automation is that it replaces jobs, it doesn't. Most organisations go into automation because they want to reduce

---

[88] *The future of employment: how susceptible are jobs to computerisation? Carl Benedikt Frey and Michael A. Osborne‡ September 17, 2013*

[89] AI won't destroy jobs it will transform them, Information Age, article by Michael Baxter

headcount, that's what they base their business case on, and they are all wrong, that doesn't happen.

"What actually happens is they put in automation and then realise that the value of their people, the value of their human capital, is much higher than they thought it was. So, they re-deploy those people. They raise them up the value chain." He cited a client who seemed to hit the nail Guy was attempting to hammer home, directly on the head, when he described what happened after robotics process automation was installed at the company: "The mood music has changed. Our people are happier, and we now measure the service in terms of compliments rather than complaints."

The second critique with the Frey and Osborne report is that from experience drawn from previous industrial revolutions technology also creates jobs.

A report from The World Economic Forum forecasts that by 2025, machines will perform more current work tasks than humans, but that the workplace could create 133 million new roles in place of seventy-five million that will be displaced between now and 2022.

However, it can also be said that many of these estimates are based on assumptions shaped by previous industrial revolutions. And that the forthcoming ones are driven by cognitive innovation, one where automation will require far fewer humans to control it.

An excellent example of the kind of job that is being created is data scientist. In 2017, The Economist magazine claimed that data is the new oil.

Data, and more importantly, the insights, is becoming incredibly valuable, and that means people are needed who understand it.

In another interview, Jeremy Achin, CEO at DataRobot, said that demand for data scientists is becoming insatiable. He says that if every person on the planet got a job as a data scientist, there would still be a shortage of people.[90]

The case for the prosecution

The problem is that the economy is complex.

---

[90] *Will 2019 see the automation of automation and push up salaries of data scientists? Information Age, article by Michael Baxter*

History tells us that there are massive time lags – the first industrial revolution coincided with a period of falling median wages and weak economic growth. Before the fruits of the second industrial revolution had dropped, like ripe cherries, into the wage packets of households in the industrial world, we first suffered economic disaster, the rise of fascism and the detonation of two atom bombs in Hiroshima and Nagasaki.

Technology will create new jobs, but there is enormous doubt concerning the job prospects of the swathes of people who work in areas that are subject to wholesale automation. Will they acquire the skills required to operate in the newly created employment roles? An entire generation, or perhaps two generations, might be lost as they will not be sufficiently skilled to meet the requirements of the new age.

Even more worrying, many of the tasks that Frey and Osborne identified as least likely to be taken over by technology are typically poorly paid — carers and nurses, for example.

No wonder there is a fear of technology.

Such fear is legitimate and does tend to correlate with the populism vote in the US and Europe where politicians offer hollow unsubstantiated promises.

Such fear needs a home; something it can focus on, so fictitious enemies are created: immigrants and globalisation. According to research from Ball State University, technology/automation was the leading cause of loss of well-paid jobs in US manufacturing. Their finding is not without critics.[91]

Those who are opposed to international trade and immigration overlook the benefits — that the net effect of both is favourable to all sides.

Most overlook the shrinking population and therefore, the workforce and the need to augment the number of people entering employment to meet the future needs and costs of society.

Trade allows nations to focus on what they have a comparative advantage in, immigrants are an essential source of innovation, entrepreneurial endeavour, and to plug the workforce deficit.

---

[91] *The Myth and reality of manufacturing in America, Michael J Hicks and Srikant Devaraj*

Deeper problem

There is a deeper problem. It is not about jobs and automation. It is about the macro effects of industrialisation, trickle-down, and potential lack of aggregate demand.

The real challenge of automation, globalisation and immigration is not that such forces cannot benefit the economy; the problem is more subtle than that: it is one of trickle-down.

The case for rising inequality is not clear cut, although it has been getting steadily worse in the US — which may be something of an outlier.

But in the UK, inequality of income deteriorated in the 1980s, then it plateaued. It is a similar story in mainland Europe. In the USA, salaries are greater than they were forty years ago; however, their purchasing power has not increased.

A more significant issue than inequality of income has been inequality of wealth, but paradoxically, the losers from growing wealth inequality have been younger generations, who are often less likely to support the populist causes of the Far Right.

Income inequality may be higher today than in any other era. Growing inequality is undesirable, not just because of moral reasons, not only because of the risk of social injustice, leading to social unrest, but because inequality can suck the oxygen of growing consumer demand out of the economy, just as the Californian sardines sucked actual oxygen from the water.

Inequality continued - Economies of scale

It is all very well having great innovation, but to be able to take full advantage of it truly, you need to make it at scale — and for that, you need a mass market. [92]

---

[92] *New technologies are often either very expensive or offer limited functionality. Take for examples: the computer, electric car, solar panels and lithium ion batteries. The computer was initially much too expensive and indeed unwieldy for consumers. So early uses were in World War 2 at Bletchley Park where it was used to break the Enigma code. Several decades later it was used by NASA. Indeed, in the early days of NASA, a computer described a large number of people crunching numbers. As the cost of electronic computers fell, their applications grew. As applications grew,*

This is one of the reasons why extreme inequality works to no one's benefit. Some inequality is an inevitable result of economic success — but too much inequality and the mass market required for products to achieve scale may not form.

A mass-market is vital to exploit an innovation fully, and a mass-market won't exist if inequality is too high. [93]

As we pointed out earlier, when he died, Henry VlII of England was one of the richest men in the world. We don't know for sure what killed him, but syphilis is a candidate. Whatever the cause, there is

---

the potential market grew, until eventually the cost was low enough for a mass consumer market. Still the applications grew, from computers used to play games, PCs for domestic use, smart phones and tablets, and now the computer devices that make- up the internet of things. Electric cars were initially bought by quite wealthy individuals, but as their cost falls, the potential market expands, and the cost will fall further. There is a case to say the creation of a rich class makes it viable for products like Tesla to work through the initial expensive stages. Alternatives might be extensive government subsidies. Lithium ion batteries found a niche in mobile phones — at first, they were expensive and cumbersome. As the market grew, cost fell, until today when the batteries can charge electric cars. Solar has only recently become competitive with traditional energy, before that it needed subsidies. Other examples might be carbon fibre, initially used by the military, then in Formula One, then in aircrafts, now it is appearing in cars targeted at a mass market. Meat created from stem cells faces a problem. It is hard to imagine anyone paying thousands of pounds, dollars or euros, just to buy meat from stem cells. So, who will be the initial customers, required to create scale? But at the mass market stage, too much inequality and demand will be inadequate to feed the learning rate.

93 Back in the second millennium on the island of Crete, in the eastern Mediterranean Sea, the printing press was created. But there was no mass market for it, the innovation stuttered, and fizzled out. Likewise, the wheel was invented in Central America before the conquistadors came. It was part of a children's toy. There were no horses in The Americas then, so demand for a wheel was limited so the market didn't evolve. When the Spanish arrived, they found in the Incas and Aztecs, a people who 'hadn't even invented a wheel'. The revolution in the motor car gained momentum once Henry Ford worked out how to make a car that was cheap enough for the mass market — in this way the car industry accelerated from meeting a niche demand and which had advanced slowly over the previous 50 years to one that appealed to a mass market. And with that breakthrough, the evolution of the motor car moved into a fast lane, such that today, cheap cars targeted at the mass market have more advanced features than the most expensive and luxurious of all cars a few decades earlier.

a good chance that today his condition could have been cured. The creation of a mass-market in health care, significantly aided by universal healthcare schemes, and more recently in HealthTech, combined with advances in computer tech, which themselves were made possible by the emergence of a mass-market, has created cures for illnesses once thought untreatable. In a way, a person on a low income who suffers from the same disease that killed Henry VIII is better-off than the former king had been, even at the height of his power.

Fiction tells stories about rich men secretly spending their fortune on trying to extend their life indefinitely. And today, there are even accounts of this happening for real. But if you really want to see technology advances such that you could live to 200, or even longer, your best option would be to use your wealth to try and create a mass market for such technology.

This is the power of globalisation, creating greater potential for a learning rate, and the real benefit of freedom of movement of people across the world. One of the greatest impingements to tech creating advances that significantly increase longevity is that not enough people can afford the tech – poverty in the third world slows back technological advances

That's s why a backlash against globalisation following the Covid-19, crises is a threat to the very forces that could avoid such problems in the future.

The rise of China, for example, has helped fund the Artificial Intelligence revolution. Its economic emergence has also helped expand the market for tech breakthroughs, and indeed the global tech R&D resources, thus increasing the chances that innovations will happen.

For example, China's growing research capabilities is enhancing the world's ability to find permanent cures or vaccines. If however, we seek to punish China, for Covid-19, as Germany was punished for the First World War through the Treaty of Versailles, we eventually end up punishing ourselves, and become self-destructive, just like the shoal of Californian sardines.

Further problems with inequality

There are two other issues with inequality – aside from obvious moral issues.

Firstly, there is the danger of social unrest – the risk, as Nick Hanauer describes it, that the pitchforks will rise-up, that ordinary folk will call for change and violently insist upon it, as they did in France in the eighteenth century and Russia in the early twentieth century. We return to this theme later in the book.

Sometimes, however, the pitchforks can be appeased by finding a scapegoat – an easy target who is blamed for their ills. In the 1930s, such a scapegoat took the form of The Jewish race. This was the case, not only in Germany but across much of the world, including the US and the UK, where the German Nazi party had considerable support. Today, immigrants are often held up as the cause of economic hardship – and unscrupulous politicians try to focus widespread ire on minorities, often hapless individuals who could be fleeing from suppression in their home country. In this way, fascism emerges.

Anti-Semitism has been on the rise, again too.

Secondly, a society which sees extreme inequality is more likely to suffer from excess aggregate savings and lack of consumer demand. This savings glut may have been an underlying cause of the US Great Depression. It might be no coincidence that the economic boom of the post-war years coincided with a period when inequality was relatively low.

High desired savings (partially caused by growing inequality) might be linked to low-interest rates. Superficially this may seem like a positive outcome, but when interest rates remain excessively low for an extended timeframe, asset prices (such as house prices) may rise to levels that squeeze out the majority of people. Low-income poor households but which own their homes, encouraged by the rise in their net wealth, may find they can still afford to spend money at the level they are accustomed to either by reducing their savings or, by increasing debt. As we found out in 2008, an economy that relies on growth through funding consumer spending via rising house prices can fall into a profound crisis.

When technology makes better use of scarce resources

A much bigger issue lies with the sharing economy.

We currently use resources inefficiently; we get sucked into buying products that need replacing every two years or so.

Linked to this is a possible change in our attitude to ownership.

Ownership is changing

It may have begun with music sharing. We used to own our musical collection; sometimes, it was almost like furniture. Our records often bedecked in stunning artwork, sitting in neat rows beneath our music system in our living room, a statement, an expression of our identity.

Today, by contrast, we instead see streaming services such as Spotify, subscription services from which you can listen to whatever you like, ad-free, for as long as you pay the monthly subscription.

Now we no longer physically own the means for storing photographs we take, they are stored on the cloud instead, once again, extracting from us a monthly fee.

Some might argue that it is a change for the worse. There was a time when an album was more than just a collection of songs. It was held together by the physical medium itself and supported by the album cover, it felt like a narrative in its own right.

But whether this is a change for the good or bad, it's a change that is occurring.

Now Amazon invites us to pay a monthly fee to have unlimited access to a million-plus e-books.

The change in attitudes is occurring in business too.

The Cloud has transformed computer hardware from being a company's overhead to a variable cost, something they pay for via regular payments and can turn up or down. But the principle of not needing or wanting to own certain goods is likely to mutate. We are approaching a point when we are likely to see a convergence between the Uber- style business model and autonomous cars?

We are rapidly approaching the end of the era when we own a car. Instead, we pay for it when we need it, or maybe pay a monthly fee for unlimited car sharing. If you see the topic of car sharing, or indeed autonomous, or even electric cars, discussed in an online newspaper article, howls of protests from readers often accompany it.

We are all victims of the tyranny of attitudes formed in our childhood.

Among mainly, but not exclusively, younger people, the concept of car sharing is not so alien.

However, if we all start sharing autonomous cars, then fewer cars will need to be made to meet demand.

If motivated by the psychology of car sharing, and by fears over climate change, we focus more on sustainability, then this would be good news that carries potential danger.

Electric cars, once the problem of battery longevity is solved, score over traditional vehicles in that they have fewer moving parts, meaning they should last longer.

The macroeconomic effects of this change will be profound. The economy thrives on waste and unnecessary spending. It creates jobs. As we cut-out waste, and share cars, aggregate demand could slump.

As we said previously, there are time lags between innovation and wealth creation. In the nineteenth century, people often became worse off, thanks to innovation in the short run. In time, the network that makes up the economy found a way to adjust, and eventually, technology innovation did lead to rising median incomes, but the keyword here is 'eventually'.

But technology is set to change at a pace that has no precedent. No sooner does the economy and government work out how to respond to one revolutionary innovation, a new one will emerge.

Such conditions are a breeding ground for social resentment. History demonstrates, and recent experience testifies that such conditions are often followed by fascism, ruling us like the Sith from Star Wars.

The biggest despot of the lot

But the biggest despot of the lot is us.

Nothing can be more unreasonable and terrifying than a crowd, infected with groupthink, subject to group polarisation, and fragmented by echo chambers.

In the age of social media, especially as new technologies such as virtual reality may make social media even more pervasive, the most likely driver of fascism will be the crowd. In the aftermath of Covid-19, where growing economic pressures, compounded by the fourth and fifth industrial revolutions changing our way of life, will exacerbate the risk.

And the crowd is made up of people like you and me. We pose this significant threat to ourselves.

As the 1970s rock band Supertramp said:

> "Now they are planning the crime of the century…
> Who are these men of lust, greed, and glory?
> Rip off the masks and let's see!
> But that's not right, oh no, what's the story?
> For there's you and there's me."[94]

---

[94] *From the album Crime of the Century, from Supertramp*

Chapter 8

Sloth and the end of empathy

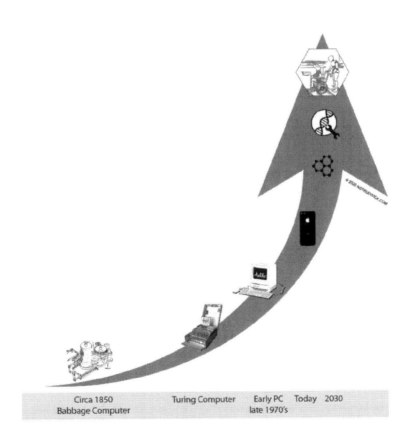

Circa 1850
Babbage Computer

Turing Computer

Early PC
late 1970's

Today   2030

 Learning a second language while you are young is good for you – at least it's good for your brain. Studies show that people who do learn a second language when young tend to have a superior attention span to those who don't.[95] Another study found that bilingualism seems to be associated with the delayed onset of dementia.[96]

But why should we? Language translation apps are becoming more accurate. It won't be long before, via the aid of earphones/hearing aid type devices, wirelessly linked to the cloud; we will be able to have every language known to humanity translated in real-time. But the technology won't just stop improving at that point. Just as AI can now be used to manipulate images, it will in due course be able to manipulate sound. Real-time voice translation will reflect an individual's way of talking, the way they emphasise certain words, their tone of voice, making the technology extraordinarily nuanced. In time it could even do this to song – opera translated into different languages, with AI generating the sound such that it seems as if you are still hearing the singer. Such technology does not exist now, but there is no reason not to assume it will exist within a relatively short timeframe, and certainly within the lifetime of most readers of this book.

Consider the implications – "You like tomato, I like tomato:" the joke is meaningless when seen in print, but when sung by Fred Astaire and Ginger Rogers, it becomes famous. But would an AI voice be able to capture that? "You like tomato, and I like tomahto', sung in a voice translating the famous duo in real-time.

---

[95] *(ORIGINAL RESEARCH ARTICLE From. Psychol., 26 May 2014 | Never too late? An advantage on tests of auditory attention extends to late bilinguals Thomas H. Bak1*, Mariana Vega-Mendoza1 and Antonella Sorace2).*
[96] *Dementia in developing countries: Does education play the same role in India as in the West? Gowri K. Iyer, Suvarna Alladi, [...], and Subhash Kaul*

But why should we bother to learn a foreign language if there are such sophisticated translation tools? Purists tell us that there are other advantages of learning a foreign language — an appreciation of poetry, or puns. But two languages may be too much to learn for me 'et tu' because of some vague benefit of understanding a play on words.

Learning a second language may help promote a deeper cultural understanding, but when we learn we need rewards "Great, I've only been learning such and such a language an hour, and I can already order a cake." But in an era of sophisticated and ubiquitous voice translation tools, the rewards of learning a second language are subtle and only tend to pay out over a long-time horizon. Most of us will have given up long before. For learning to be effective, it needs rewards; the learner needs to feel as if they are making useful progress. In the era of AI-enabled highly sophisticated real-time language translation technology, never more than a second away, we might have to spend years learning a second language before any benefits emerge. As a result, maybe many of us wouldn't try to learn a second language in the first place. The hidden advantage of learning a second language that it is good for our cognitive functions would never accrue.

A similar argument might apply to learning your multiplication tables. When we are linked to a computer directly via a brain interface controlled by thought, we can work out the cubic route of 6,945.67 in a moment. Why would we need to memorise what six times seven is?

It might be that there are hidden benefits of learning tables, or indeed of practising arithmetic, especially mental arithmetic. It might be that learning tables provides us with a more intuitive understanding of numbers. Practising arithmetic and being adept at 'doing sums' in our heads may be a form of exercise for our brain. But if technology devices augment these abilities, it might be tempting for us to rely entirely on the technology.

This takes us to one of the dangers of tech. Might we lose our intuitive understanding of numbers? Will some technologies make our minds lazy? Will it suck away our ability to concentrate for an extended timeframe?

Boredom can be vital. Moments with nothing to do might encourage us to allow our minds to wander, maybe leading to creative solutions to problems that have been vexing us or create a deeper understanding of some issue. These days, what were once moments of boredom seem to be jam-packed with activities involving our smartphone — checking out Facebook, watching Netflix or playing a video game.

Dangers of smartphones

Have you ever gone into a panic because you can't find your smartphone? Worse, have you ever gone into a panic because you can't find your smartphone while you are using it? The author of this passage has. It must have something to do with the way the mind struggles to hold more than one idea at once. So, you are making a phone call, and someone asks you a question. "Hold on; I'll Google it, you say." Then you panic – "Where's my phone? I was looking at it just now," desperate searching of the back of the sofa follows, while the person you are talking to tries to stifle their laughter.

According to one survey, the average American checks their smartphone fifty-two times a day. There is a recognition by people that they over-use their smartphones, thirty-nine per cent of those surveyed admitted to this, but can they crack the habit?

Has picking up a smartphone become akin to scratching an itch?

Recent analysis of smartphone usage shows that it is dominated by social networking, games, messaging, and media streaming with books and news way down the list. Are we taking advantage of this unique opportunity of enriching ourselves or simply continuously seeking superficial entertainment and self-gratification?

But smartphones are just interim devices. As we move to augmented reality devices, and smartphones mutate into computers embedded into our glasses, contact lenses or even our brain, information displayed on virtual screens, what then?

Will we be permanently connected? Might this make our brains lazy?

Diminished Homo sapiens

Technology could augment us, but it could diminish us. Perhaps it already has.

By divorcing us from the cognitive effort involved in learning or communicating, technology may make us less than human.

Science fiction writer, Ian M Banks, in his books that introduced the idea of neural lace, teased out the idea that AI creates gods, humans little more than pampered pets.

Some characters in his books were dissatisfied with the comfortable and perhaps superficial life that had been created. They chose to live on the fringes of society instead.

Or, as the famous technology entrepreneur, Elon Musk, said: "We'll be like a pet Labrador if we're lucky."

Some studies suggest that technologies such as the internet and social media are lessening our concentration and attention spans. Maybe then, technology is making us less than Homo sapiens sapiens.

According to media reports, a survey by Microsoft found that the average human attention span decreased from twelve seconds in the year 2000 to just eight seconds in 2013. - "One second shorter than a goldfish!" cite the media reports.

It is just that the media reports were not strictly accurate. In fact, the Microsoft study quoted The Statistic Brain website, which, according to Simon Maybin, from the BBC's More or Less Programme, the sources for these numbers were quite vague.

Mr Maybin quoted one academic who specialises in attention in drivers and witnesses to crime. She said that the idea of an "average attention span" is pretty meaningless. "It's very much task-dependent. How much attention we apply to a task will vary depending on what the task demand is."

That's the problem, many of the people who say evidence shows digital technology reduces attention spans, are themselves applying limited attention to detail.

In a paper, Shannon Vallor, a philosopher of technology at Santa Clara University in Santa Clara, cites evidence that multitasking entails "considerable cognitive costs." She said that "chronic multitasking may have lasting negative effects on human cognitive abilities, leaving us more distractible and less efficient at refocusing our attention."[97]

The main weakness with these studies is that they assume falling attention span is somehow new. Pick up a book by Dickens and note the sentences that drag on and on. Look at books from 100 years

---

[97] Moral Deskilling and Upskilling in a New Machine Age: Reflections on the Ambiguous Future of Character, Shannon Vallor

ago, and further back than that and it is hard not to conclude that Victorians and before that, Georgians, had superior attention spans.

Perhaps our attention spans began to diminish when the majority of people learnt to read, doing away with the need to focus hard, memorising the spoken words or stories, instead we could just go back and re-read a passage again.

Read the complex sentences in the Bible, then, bearing in mind the stories that make up the Bible were actually read by very few people – one can start contemplating the concentration powers that our illiterate ancestors may have applied.

Go back further, maybe, to before farming, when we hunted and gathered instead. The patience, concentration and memory functions required were often far higher even than those applied by medieval illiterate peasants trying to understand the Bible, or Victorians reading Dickens.

Have concentration spans fallen? Maybe they have been falling for millennia? More likely, they have been falling in some respects, improving in others.

The TV series Game of Thrones, such a hit with the millennial generation has a complex storyline, with a character list that can be overwhelmingly confusing to the casual viewer.

This takes us to the so-called Flynn Effect, which states that population intelligence quotients increased throughout the twentieth century, although recent years have seen a slowdown or reversal of this trend.

But how meaningful are IQ tests? They are usually created by studying a population and creating questions that show a breakdown of intelligence within that population, with an average score of 100. By definition, average IQ will always be 100. Maybe, if you were to take individuals from a modern-day hunter-gatherer society, IQ scores would be lower in tests produced with Western culture in mind. But if IQ tests were created specifically for people living in isolated hunter-gatherer tribes – with an average score equating to 100 in that tribe, there is a likelihood that westerners would achieve low scores in those tests.

Beware of any study purporting to compare IQs among people of very different cultural backgrounds, including between people of different generations – the results of such studies might be as useful as a 5G enabled smartphone when there is no internet connection.

It is clear, however, that smartphones are changing us, the next generation of devices, and the generation that follows, which may consist of chips inside our heads, which we interact with via thought, will change us by even more.

We absolutely cannot trust to luck and just assume the results will be positive.

The risk that such technology may diminish our intellect needs to be understood, and it needs to be studied in-depth, and this needs to happen now.

Obesity

We are getting fatter.

According to international researchers, led by Professor Emmanuela Gakidou of the Institute for Health Metrics and Evaluation at the University of Washington, overweight and obesity rates have increased 27.5 per cent over the last thirty-three years and by 47.1 per cent among children and adolescents.[98]

It's hardly surprising – we are hardwired to exist in a hunter-gatherer society where food supply can fluctuate, from scarce to plentiful, when sugar or honey was rare. When we eat to excess and consume food packed with sugar, we are merely obeying the instructions in our genes. It takes considerable efforts not to follow these instructions, and some people find it easier than others to resist the temptation of sugar and processed foods.

But consider how modern technology makes things easier. From washing clothes by hand to using a washing machine, from sitting on the ground with others, listening to a storyteller, to lounging on our sofa watching TV, technology replacing the need to have to get up now and then, and travel all the way across the room to the TV to turn to another channel, to just touching the remote control – our exercise limited to those occasions when we have to turn the sofa upside down to find the remote. But even using a remote is seen as too much work, now we can bark instructions at our speech recognition

---

[98] *Artificial intelligence yields new antibiotic, February 20, 2020, Science Daily,*

virtual assistant. AI is increasingly anticipating our needs. No need to research what we are going to watch, AI will know.

In the movie WALL-E, robots did everything for us; humans were slothful creatures for whom almost everything was too much effort. Could that be our fate?

The giant sloth has an undeserved reputation. But maybe slothful humans, or Homo sapiens teporis torporibus is what we are at severe risk of becoming.

Universal basic income

The idea that technology may make us lazy or slothful takes us to the danger implicit in the promise of living in an age of plenty. Could we return to Eden, but this time digital Eden? If so, universal basic income must then enter the debate.

Maybe, though, to live in an age of plenty, we don't require technology to help us create more, instead we need technology to help us make better use of what we already have.

What we want and what we need are different.

Recall Maslow's hierarchy of needs, described previously. We show the chart again, below. Many of the products and services we consume barely show up on the hierarchy. We want status, but that is not the same thing as buying more food than we can eat, creating waste. We want fun, but do need, for example, an advent calendar for our pet dog?

To put it another way, we labour in fields, offices, in factories, construction sites, retail stores, warehouses and in countless ways to earn money to live. But a lot of the goods and services we produce are wasted. For example, in the western world, up to forty per cent of food is not consumed, presumably left to rot away.

There is even evidence that a lot of us do so-called 'bullshit jobs'.[99]

Smart technology, applying the internet of things, data and machine learning offers the potential of making more efficient use of technology without comprising our desire to fulfil our needs, wherever those needs fit on Maslow's hierarchy. Furthermore, if technology can allow us to make smarter use of resources, wasting less, buying less things we don't need, making more informed purchasing decisions, maybe our needs could be met from less labour.

So, if by sharing autonomous cars, our needs for private transport are fulfilled with 90 per cent less cars, if smart energy means we minimise the amount of energy we waste, if smart devices create a situation in which we waste less food, then maybe it won't be necessary for us to work so hard to fulfil our needs.

As mentioned previously, Jack Ma, founder of Alibaba, has argued in favour of a "996" working week: nine hours a day (nine am to nine pm) six days a week. Hard work is good for us, is the gist of his argument.

As Pope Paul said: "All life demands struggle. Those who have everything given to them become lazy, selfish, and insensitive to the real values of life. The very striving and hard work that we so constantly try to avoid is the major building block in the person we are today."

Universal basic income, on the other hand, is the idea of providing every adult, and in its purest form, every adult and child, a monthly income, irrespective of what they do.

In short, they could get money for doing nothing. And if we live in an age of plenty, in which all our needs can be satisfied, there may be no obvious economic reason against universal basic income.

The risk that this might make us lazy, even remove the dignity and satisfaction that is conferred by working, and earning one's way in the world, is perhaps the single biggest argument against universal basic income. Such a policy can surely only be justified if a compelling

---

[99] David Graeber book published in 2018.

181

reason can be found to show that it can be packaged and perhaps tweaked in such a way that this does not happen. Then again, even the strongest advocates of universal basic income only believe in providing a level of income that is sufficient to provide essentials. People would still have to work to buy non-essential items.

Yet there is something strange in this argument – and it lies with inheritance. If there is a risk that plenty, or universal basic income, might make us lazy, then could not the same argument be applied to those who inherit enough money to the extent that it is not necessary to work ever again? Ironically, those who argue most vehemently against what they call an entitlement culture, or receiving something for nothing, are often the most riled when the topic of inheritance tax is brought up. Inheritance tax destroys incentives say the critics, but maybe nothing crushes motivation more than knowing from a young age that you need never work to enjoy the benefits that sit at the top of Maslow's hierarchy. This is not an argument against inheritance; merely we are trying to demonstrate that if you are applying the 'earning money for doing nothing makes us lazy' rationale, it is inconsistent to argue against inheritance tax and universal basic income simultaneously.

Morality, empathy and will technology make us more or less decent human beings?

So, technology may suck joie de vivre from us.

Linked to this is the argument that it may also rob us of our empathy.

Naturally nice

You are probably a nice person. You probably occasionally engage in acts of pure altruism, get pleasure from other people feeling happy, or laughing, feel sad or even distressed by other's suffering, and quite often, you behave unselfishly too.

You are not always like that of course, sometimes, just like everyone else, you are a right so and so.

Evolution has created in us Homo sapiens sapiens, an animal who often (but not always) behaves, by obeying the hardwiring in our genes, quite unselfishly.

The question is, will technology change that? As we artificially mutate, is there a danger that technology will lessen us, make us a more greedy, self-obsessed creature?

Or will technology change us from a species made up of individuals who can occasionally be nice to one another, to one made up of several billion souls who, with respect to our morality, might as well be carbon copies of Mother Teresa of Calcutta?

Evolution and altruism

There is a mathematical, evolutionary and physiological reason for altruism, and by extension, empathy.

To understand the mathematical reason, we need to take a brief detour into the world of game theory.

Assume you and an accomplice have committed two crimes, a serious and not so serious crime. And you are arrested. Assume that you feel no guilt, no desire for self-retribution, but want to minimise any punishment. The police have enough evidence to prove you committed the less serious crime which carries a mild sentence. They can only prove the more serious crime if either you or your accomplice confesses. You are both questioned away from each other, with no idea what your accomplice says. If you both confess, you go to prison for a number of years, say ten years. If you confess, but your accomplice doesn't, you get off with a 'pardon'. If you stay quiet, but your accomplice confesses, you receive a severe punishment, say twenty years in prison. If you both remain silent, you are only punished for the minor crime, maybe you go to jail for a few months, or have to complete community service.

What do you do?

If you distrust your accomplice, you should confess. If you trust your partner in crime, it would be better to say schtum.

Suppose, during our lifetime, we are faced with countless situations in which we have to choose an optimal path. When we buy a cappuccino, do we take the drink and then pay for it, or pay upfront? If we pay upfront, how do we know the drink will be delivered? (We will return to this scenario, bringing in the law, shortly.) Suppose we experience what one might loosely describe as prisoner dilemma type situations over and over again, not literally prisoner dilemma, but scenarios in which we have to decide whether or not we act in the same way that we hope others act towards us, or we behave in a way that works solely to our benefit. What should we do?

The mathematician Charles Nash, subject of the 2001 film A Beautiful Mind, starring Russell Crowe, devised a method for calculating this optimal path, known as the Nash Equilibrium.

But the American political scientist, and Professor of Political Science and Public Policy at the University of Michigan, Robert Axelrod, found that the optimal scenario involves a degree of trust. You assume the other party will act in your interest. If they don't do this, the next time you are in such a situation with this person, you punish them, by, for example, in a Prisoners Dilemma situation, confessing.

Axelrod calls this approach Tit for Tat. It's a profound theory; it provides a mathematical reason to trust people. (Although some researchers question whether other approaches such as Tit for two Tat (when you give people a second chance) or scenarios in which you occasionally diverge from Tit for Tat altogether, can work).

Evolution

If Tit for Tat is such an appropriate strategy, would it not make sense for evolution to hardwire a tendency to follow this approach into us?

In his book The Selfish Gene, Richard Dawkins looked at the ideas of Robert Axelrod to explain altruism in the natural world.

But there is another factor at play. Sometimes, the successful reproduction of our genes – and from an evolutionary point of view, this is all that matters – depends on us apparently acting unselfishly. So, for example, a bee might sacrifice its life by stinging something that poses a threat to the hive, but in the process increasing the likelihood that its genes will reproduce via the queen bee, who accounts for half of the suicidal bee's genes.

Many evolutionary biologists agree that there is such a thing as altruism but disagree on the specifics. In particular, there is massive disagreement between E. O. Wilson, the multi-award-winning biologist, known as the world's foremost expert on ants and two times winner of the Pulitzer Prize and Richard Dawkins. Wilson was closely associated with the concept of kin selection – an evolutionary strategy that favours the reproductive success of an organism's relatives.100However, Wilson later renounced the theory, arguing that altruism is not just about supporting relatives but can be about protecting the social group an organism belongs to, whether it be kin or not.[101][102]

Dawkins disagrees, and for his part, Wilson resorted to a polemical response: "There is no dispute between me and Richard Dawkins, and there never has been" he said on a programme aired on the British TV Channel, BBC Two, called Newsnight, "because he's a journalist, and journalists are people that report what the scientists have found and the arguments I've had have actually been with scientists doing research."[103]

But the disagreement, interesting though it is, is not crucial to the theme of this book. What is important is the idea that altruism can exist in the natural kingdom as well as with humans and that among humans, technology can either support or undermine this.

In other words, it seems that evolution can make us 'nice'. Technology could make us even nicer, or it could make us bad.

Darwinism and morals

Taking a different approach, Charles Darwin could see how evolution could hardwire collaborative behaviour into a species.

He stated: "When two tribes of primaeval men, living in the same country, came into competition, if the one tribe included…a greater number of courageous, sympathetic, and faithful members, who were always ready to warn each other of danger, to aid and defend each other, this tribe would, without doubt, succeed best and conquer the other…. A tribe possessing the above qualities in a high degree would spread and be victorious over other tribes; but in the course of time, it would, judging from all past history, be in its turn overcome by some

---

[100] *E.O. Wilson's Theory of Altruism Shakes Up Understanding of Evolution, Pamela Weintraub, Discover Magazine*

[101] *E.O. Wilson's Theory of Altruism Shakes Up Understanding of Evolution, Pamela Weintraub, Discover Magazine*

[102] *The Selfish Gene, Richard Dawkins*

[103] *Biological warfare flares up again between EO Wilson and Richard Dawkins, Chris Johnson, The Guardian*

other and still more highly endowed tribe. Thus, the social and moral qualities would tend slowly to advance and be diffused throughout the world." - Charles Darwin, The Descent of Man, 1875.[104] It does not take a great leap, to assume that in a sentient species such as us, moral behaviour could be hardwired into us.

When we lived in communities of around 148, it is not difficult to see how a system of Tit for Tat worked. Everyone knows everyone, and it would be common knowledge if one individual behaved in a way that was not conducive to the well-being of the community. If they were to in some way hit the community with a Tat, the community might respond with one big Tit!

In much larger communities, in which we no longer know everyone else's business, a system of laws, possibly enforced by officers of the law, might apply the principle of Tit for Tat, punishing people who diverge from the greater good.

The idea that we can behave altruistically was supported by no less a person as Adam Smith, arguably the father of Capitalism. He is famous for saying: "It is not from the benevolence of the butcher, the brewer, or the baker that we expect our dinner, but from their regard to their own interest." It is one of the founding principles of capitalism, by acting selfishly we serve the greater good.

But Smith also said: "How selfish soever man may be supposed, there are evidently some principles in his nature which interest him in the fortune of others, and render their happiness necessary to him, though he derives nothing from it except the pleasure of seeing it."[105]

It is not a widely quoted statement, but then again, the arch capitalists – the greed is good creed – maybe don't like the idea.

Ayn Rand, arguably the mother of the 'greed is good' idealism, and arguably the mother of neoliberalism preached the idea that we should always act in our own interest. "I swear by my life and my love of it, that I will never live for the sake of another man, nor ask another man to live for mine," states an oath taken from Rand's massively successful book: Atlas Shrugged (Ayn Rand, 1957).

Maybe a whole philosophical approach to capitalism that culminated in the banking greed that underpinned the 2008 crash can

---

[104] *Charles Darwin, The Descent of Man, 1875.*
[105] *"Adam Smith, The Theory of Moral Sentiments, 1759*

be traced back to Rand's ideas – ideas that were born in a cauldron that seemed unaware of the concept of Tit for Tat and the evolutionary benefits of altruism.

Physical reason for morality

Evolutionary benefits can show up in physical characteristics, and so it is with empathy. Studies involving MRI scans have uncovered mirror neurons,[106] which have been observed firing – forming synapses with other specific neurons – not only in response to a particular stimulus, but also if they witness it in others.

In this way, other people can literally feel your pain, or at least imagine it vividly.

This should come as no surprise. That's why our ancestors so liked listening to stories, why we enjoy reading novels or watching movies. We put ourselves in the position of other characters.

Is there an empathy muscle?

But physical attributes need exercise. A child brought up in an environment devoid of say the colour red, grows up unable to see that colour.

Maybe a child who grows up never having the opportunity to exercise mirror neurons does not develop empathy.

Perhaps, it is as if empathy is a muscle, that goes weak with lack of use.

The idea that empathy is like a muscle goes back to at least the time of Aristotle, who in the fourth century BC said:

---

[106] *Mirror Neurons were discovered by mistake thanks in part to a pistachio nut combined with serendipity. Researchers at the University of Parma were conducting research into fMRI (Functional magnetic resonance imaging). During a respite, they left a macaque monkey and a human still connected to brainwave detectors. The hapless human was trying to crack open the nut. Researchers noticed that the brain activity in the human and observing monkey were very similar. WINERMAN, LEA, the mind's mirror, American Psychological Association, Monitor on Psychology, October 2005Monitor on Psychology.*

> *"Excellence is an art won by training and habituation. We do*
> *not act rightly because we have virtue or excellence, but we rather*
> *have those because we have acted rightly.*
> *We are what we repeatedly do. Excellence, then, is*
> *not an act but a habit."*

This is one of the arguments put forward to having a family pet, when children are growing up.

As the philosopher John Locke (1632 – 1704) said, children who are encouraged to care for animals can "be accustomed, from their cradles, to be tender to all sensible creatures." Studies appear to back this claim up; it seems that having a pet from a young age can help create in us, a greater tendency to be empathetic.

In fact, we know that the development of mirror neurons can be enhanced by our upbringing - supportive parents can give us greater empathy. (Miller & Eisenberg, 1988). On the other hand, overly supportive parents can turn us into Veruca Salts – spoilt little darlings 'who want it now.'

Morality over time

It is to be hoped that all readers of this book consider any form of slavery an abomination. Yet 250 years ago slavery was common, and presumably otherwise decent people thought nothing of it. Does that mean we are more moral today? If we are, there has certainly been no genetic change; our DNA is virtually unchanged; instead, it seems we have learned to change our views over what is moral so that today slavery is thought of as implicitly evil.

Various factors lie behind changing attitudes to slavery, but the works of Mark Twain must have been a factor, especially in the US. For example, books such as The Adventures of Huckleberry Finn extol the evil of slavery.

Turning from slavery, to poverty, Dickens brought attention to poverty and social challenges in Victorian Britain. The influence of both Twain and Dickens was amplified many times over by the technology of the printing press, in the process eventually changing attitudes and deeply held beliefs. So, in that sense, maybe technology (the printing press) gave us more empathy.

Consider more recent technology. It can feel as if many of the studies looking into the effect of technology on our empathy, were designed at the outset to show a negative link.

As we said previously, it is human nature to dismiss the 'youth of today' or be cynical about new technologies -- 'nothing but harm will come of it'. Sometimes it feels as if studies purporting to show how technology can adversely affect the young were produced to elicit that very outcome. If technology creates lower empathy as some studies suggest, explain how is it that globally, violence has been in steady decline.[107]

People who cite TV as an example of a medium desensitising us, a contributory factor to violence, need to explain how it is that the rate of that violent crime per capita has been steadily falling over time. They need to explain why causes associated with tolerance, such as gay rights and sexual and racial equality, now have more popular support. On the 7th June 1954, Alan Turing, a vital figure in the allies' victory in World War Two, and one of the fathers of computer science died, possibly because of suicide, after he was hounded for his sexuality. The treatment of this hero was 'a crime' committed by both government and society, but gay rights have been transformed since then. Although TV typically reflects the attitude of society, it can also influence attitudes. Whatever the cause of changes to gay rights, and clearly the 1960s' popular revolution, leading to the likes of David Bowie, with his ambiguous attitudes towards sexuality, was a factor. TV was like a megaphone that emitted a message that in a previous era, may never have gained traction across a global audience.

In the early 1990s, at a time when fears over AIDS and associated prejudice was at near-hysterical levels, the British TV series Eastenders began a storyline to last ten years featuring a character called Mark Fowler who was diagnosed as being HIV+. The storyline showed the prejudice encountered by the character. It is hard to believe that the TV show, which back then, regularly had viewing numbers in excess of twenty million, did not play a role in changing attitudes to people who were HIV+.

---

107 *Stephen Pinker, Better Demons of our Nature.*

TV history is rich with examples of storylines advancing ideas that could have helped change attitudes. There was Anna Friel's lesbian kiss in the British TV series Brookside in 1994, Peter Dinklage's (who is one metre thirty-five tall) colourful character in Game of Thrones, or going back further, to the US TV series Gunsmoke, (ran from the 1950s to the mid-1970s) which tackled an assortment of social issues including the treatment of minority groups.

In the twenty-first century, calls for gay rights and sexual equality have gained mass appeal. It is a great irony. While fears over growing inequality, and a reaction against globalisation and immigration threaten to undermine the fabric of society, in other respects, an era of greater tolerance emerges too. Media made possible by technologies such as TV, and causes echoed across Facebook and Twitter, may have advanced higher understanding in some respects. In contrast, in other respects, we see the ever-greater polarization of society.

Some blame social media for the rise of political extremism – a more likely explanation is growing inequality and the hollowing out of the conventional labour markets, in which the echo chambers, facilitated by social media, propagate misinformation and disinformation. But if the move towards greater gay rights and sexual equality is a sign of growing tolerance, it may also be a sign of greater empathy and a more moral society, enabled in part by technology.

The danger and opportunity

If, via the filter of the internet bubble, weeding out views that clash with our own, social media can divorce us from any sense of objectivity, magnifying the more extreme opinions held by a vocal minority, we risk becoming warped in our thinking.

But if altruism is something we get better at via practice, is there a danger that technology may distance us from the kind of human contact that requires empathy and that strengthens the synapses in our brain associated with kindness?

The danger is that if we spend too much time behind screens, or relying on robots, we spend less time interacting with others, our empathy muscle weakens, or fails to grow.

Conversely, some argue that some forms of entertainment, such as video games, or in the future, virtual reality, desensitises us — through over-use, making our mirror neurons less responsive.

On the other hand, by putting us in contact with people of more diverse backgrounds, technologies such as social media and in the future augmented and virtual reality, may promote more significant interaction and therefore, understanding. Technology may create the opportunity to foster greater understanding and tolerance by promoting closer communication between peoples from different backgrounds.

Because of the immersive experience it offers, Virtual reality, could arguably strengthen our empathy muscle.

The threat and opportunity of anonymous

Suppose uncooperative – you might call it trolling — behaviour appears on social media, but advanced by an anonymous source. If Tit for Tat is nature's way to punish transgressions from unacceptable behaviour, how can this occur if we have no idea who the individual is behind specific tweets or Facebook comments?

The internet is a force for the democratisation of society because it gives power to individuals to extol their views, vent their frustrations and try to convert others to their way of thinking. But if you have stopped to read reviews of a hotel, before booking a holiday, you will know that many, often anonymous, users resort to polemic displays, which seem to serve some kind of hidden agenda. A rude customer who behaves abhorrently can push the maxim: 'the customer is always right' and utilise social media to take revenge on exasperated staff. Or in a medical setting, an individual can destroy a well-earned reputation for providing the highest standard of care because of some imagined slight.

Social media can provide power without any sense of responsibility – may be through anonymity, but maybe just by creating a protective barrier made of ether – physically distancing the architect of some unjustified written vitriol, from the consequences.

Maybe social media can give some people the courage to speak their mind in a way that they would not experience in a setting involving direct human contact. This may be a good thing.

On the other hand, social media can also empower people to vent the darker sides of their nature – direct human contact, and the simple rules of social engagement, which most of us learn as we grow up, act as a kind of brake on our darker thoughts. Liken social media to a diary: many of us use our diary to express our darkest insecurities in a way that we do not truly feel. Social media may be akin to a diary in that sense.

The rules of society demand tact and diplomacy, which in turn usually force us to pause and consider our conversation before we articulate our views. Social media, however, can remove those natural barriers — and we can release our toxic thoughts, sometimes magnified by like-minded others, in a way which might not happen in a physical setting, unless we are inebriated.

In short, the internet can make some people behave like an obnoxious drunk at a party – full of anger and poisonous views – with little in the way of barriers.

Divorcing us from reality

If empathy is like a muscle that can strengthen with use, is it the case that the more often we act altruistically, we become more likely to do so in the future? Equally, might we become desensitised by viewing violence in a semi-realistic setting, such as TV or video games, or an ultra-realistic setting such as virtual reality, making our mirror neurons less responsive? If empathy really is akin to a muscle, it is clear that incredible opportunities and terrifying dangers arise from our use of technology.

If watching violence on TV can desensitise us, making our mirror neurons less responsive, consider the effect that video games, in which we are responsible for the violence we observe. Virtual reality, however, will take interactive entertainment to a new level of realism.

In video games, we may shoot an alien, and presumably suffer no internal moral conflict, because of the distance from reality, but if we shoot a representation of a human being, the dangers are clear.

However, while there is some evidence suggesting that violence in video games can desensitise us, the paucity of this evidence might suggest the link is not significant.

Virtual reality is different. If we immerse ourselves in a 360-degree orientation, and maybe not just our sight, but our hearing and perhaps our sense of smell, and touch can be subjected to an ultra-realistic experience, our empathy muscles may become all the more vulnerable.

In virtual reality, we can be cruel or kind, vicious or gentle. It may not seem to matter: such acts would be part of a game, the victims or beneficiaries of our actions are just computer graphics, people represented by avatars that can feel no pain. It is just that the mirror neurons that are exercised, for better or ill, are real: and the more realistic our virtual experience, the more they might be changed.

There is a more important point.

If empathy is something, we learn from interacting with others, then it becomes essential we practise this skill: social media can bring people together, communicating in virtual reality can enhance this. But it can also shut us off from interacting with people in the flesh, virtual more engaging than reality.

Some practical examples

Shannon Vallor, looks at the possibility that we can be morally de-skilled by technology, in much the same way that the skills of artisans can be lost to technology via the inexorable force of automation.

And she takes three particular cases involving technology and how it could be used to either deskill us of certain morals or enhance them.

Firstly, she takes a military setting. We are all aware, perhaps through viewing movies such as Killing Fields, how soldiers, who we might typically consider to be upstanding citizens, can behave in an appalling way under certain circumstances. Sometimes we can be quick to forgive our own soldiers for atrocities they commit, because "they were in abnormally stressful circumstances" but castigate as evil, others living in equally stressful circumstances, who resort to violence.

In fact, Vallor says that "the conduct of killing in war demands considerable moral skill if it is not to descend into utter moral chaos." She suggests that most professional armies put considerable emphasis on education in the context of virtue. She says that "the broad concept of 'military virtue,' and the specific norms such as courage, loyalty, discipline, and service that go along with it, carry special resonance." But education in itself is not enough. We all know that the best way to learn is by doing, and maybe this applies to learning virtue too. Vallor says: "Only in the actual practical context of war, where situations are neither stable nor well-defined and where success and failure have lifelong moral consequences, can words like 'courage' and 'discipline' be more than empty slogans or aspirational terms."

In her second scenario, Vallor looked at new media and the practice of multi-tasking.

Vallor cited research[108] that suggests that the habitual media multitasking does not bring greater knowledge, even though this might be the intent, but becomes almost self- fulfilling: "Multitasking did provide strong gratifications of a habitual sort – it 'scratched the itch.' Yet, as anyone with eczema will confirm, once you start scratching an itch, it is difficult to stop.

She says: "A person who cannot be counted on to pay attention when you tell her about the recent death of your closest friend, or who is unable to stay focused on the grave and imminent danger to which you're trying to alert her, or who cannot attend to the expressions on your face during an intense conversation, is not someone who can be said to be virtuous. This is true even if a person who makes a sincere effort to pay attention to her social environment but who has unwittingly lost the cognitive ability to succeed in this task."

Finally, she looks at care. Caring for individuals is not merely a duty, a task that needs to be fulfilled. It is also a fundamental part of being human. The ability to care for people helps define us as human. Suppose robots take on the role of caring – not just the heavy lifting, but take care of all our practical needs, relegating our social needs

---

[108] *Wang, Z., & Tchernev, J. M. (2012). The myth of media multitasking: reciprocal dynamics of media multitasking, persona* needs, and gratifications. Journal of Communication,

to luxuries. There are implications for the carer as well as the person being cared for.

Vallor proposes solutions to these problems.

For example, in a military setting, if robots could divorce us from the business of killing for military success, there are dangers we lose a human element. She cites: Mark Coeckelbergh's analysis of drone pilots.109 He "notes that while technologies that distance soldiers from killing appear to 'de-skill' them by depriving them of 'knowledge that is grounded in lived bodily experience, in handling things on the ground, in skillfully engaging with what happens on the battlefield and with others, the extended surveillance and acute visual imaging of drone targets actually end up enhancing the pilot's moral knowledge of what they are doing, and to whom."

Within the caring profession, Vallor refers to various studies that show the importance of eye contact and touch in caring relations. Using the example of an automated system for lifting patients, she notes that a nurse "lifting" a patient with the help of a machine is hardly engaged in skilful caring if the nurse's attention throughout must be devoted to monitoring the machine controls and not the patient – even if the end result is a safe and efficient lift. Far better would be a design such as a mechanical exoskeleton that ensures a safe outcome while still allowing the nurse to maintain eye contact with the patient, verbally enquire after the patient's comfort and sense of security and offer reassuring touch throughout the process.

Let AI become our conscience

Maybe, we can be nudged into behaving morally. In China, the social credit system rewards us for good behaviour.

If we then continue to behave in a way considered moral, maybe the practice becomes hardwired into us

Or maybe AI will be able to achieve this. If our smartphones mutate into 'always with us' AI assistants which encourage us to act unselfishly, will we become less selfish individuals?

---

109 https://www.researchgate.net/publication/257560397_ Drones_Information_Technology_and_Distance_Map ping_The_ Moral_Epistemology_Of_Remote_Fighting

195

But who determines what constitutes good behaviour? And isn't a little bit of rebellion, from time to time, good for our soul?

Maybe, realistic avatars of our parents could be created, then perhaps we can take them with us – our conscience, telling us off, like they did when we were kids.

Or maybe an avatar could be the embodiment of a religion, reminding us that certain activities are tantamount to a sin. If God is with us all the time, so might our AI guide, but this time, whispering in our ears, smiting us with a virtual admonishment when we transgress.

Our AI conscience could even be ourselves — but when we are at our best. An AI conscience reflecting our mood when we are recovering from a hangover may advise against taking another drink.

We could change the controls – turning the digital dial to a barely audible warning, rather than a painful screech if we are about to have one drink, chocolate bar, packet of crisps or cigarette too many.

Jiminy Cricket was Pinocchio's conscience – and was distinctly ineffective too. But then in an era when privacy may become a distant memory, our lies won't be betrayed by a growing nose, instead, AI, after cross-referencing multiple data streams, will indicate when we are less than truthful.

"A little boy who can't be good, just might as well be made of wood," or so we were told, while watching Pinocchio, but technology that can't accentuate the best of human traits is no good: we want technology that liberates us without such liberation being at the expense of others. We might want to say: "there are no strings on me," but a wireless moral compass supported by AI might not be so bad.

Chapter 9

When virtual reality is
better than reality

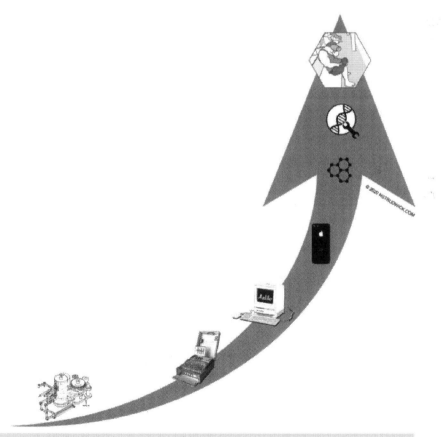

| Circa 1850 | Turing Computer | Early PC | Today | 2030 |
| Babbage Computer | | late 1970's | | |

We live on a crowded planet; it takes too long to get anywhere. Holidays can be fraught with stress, and travel arrangements can be filled with challenges. As the world becomes ever more crowded would it not be more comfortable if we just escaped to virtual reality, assuming, that is we have not already done so.

Then there is sex.

Sex in the digital age

Sex and love! Neither defines us as human because they are not unique to humanity. They are both rather crucial though if there is a chance technology could change either, for better or worse, then that is something we need to start thinking about, and quick.

There is one important way in which it already has. We refer to Sildenafil (better known by brands such as Viagra, an erectile dysfunction drug marketed by Pfizer.) It may be the cause of millions of spam emails, but this medication, because it has enabled couples to enjoy a sex life to an age that might otherwise have been impossible, is a superb example of technology bringing enjoyment to millions. To a cynic who scoffs at modern technology, dismissing it as solely bringing trivial entertainment, respond by saying: "Isn't sex important then?" Or just say: "Viagra."

We all know why sex is enjoyable — it does not take a great intuitive leap to assume evolution made it pleasurable as a way to ensure reproduction – if you like, the continuation of the selfish gene. But sex is also associated with various rituals, both in the animal kingdom and among humans.

By linking sex to long-term commitment: creating a stable environment for offspring, with our species, we have marriage. Other rituals, potentially seen as a precursor to foreplay, might include a night at the cinema followed by a meal.

Suppose technology changes this. Suppose it can make sex more physically stimulating without direct body contact. The implications are as profound as you can imagine.

The potential disruption of sex lies with convergence.

Three distinct areas coming together could dramatically transform the sexual act – it is time to consider the implications.

The convergence consists of advances in prosthetics/ robotics, AI and virtual reality.

As a report looking at our sexual future with robots, says: "Modern sex dolls, unlike their vinyl blow-up counterparts, have a silicon skin with a human-like feel and touch. They often include an 'articulated metal skeleton' so that they can be manoeuvred into a variety of positions and are increasingly customisable – down to the nipple shape and fingernail type/colour." [110]

The dolls are not exclusively gendered female, either. Some modern dolls correspond to males, complete with realistic penises that can be turned from flaccid to erect.

Surveys suggest that some people would indeed be happy to have sex with a robot, although more men than women suggested this the proportionate differences between the sexes was not as high as some might suppose.

---

[110] *Sex dolls. with-artificial-intelligence, sexdolls.com*

Some people may assume that it is almost entirely males who use sex robots. But surveys reveal that female demand is not trivial. One study conducted in the US among 100 respondents, found that two-thirds of the males were in favour of using sex robots and two- thirds of females were against the idea.[111]

But how many people would? Another survey conducted in the UK found that seventeen per cent of respondents would be willing to go on a date with a robot.[112]

The so-called uncanny valley is a barrier – it seems that people can take sexual gratification from an object that looks vaguely human or has some characteristics that support sexual satisfaction. But as an object becomes more human- like, there comes a point when it becomes repulsive. But when this valley is crossed, and sex with a robot becomes, or can become desirable. Almost the Turing Test of sex!

This begs the question, what kind of relationship with a robot is possible? Given that robots are programmed and not – as of yet, at least – sentient, is it possible to have a meaningful relationship with a robot? An episode of Black Mirror, a Netflix series, comes to mind here, when a woman ordered a robot that had the physical and mental traits of her dead husband.

---

[111] *40% of Americans would have Sex with a Robot, Study Finds, SWNS Digital Would you date a robot? More than a quarter of millennials say they would replace a human lover with a DROID, Daily Mail Sick sex robot fantasy BANNED from world's first cyborg brothel, Joshua Nevett, Daily Star, 8 October 2017*
[112] *https://www.telegraph.co.uk/science/2017/11/26/rise- digisexual-virtual-reality-bypasses-need-human-intimacy/*

Further moral implications of technology and sex

Several further moral and ethical questions emerge:

- Robot brothels and prostitution. Robot brothels already exist. They apparently cater to all kinds of tastes, some not encouraged. Sergi Prieto, the co-founder of the Lumidolls, sex doll brothel, told the Daily Star: "Some customers prefer the service because they have a rape fantasy. Obviously, we don't want to promote this kind of activity." The issue of technology disrupting jobs is a topic for a later chapter. It is interesting to speculate, however, will sex robots disrupt one of the oldest 'professions, ' namely prostitution?[113]
- One highly debated area is whether sex robots objectify the human form. This is a topic that is hotly discussed and controversial.
- Could sexual intimacy with robots lead to greater social isolation? To an extent, the answer to this depends on how isolated an individual is in the first place. Controversially, some argue that sex robots could be supportive of older, lonely people. There is a genuine fear, however, that some individuals may become isolated from society. Linked to this is the question of de-skilling social skills, as referred to in chapter nine, on morals and the work of Shannon Vallor. Is there a danger that sex robots might deskill someone from being able to practice intimacy with other humans? On the other hand, maybe sex robots will help us become better lovers.
- Could robots help with sexual therapy? In this case, robots could help people with emotional blockages.
- Would robots help to reduce sex crime? The question here relates to whether sex crime is a habit. If people can perform rape fantasies on robots, will this alleviate them of the need to apply such fantasies on a real person, or will it make them more inclined to do so? Linked to this is the issue of paedophilia, the idea of sex robots looking like children fills most of us with revulsion. Whether sex robots can help in these matters would be very dangerous to test.

---

[113] *Sick sex robot fantasy BANNED from world's first cyborg brothel, Joshua Nevett, Daily Star, 8 October 2017*

The above areas are all critical – there can be surprising benefits of sex robots. Still, the dangers in terms of creating an addiction or removing the link between sex and intimacy with a human being are clear.

When we see convergence with AI/machine learning, in which a sex robot can communicate with us, learn about us, hold conversations with us, then the issues referred to above, become magnified multi-fold.

But it is convergence with virtual reality when the disruptive potential of technology on sex becomes the most extreme. In virtual reality, you can be represented by avatars, and via this avatar communicate with others. The avatars don't have to look like you, or even be the same sex as you. In virtual reality, you can be anyone you like. You will, via the aid of sex robots, simulating the actions of other people you meet in virtual reality, who are similarly linked to a sex robot, be able to have sex in virtual space and real space simultaneously. The barrier of distance will be removed by robots using AI, mirroring the actions of your partner. You and your lover will be entwined both virtually and by proxy. You could conceivably have sex in augmented reality, with the image of your distant partner superimposed onto a robot – which admittedly sounds a bit weird.

These things are not going to happen next Tuesday. But then this book is not about how technology is going to change the world in the next week. It is about how technologies, such as those described earlier will change the world in our expected lifetime. Sex robots converged with AI, and virtual and maybe augmented reality will have massive implications during this period. We must not leave it too late to consider these issues. If we leave it for too long, we may no longer be able apply objective analysis.

Virtual Life after death

Sadness seems to be an emotion of living. But sometimes it can occur thanks to the fact that we all die, eventually. There is undoubtedly nothing that makes us sadder than the death of a loved one.

A company called eternity.me thinks it may have cracked that one. The idea, to quote from the company, is to "collect your thoughts, stories and memories, curate them and create an intelligent avatar that looks like you. This avatar will live forever and allow other people in the future to access your memories." At the moment, we have photos and videos, which we stare at after our loved ones leave us. eternity.me takes that idea a step, or maybe several steps, further.

Another Netflix series called Altered Carbon which is set in the year 2384 has people of Earth uploading their consciousness into a new "sleeve" body, one whose quality is determined by wealth. The sum total of one's personality, memories, and abilities boil down to a Cortical Stack (think of an advanced memory stick) located in the back of the neck. The Stack can hypothetically be "re-sleeved" until the end of days – but once it's destroyed, its owner is dead forever.

Consider ten or twenty years from now. Let's say that we have augmented reality assistants that get to know us even better than our partners or parents know us. The AI assistant is there, with us all the time, it knows how we react to different circumstances. By comparing data streams, it knows that a specific type of joke makes us laugh, but only after we have had a certain kind of day. If we bang our head, we get a payment reminder in the post, and our computer crashes all within five minutes of each other, our AI assistant may know that we tend to react by screaming, or taking our frustration out on the poor unfortunate person whose shadow crosses ours, or we reach for the music player to listen to melancholy music, or we reach for the alcoholic beverage. We react differently; over time, the AI assistant knows how we will respond.

People who know us well might be able to guess what we are going to say next. My children can second guess a joke I might crack after a given event, I used to try and wind my dad up, getting him to repeat a story he had told a hundred times before. We all become predictable, and the people who know us best might find that we are especially predictable. David Bowie overcame the problem of creating predictable lyrics by cutting up newspapers into individual words and putting some of them back together randomly.

If we are so predictable, consider how predictable we might become to our AI assistant.

By cross-referencing recordings of our comments with video footage from other people's AI assistant of our own physical appearance when making those comments, the AI assistant may not only be able to know how we will react to a given stimulus, it might be able to extrapolate our facial expression and body language, from the perspective of other people.

And from this, it could create an avatar, to act either when we are dead or even when we are still alive. We may have to apologise for our avatar – it may have uttered a rude comment to someone else. We may not have said it, but the reaction of our avatar shows we would have said it if we had been there. We end up apologising for what we would have said if we had been there.

In this way, we can have engaging conversations with the avatars of the deceased certain that if they had still been alive, the conversation would have been near-identical.

We might even be able to make love, via the aids described in the section above, with our deceased partner.

We are not suggesting that these are good things, merely possible things, and within a few decades too, quite possibly during our lifetime: The year 2040, as the date when these ultra-realistic avatars exist, seems viable.

Virtual reality

"If a virtual knife stabs you, you are not going to be physically injured but nevertheless might feel stress, anxiety, and even pain," said Mel Slater and Marie Sanchez-Vivek. [114] In a paper looking at the applications of virtual reality, (VR) they say VR simulates reality, it does not create a new reality. They say it operates in a space just below "The reality horizon." "If a virtual human unexpectedly kisses you," They explain further, "you may blush with embarrassment, and your heart starts pounding, but it will be a virtual kiss only."

But is this really so? Pain is not felt at the point of impact or injury but in the brain. Thus, the brain can be tricked. Psychology 101 explains how illusions can fool the brain.

We know that mirror neurons can simulate the pain felt by others, such that it is as if we feel that pain. Suppose though, instead of us observing another individual. We are watching a simulation of ourselves, in virtual reality. The simulation can be given extra reality by

---

[114] *Enhancing Our Lives with Immersive Virtual Reality, Mel Slater and Maria V. Sanchez-Vives, Frontiers in Robotics*

linking our physical actions to the movement of the avatar. We lift our hand; the avatar lifts its hand. Maybe we walk on a treadmill, but the avatar walks at the same speed, but in some simulated environment. Perhaps the simulation can be physically enhanced, in much the same way that movie theatres can enhance the viewing experience through water sprays, and certain smells. Maybe in time, technology will stimulate neurons responsible for certain sensations – for example, if with the help of quantum computers, we can map out the neurons and synapses in the brain and identify which neurons are responsible for which activities. If you in the VR environment, simulating a situation that should elicit the smell of sulphur, the neurons responsible for this smell could be stimulated.

Even without such stimulation, maybe the brain can, thanks to our imagination, be fooled into feeling as if a simulation is real.

In an article for The New Yorker, Joshua Ruthann [115] reports on an attempt to use virtual reality to create the sensation of out-of-body experiences.

Ruthann quotes philosophers Thomas Metzinger and Michael Madary, who have drafted a virtual-reality 'code of ethics' saying that embodied virtual experience can change us profoundly. It can affect us in ways we barely understand, redefining "the very relationship we have to our own minds."

We consider other applications of virtual reality, as follows:

- VR in science, especially psychology and neuroscience
- Sports and exercise
- In social psychology, including on how it has been used in the preservation of and access to cultural heritage
- Moral behaviour, including an example of how it might be used to train professionals such as medical doctors when confronting serious dilemmas with patients
- In travel
- And in the presentation of news.

---

[115] *Are We Already Living in Virtual Reality? New Yorker, Joshua Rothman, March 26 2018*

Consider for a moment the implications:

Humans are great storytellers. Indeed, when ideas are expressed as a story, they often take on far greater resonance. That is why the parables from the New Testament became so influential. There was a time when we gathered around a fire hearing tales of the spirits and demons, but these tales often had a purpose, educating us on plants to avoid, or hunting techniques, for example. Stories were passed, from parent to child, held in memory, gradually changing over the aeons, maybe creating myths and legends. With writing, such tales became fixed, and with the print, they were disseminated to a broader audience. But TV and cinema took the practice, which was as old as humanity, and transformed it. Virtual reality will be even more transformative. It will be as if we are experiencing the adventures in a tale, ourselves.

Add to the equation interaction. By our own actions, we are able to change the outcome of the narrative.

At this point, we see a convergence with video games. The popularity of computer and video games has always been a function of the power of the hardware and realism of the experience. During the 1980s, when computer games were played on ZX Spectrums and Commodore 64s, the industry was small and niche. The broader media even questioned whether it had a future.[116] With each leap in computer power, from Commodore 64 to Commodore Amiga, from Sega Megadrive to Sony PlayStation, the industry became more mainstream. With virtual reality, computer and video games could become the dominant form of entertainment. But will they become so addictive that the human race, living off universal basic income, will decide simulated reality is more enjoyable than reality?

We may even holiday in virtual reality, walking down the Grand Canal, Venice, replete with the aroma for which Venice is famous. Maybe, in time, there will be multiple simulations of Venice, virtual gondoliers, steered by real people, in their own virtual reality environment, as we jostle with the crowds, like-minded people who have chosen the same simulation as us.

Or maybe, our touristic escape will be via augmented rather than virtual reality. We may eat at a restaurant overlooking the Rialto

---

116 *The author had first-hand experience of this, as during the 1980s when he worked in the video game industry, providing a PR service*

Bridge, gazing at our loved one in this most romantic of settings, when in fact we might be sitting in the Rialto Restaurant Green Screen Simulation, New York. Our partner could be in the Rialto Restaurant Green Screen Simulation, London. Might virtual reality become more appealing than reality? The philosopher Nick Bostrom argues that the laws of mathematics suggest we already are. If it is possible, goes the argument, to create a simulation so realistic that it fools us into thinking it is real, then might the simulation of reality itself generate a simulation of the simulation of reality in which we already live. You can liken it to two mirrors facing each other – you see a reflection of the reflection going off into infinity. Maybe we could eventually see simulations of simulations of simulations of reality. In a scenario in which there are a thousand layers of such simulations, what are the chances we actually live in reality and not a simulation? Are they 1000 to one? Maybe they are infinity to one. Studies of the quantum world reveal that particles behave differently at the quantum level. Perhaps they behave differently because of glitches in the simulation. Elon Musk had often spoken up for this simulation hypothesis. He suggests that reality must be boring; why else create a simulation? [117]

Is this a risk, might we decide virtual reality is better than reality and choose to exist in a simulation like the movie Matrix envisioned? Would that be a bad thing?

Might we find a kind of simulated version of nirvana, or might we denigrate ourselves, lose our humanity, instead of being Homo sapiens sapiens, we just become homo subsunt res quarum habent — insubstantial humans.

---

117 *We're Probably Living in a Simulation, Elon Musk Says By Mike Wall 07 September 2018,*

Chapter 10

When Orwell meets the fifth industrial revolution

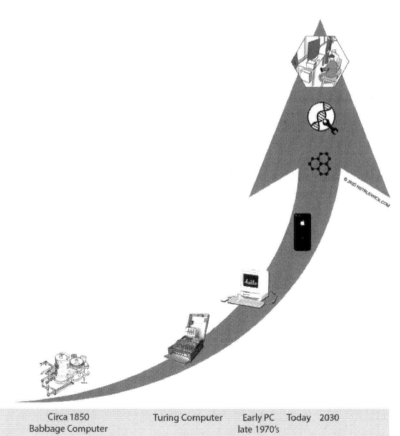

| Circa 1850 | | Turing Computer | Early PC | Today | 2030 |
| Babbage Computer | | | late 1970's | | |

> *"Freedom is the freedom to say that two plus two make four. If that is granted, all else follows."* George Orwell 1984
> *"Freedom's just another word for nothin' left to lose."* Janice Joplin singing lyrics by Fred L. Foster and Kris Kristofferson
> *"Do you want to be remembered as the handmaidens to authoritarianism… as we play with our phones as darkness falls?"* Carole Cadwalladr, interviewed as part of the Netflix programme, 'The Great Hack.' *"Silicon chip inside her head, gets switched to overload,"* Bob Geldof, The Boomtown Rats.

How well do you know your friends? How well do you know your partner? How well do you know yourself?

When was the last time you had a thought, maybe you shared it with someone, such as: "I would love a chocolate bar, right now!" Five minutes later, a pop-up appears on your social media feed for yummy, soft, melt in your mouth, chocolate!

"They are watching us...they are listening to us," you conclude.

It's not quite like that. Data can provide such insights that it can reveal things about yourself, maybe even before you are aware of them. The ads don't appear because someone has been listening in to your conversation; instead, the ads have been pushed at us because we are all more predictable than we realise.

It's not that the technology does not exist to listen to us in our homes it does, it's called Alexa, Siri, amongst others but 'they wouldn't, would they?'

Not only don't we know ourselves as well as we think, we are easier to manipulate than we might possibly admit.

As Chris Wiley, data scientist, and former employee at Cambridge Analytica, the data company that fell into controversy over using data to manipulate people's voting in the US election of 2016 and the UK

Brexit referendum of the same year, said in the Great Hack:[118] "People don't want to admit that propaganda works, because to admit it means confirming our own susceptibilities."

We are a gullible species. Every single one of us form views that were moulded by the network that surrounds us. If we had lived in Ancient Greece, the existence of Zeus would have been something we would almost certainly have accepted.

We invariably comply with the crowd, or group or network that surrounds us.

The psychologist, Solomon Ash, showed that we don't like speaking against the crowd. Hand a group of actors, and one person (the test subject) who is oblivious to the identity of the others in the group, two pieces of paper. On one piece of paper, have a single straight line. On the other have three straight lines of varying lengths. Make it so that one of those three lines is roughly the same length as the line on the first sheet. Ask each member of the group which line on the second sheet of paper is the same length as the line on the first sheet. The answer is obvious. But, unbeknown to our test subject, the actors lie. They all, without exception, point to the same line, but not the right line. What does our test subject say, when asked out loud, in front of the group? Our unfortunate subject gets nervous, their pulse races, and they feel sweaty. Often, but not always, the test subject lies. They go along with the rest. They point to the line that is obviously not the correct answer.

Then Ash repeated the experiment, with different test subjects.

In the original experiment, 32 per cent went along with the group; they put conformity before truth.

The study has profound ramifications. If we are naturally inclined to conform, even if this means ignoring the truth, the opportunity to manipulate us becomes many times greater in the age of social media.

There is a more subtle danger. Ideas also become moulded by the group. Social media amplifies. It exaggerates. We latch onto people with similar views, and our views become confirmed and then embellished. It is not just that we are vulnerable to the deliberate manipulation of companies and political movements. In the age of social media, we are susceptible to the greatest authoritarian of the lot – the crowd.

---

[118] The Great Hack, Netflix

As virtual and augmented reality becomes the method by which we communicate, the group can become even tighter, even more closely aligned.

But there are nuances to the Ash experiment.

When asked why they got the answer wrong, some test subjects insisted they thought they had pointed to the correct line. It seems we would rather admit to stupidity then deliberately getting the answer wrong so as to conform with the group.

If the experiment is changed, and one actor pointed to the correct answer, then in nearly every case, our test subject goes against the majority and says the correct answer. But it takes less than that for our test subject to go against the group. If one of the actors, points to the third line, still incorrect, but different from the answer the other actors give, then our test subject is more likely to identify the correct answer.

The Ash experiment has been repeated countless times and around the world.

It turns out that people from some nationalities are more likely to conform with the group by giving a false argument, than other nationalities. The rate of conformity amongst Chinese, for example, is higher than amongst Americans.

It ties in with the idea that the Chinese are more tuned into the concept of loyalty to the group, of emphasising the needs of the many, the greater good, while the European, and American ideal, in particular, puts more emphasis on individuality.

The reason for this may have roots in agriculture. Success in growing rice is directly proportional to the effort you put it, and benefits from group farming, mass collaboration.

In Europe, the nature of the hilly landscape often created small isolated communities – small farms. European crops require less labour-intensive input too.

Maybe that explains why the Chinese seem to put more emphasis on group loyalty and hard work.

For the US, immigration may have been another factor.

Maybe the pioneering instincts of immigrants mean they are more likely to be entrepreneurial and individualistic. All this is changing, the US was typically a nation of first, second or third-generation immigrants, and perhaps this forged cultural attitudes. This immigrant effect may be slowly waning, as a higher proportion of nationals might be several generations – several great grandparents – from their ancestor settlers.

Whatever the reasons, the Chinese emphasis on group loyalty means that it is likely that China will recover from the Covid-19 crisis more quickly than any other large economy.

For the same reason, China's rise to dominance and the end of Western supremacy seems closer. And the reason why this is so, takes us into data, a surveillance state, privacy and whether it matters.

The surveillance state

What price freedom? What price privacy?

Surveillance! During the depths of the Covid-19 crisis, our right to freely go out when we want and even our right to keep our whereabouts to ourselves, was sacrificed on the altar of defeating a disease.

And very few people disagreed. Most of us, including the authors, felt that this was a price worth paying to stop the spread of the virus.

In some countries, furthermore, countries that were quicker in defeating the spread of Covid-19, went further in imposing rules and in sacrificing the privacy of citizens. It seems that the more willing a country was to overlook privacy concerns, the quicker they could defeat the disease.

In China, for example, a traffic light system was developed. Based on an enormous amount of data, each individual was, or is, presented with a colour donating their right to travel outside of their home. Green gave them, well it gave them the green light to leave their home. Red meant they were either strongly suspected of being Covid-19 positive or had been in close proximity with someone who had. They had to self-isolate for a specific period. Amber meant they were somewhere in between, there was no evidence they had been near someone who had the virus, but they had carried out an activity, like flying into China from abroad, that was seen to suggest high risk. Such people had to self-isolate but not for as long as someone who fell into the red-light category.

But privacy was almost entirely sacrificed in an attempt by authorities to track every citizen's movement. That way, if someone tested positive for Covid-19, authorities could ascertain the identity of every other person with whom they had been in touch.

Such approaches to defeat the virus were not only applied in China, or Asian countries where sensitivity to privacy is not considered to be as crucial as in the West. In the UK, on March 25 the Coronavirus Act of 2020 received Royal Assent.

The Act gave the government permission to track the digital footprint of every person in Britain.

The Act gained very little publicity, but it is doubtful many people would have objected if they had known about it.

That was the way of the world, even in libertarian orientated countries, the idea of authorities tracking our movement was considered perfectly acceptable.

The Act had an expiry date, after this date, another agreement by Parliament could only extend it.

But the nagging doubt remains, if it is okay to track citizens for this reason, what other purposes might be found?

When Covid-19 is finally relegated to history books (and by the time you read these words, that might have happened) won't there be a new heightened awareness of another potential threat from a pandemic? Maybe authorities won't actively track us, but instead leave the tracking laws and technology in place, just in case.

Or maybe, it will be felt expedient to maintain tracking just in case a new virus emerges so that authorities can, as it were, nip it in the bud.

Or instead, the technology may be maintained to track suspected terrorists. To an extent this was already happening pre-Covid, but maybe it will be felt appropriate to widen the scope.

Public opinion is a strange thing, so for that matter is individual opinion. Once it becomes accepting of one idea, it is more likely to concur with a little more extreme version of that idea.

So, we risk gradual erosion of our privacy – surveillance gradually creeping more and more into our lives. At first state surveillance is considered acceptable to stop disease and track known terrorist sympathisers. Then it is used to track someone who it is thought could become a terrorist sympathiser. Then authorities develop a profile of the characteristics that terrorist sympathisers have in common. Authorities ascertain who has those characteristics and track them. Then they apply the technology to tracking individuals who fit the profile of potentially becoming violent – not just in a terrorist setting but in any context.

It could become a little like the movie Minority Report, when Tom Cruise is a cop who can arrest people for murder before they commit the crime. In the case of the movie, the criteria for predicting these crimes is 'visions from the future.' In the real world, it could be a combination of AI and big data.

But what constitutes an act that justifies state surveillance? We have established that a live pandemic does, as does strong evidence of being a terrorist sympathiser. But what about some evidence that someone could become a terrorist? What about evidence-based on an individual's DNA or upbringing that they could become violent? What about suspicion that an individual is a shoplifter? What about evidence an individual doesn't like the government, or the President? Might that justify surveillance?

Or might state surveillance be used to encourage us to become 'better' citizens'?

If sensors are encoded into us and in the objects that make up the Internet of Things, we could be encouraged to be unselfish; we are penalised for undesirable behaviour.

In China, a system called social credit has been applied for that very purpose. People earn points for specific actions and lose points for other types of behaviour.

The idea is that people with low a social credit score might have to pay more for a train ticket, for example.

Such a system, could, in theory, deduct points for bad behaviour after drinking heavily. In this way, people are encouraged to behave in a certain way. Technology linked with AI can create the data, analyse the data and personalise the 'solution'.

If, as was suggested previously being altruistic is a habit, if taking pleasure from being a decent person can be enhanced with practice, then will forcing appropriate behaviour, using technology, be a good thing?

But who decides what is good or bad? If thinking negative things about the government or president lowers our social credit score, then the dangers are clear.

The Chinese authorities say that the rationale behind the social credit system is to promote 'trust' and 'sincerity.' An episode of the

TV programme Black Mirror entitled Nosedive illustrates the danger. In this episode, we carry with us devices which enable us to mark everyone we meet on how they behave towards us. And if someone with a higher social score than us gives us good marks, our overall score increases. Likewise, if they mark us down, our reading falls. If someone with a low social score gives us either low or high marks, it does not matter that much. So, we are encouraged to be super-helpful to people with high social credit, indifferent to those with low credit. In the TV programme, the result is an incredibly superficial, selfish and self-absorbed society, in which no one feels they can display their genuine emotions.

Technology can be used to manipulate us. Conversely, by removing secrets from society, by making it impossible to cover up our bad deeds, it could create a society where we trust more.

And what about corporate surveillance by an employer or its employees? If they are now working from home, how far can an employer go in ensuring staff are working when they say they are?

In George Orwell's 1984, the main protagonist Winston Smith, was reprimanded for not doing his daily exercises at home with appropriate enthusiasm. "'Smith!' screamed the shrewish voice from the telescreen. '6079 Smith W! Yes you! Bend over, please! You can do better than that. You're not trying. Lower please! That's better comrade'...A sudden hot sweat had broken out all over. His face remained inscrutable! A single flicker of the eyes could give you away."

Might employers intrude into their employee's home in a similar way. The Zoom teleconferencing app had a feature, currently disabled, that could tell the conference owner if one of the participants was not paying attention.

Privacy experts are alarmed. "Companies will start thinking, well, governments can track where people are all the time, so why can't we track our employees?" said Dr Vasileios Karagiannopoulos, Reader in Cybercrime and Cybersecurity, Director of the Cybercrime Awareness Clinic, Institute of Criminal Justice Studies, University of Portsmouth, in an interview with Michael Baxter.

"There is no government I have ever come across that actually hands back anything," warned Joe Dignan, a digital transformation expert who runs the Kintechi consultancy.

"This is George Orwell all over again" said Steve Wright, partner at Privacy Culture.

Enter Orwell

Doublespeak, where language is used to disguise or even change the meaning of words, alternative facts being a subset, is one example. Another example is Room 101, where our darkest fears exist. Big Brother and the Thought Police are other examples. What these phrases have in common is their origin: George Orwell's 1984, a book that defined our attitudes to privacy and dystopia.

And when, in 2015, Mark Zuckerberg listed his favourite books, he included Orwell's Revenge, by Peter Huber as one of his books of the year. "Many of us are familiar with George Orwell's book 1984, its ideas of how Big Brother, surveillance and doublespeak have become pervasive fears in our culture," wrote Zuckerberg. He continued: "Orwell's Revenge is an alternate version of 1984. After seeing how history has actually played out, Huber's fiction describes how tools like the internet benefit people and change society for the better."

And that's the paradox of the internet and other technologies that bring us closer together.

We all want privacy, but most would agree transparency is essential in the digital age.

Surveillance seems acceptable if it makes us safer, less likely to be a victim of a crime. But we don't want to feel as if 'they', whoever 'they' are, are watching us all the time.

Secrets sound like bad things, privacy a good thing – but where does one end the other begin?

During the last year of the 20th Century, Scott McNealy, the then chief executive of Sun Microsystems said: "Privacy is dead, get over it".

In 2011, Mark Zuckerberg himself said: "People have gotten really comfortable not only sharing more information and different kinds, but more openly and with more people." He suggested that such lack of privacy has become a "social norm."

Zuckerberg surely regretted saying that when, a few years later, the world reacted in horror over fears that Facebook data was used to influence democracy.

The danger lies with manipulation. We know that our species is subject to manipulation. That's why advertising works, not that advertisers would use that word — maybe they would say that they persuade, or even inform, but not manipulate. But that which we call manipulate, by any other words smells so foul. And maybe there is nothing wrong with ads which persuade us to buy one brand of washing liquid over another. And just about all products, including this book, need promoting. The argument is less clear cut when ads try to persuade us to do something that isn't good for us, such as smoke. What about when the arguments are subjective?

When we are manipulated to hate, or become intolerant, data which is used to 'persuade' takes on a terrifying persona. We do know that in 1994, the Hutu government of Rwanda, was able to manipulate its demographic to hate their neighbours, even people they went to school with, resulting in the slaughter of up to a million people, wiping out 70 per cent of the Tutsi population.

Perhaps the single most negative characteristic of our species is how we can be manipulated in such a way.

We can also be manipulated in softer ways, indoctrinated. And from information about our likes on social media, those who understand these things, or worse, AI, after crunching data, know how we can be manipulated – know our soft spots, our weaknesses, our tendencies.

In 2014, Facebook conducted a study, in conjunction with Cornell University and the University of California, involving 689,000 users. It filtered their news feeds; for example, in one experiment, it focused on some users' exposure to their friend's positive emotional content. Its conclusion: "Emotions expressed by friends, via online social networks, influence our moods, constituting to our knowledge, the first experimental evidence for massive-scale emotional contagion via social networks." [119]

The study also said: "We show that emotional states can be transferred to others via emotional contagion, leading people to experience the same emotions without their awareness. We provide experimental evidence that emotional contagion occurs without direct

---

[119] *Adam D. I. Kramer, Jamie E. Guillory, and Jeffrey T. Hancock, Experimental evidence of massive-scale emotional contagion through social networks,*

interaction between people (exposure to a friend expressing an emotion is sufficient), and in the complete absence of nonverbal cues."[120]

As mentioned before, in 2017, The Economist described data as the new oil. Maybe it would have been more accurate to liken it to the 'new electricity', furthermore, electricity that can be generated by renewable resources.[121]

Not all agree with such a description. Others refer to big data as the new asbestos.

If all big data can achieve is support marketing activities, helping companies target their advertising with newfound accuracy, the effect on society as a whole may not be so dramatic. After all the media and sport, which presumably most would agree do provide a service to society, have been funded by ill targeted advertising for years. One result of the data age has been to redistribute the profits from advertising from a plethora of publishers and media companies, to a handful of dominant tech firms such as Facebook and Google/Alphabet.

But big data is also enabling them to test new products, and based on the results, tweak them, making society richer with the resulting variety.

In healthcare, the combination of data and AI will help create significant new opportunities including developing new cures for illnesses that are currently incurable and help target individual patients with the treatments that are uniquely right for them. This is now a reality! In February 2020, using a machine-learning algorithm, researchers discovered a powerful new antibiotic. In tests, "the drug killed many of the world's most problematic disease- causing bacteria, including some strains that are resistant to all known antibiotics," it was stated in a paper produced by the researchers.[122]

Data save lives and radically improve the quality of life for millions.

But if misused, it could be used by companies and governments to manipulate us.

Such manipulation is not always undesirable. Advertising designed to persuade us to give up smoking, or wear a seatbelt when driving,

---

[120]

[121] *The world's most valuable resource is no longer oil, but data, The Economist, 6 May 2017*

[122] *Artificial intelligence yields new antibiotic, Science Daily*

or even to eat less sugar, can nudge us in a positive direction. But would it be acceptable if data, analysed by AI, enabled the government to nudge us, or manipulate us, into never drinking more than two units of alcohol a day, or going to the gym three times a week, never dropping litter, always helping old ladies cross the road, and never so much as saying 'boo to a goose'?

There is a narrow divide between nudging us to act on our own best interests, and to the benefit of someone else. A dictator may think it is in society's best interests if everyone loves him/her. Regulators have responded to the threat posed by data. In Europe, the General Data Protection Regulation (GDPR) is designed to support the use of data in a way that underpins technological evolution, while protecting our privacy.

The regulation starts with the phrase: "The protection of natural persons in relation to the processing of personal data is a fundamental right."

Maybe these are words that we should all heed; privacy is a human right. But enforcing such regulation is quite different from imposing it. When money is at stake, when technology becomes enormously complex, the scope to navigate around a regulation grows.

And what about the use of our personal data by governments and security forces?

One way in which data can be used for the benefit of society, without compromising privacy, lies with what is known as the anonymisation of data. But there is a problem here, too. It may be impossible to make data genuinely anonymous. In one study, "Vijay Pandurangan, a former Google engineer and founder and CEO of a company called Mitro, analysed data on 20 gigabytes worth of trip and fare data involving New York cabs, comprising more than 173 million individual rides.

The data was anonymous. His conclusion: "This anonymisation is so poor that anyone could, with less than two hours work, figure which driver drove every single trip in this entire data set. It would even be easy to calculate drivers' gross income or infer 'where they live.'"

Privacy could be compromised in another way; technology could provide information on the whereabouts of a person or thing. This would be great if it can tell us where our smartphone is, or our missing dog, an odd sock, or even an elderly relative with advanced dementia;

not to mention the much-needed requirement to track and trace in a pandemic environment. But the potential downside is clear.

But suppose we carry devices that record all that we see and do during the course of a lifetime. In this way we need never forget; forget the name of that place we visited on our tenth birthday, never forget the people we have met and what they said during our lives.

But suppose such data is hacked? So, twenty years ago, you became drunk, made a fool of yourself, and wished the night never happened, and prayed all the people who witnessed it would forget about the occasion.

If, however, people automatically record the events of their lives, they will never forget, or can at least be reminded. Instead of memories fading over time, they could be recalled. Our friends, ex-friends, lawyers representing our former partner in a divorce hearing, or chance acquaintances, will be able to privately or publicly re-play our most embarrassing moments.

Under GDPR, there is the right to be forgotten when data subjects can require organisations to delete data relating to them. But whether it is possible to have all the data recorded by individuals relating to us deleted is another matter entirely.

There is an even more pervasive element, one that has terrifying implications.

In 2017, Mark Zuckerberg said: "We're working on a system that will let you type straight from your brain about five times faster than you can type on your phone today. Eventually, we want to turn it into a wearable technology that can be manufactured at scale. Even a simple yes/no 'brain click' would help make things like augmented reality feel much more natural."

Other products under development are said to be able to pick up subtle movements from our neck and facial muscle to give instructions, such as 'turn on the light', or communicate with other wearers of the device. It is not literally telepathic communication, any more than creating light by the application of electricity is magic, but just as modern tech may seem like magic to the uninitiated, communication by thought seems like telepathy.

Imagine, however, the privacy implications if businesses, your boss, security forces or hackers can obtain the data generated by our thoughts.

In the famous Boomtown Rats song "I don't like Mondays"; the lead singer Bob Geldof sang "Silicon chip inside her head, gets switched to overload. Maybe it would be appropriate to change that to "silicon chip inside her head, so they could switch to overload."

Chapter 11

Homo sapiens augmented

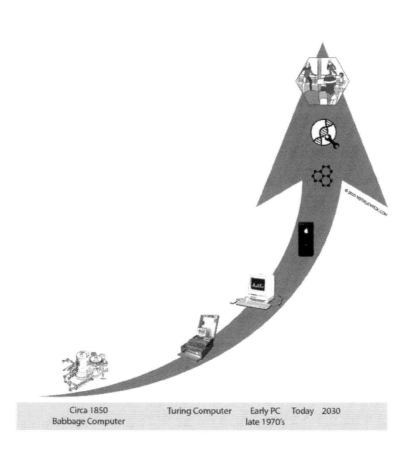

Circa 1850
Babbage Computer

Turing Computer

Early PC
late 1970's

Today

2030

In the 1970s TV series, the Six-Million- Dollar Man, the character Steve Austin, an astronaut, played by the American actor Lee Majors, was seriously injured in an accident.

He was subjected to expensive surgery, (six million dollars was a lot of money in those days) augmenting his physical prowess with robotic parts. He was enhanced with bionic eyes, giving him super eyesight, bionic legs making him super-fast, and a bionic arm giving him super strength.

The technology to boost our strength and boost our physical limitations via prosthetics or exoskeletons is not far off. Beyond its natural use by the military to create super- human soldiers, we will see enhancement in logistics and in healthcare enabling nurses to move bedridden patients without injury, for example.

But what about our brains? We are feeble creatures compared to most of the animal kingdom, but our mind is not. Can technology augment us, making us super- intelligent?

Extending the Dunbar number

The evidence that we are designed to live in communities of 148, the so-called Dunbar number, usually rounded up to 150, is far from proven.

It's just that too many people, the theory chimes with what they feel is instinctively is right.

If we only have the cognitive functions to engage with 150 or so people at any one point in our life, how can we cope in the internet age? How do we find the cerebral abilities to manage in the Facebook age, let alone in the physical world when many of us, especially in business, attend networking events regularly? Interestingly, despite having access to a potential 2.5 billion

How many people have you met, but forgotten, how many times have you met someone for the second time, but only have the vaguest memory of the first meeting? As you talk, flashes come back to you, but you never fully remember.

Technology can solve this. AI providing image recognition, wearable technology recording previous meetings, even little cameras embedded into our clothing, or even our skin, maybe just above the eye, could store a record of everything we have ever seen or done.

"I recognise this place," you think. We have all had that experience as scattered memories come flooding back. Often we only remember tantalising moments; we are left with an impression of a past moment but not a full recollection.

Sometimes such impressions can mislead. We get a distorted view of the past – we confuse past events, we can swear blind that 'so and so' was at 'such and such' an event, but we are mixing 'so and so' with 'what's her name'.

This is all set to change.

When we meet someone at a party who we are vaguely aware we have met before, our AI assistant will whisper in our ear, or profile them via our glasses or contact lens.

You won't always be reminded of positive things. Maybe they were a bore, or that you owe them money. They may have been a bore because they were exhausted on that occasion or suffered a tragedy the day before. Or maybe it was you; perhaps you made a fool of yourself. Do you want this person, via their AI assistant, to be reminded of how drunk you were, how embarrassing your behaviour was? For that matter, do you want to be reminded? Sometimes we are better off if our actions are forgotten.

Such technology will clearly change us.

If we can, via the support of our AI assistant, be able to have meaningful interaction with more than 150 people at any one point, are we still Homo sapiens sapiens? Have we not supplanted that which makes us human, or at least the species of human that we have been for the last 200,000 or so years?

Augmenting our memory

Memories are frustrating things. Too easily do we forget, or so they say (whoever, they are). Suppose our memories can be enhanced. We could improve our memories via computer storage – a hard drive linked directly to our brain, into which we can download memories to recall at will.

Or instead, we could have RAM (Random Access Memory, used by computers to store information we are using at any particular time) linked to our brain, to support our working memory. Famously, in 1956, George, A Miller,[123] a psychologist from Princetown University, suggested that young adults can only process seven pieces of information at one time. Although, subsequent research has revealed that the reality is a little more nuanced than that.[124]

The limitation to our working and short-term memory is presumably the reason why a pencil and paper can be so useful, in this way we can jot down more than seven pieces of information, effectively artificially enhancing our cognitive ability. Suppose, however, our working memory is enhanced, via a computer chip, displaying additional bits of information on a computer screen viewable from the corner of our eye, via augmented reality contact lenses.

Computer chips are not the only way. Theodore Berger and Dong Song, and their team from the University of Southern California, have been working on a device that can apply electrodes to give small electric shocks to the hippocampus (a region of the brain that is vital for learning). In the process, our memory can be improved by up to around 25 per cent.[125] The team tested the device on twenty volunteers who were, in any case, having electrodes placed in their brains to treat epilepsy. In one test, the volunteers were asked to recall specific 'blobby'

---

[123] The Magical Number Seven, Plus or Minus Two: Some Limits on our Capacity for Processing Information, George A. Miller (1956), Harvard University, First published in Psychological Review, 63, 81- 97

[124] and our short-term and working memory's ability differs depending on the nature of the bits of information we are *processing*. *(Indeed, short-term memory and working memory are not the same. The latter can take information from both short term and long-term memory and manipulate that information / Difference Between Short-Term, Long-Term, and Working Memory, examinedexistence.com*

[125] *Prosthetic Memory System Successful in Humans, Study Finds, wakehealth.edu*

shapes that they had seen a few seconds earlier. A second test involved the volunteers making decisions based on their recall of objects that they had seen 10-40 minutes earlier. In this way, both short-term and working memory was tested.

After the device was used to stimulate the brain, the short-term recall was enhanced by 15 per cent and working memory by 25 per cent.

Using chips to enhance memory may not feel like proper enhancement – these are tools, no matter how seamless the interaction with the brain. But applying electric shocks to a region of our brain feels like bona fide enhancement.

The immediate applications of such technologies might be to support people with memory difficulties, such as dementia. It is not hard to see how they could be used by students studying for an exam.

Might students be expected to undergo random testing for hippocampus stimulation, in much the same way athletes are tested for drugs?

If, however, our memories can be enhanced by 25 per cent, and additionally supported by computer chips, are we still the same? We might have the all too familiar human frailties, but our enhancement might be such that we are also something more than just human.

Augmenting intelligence

Meanwhile, researchers at Oxford University and University College London have tested a technique, again using electrodes, but this time applying electrical brain stimulation every day, by using transcranial direct current stimulation (TDCS) – which entails constant, low direct current delivered via electrodes on the head. The researchers found, depending on whether the electrical currents passed through the left or right parietal lobes, that volunteers either saw an improved or worse performance at certain mathematical puzzles. Roi Cohen Kadosh, a neuroscientist at Oxford University, told the Guardian newspaper: "We've shown before that we can temporarily induce dyscalculia [a mathematical disability], and now it seems we might also be able to make someone better at maths.

Electrical stimulation probably won't turn you into Albert Einstein, but if we're successful, it might be able to help some people to cope better with maths."[126]. The study found that any resulting improvement in mathematical ability could last for six months.

Teaching old dogs new tricks

Another technique, so far tested with mice, has extraordinary ramifications if it can be applied in humans. It could give adult brains the kind of plasticity usually restricted to children.

It is well understood that children can learn faster. What we learn in the early years of our life can determine so much of who we are later in life. Consider the act of learning a language. A young child who moves to another country can not only learn the local language but will grow up to speak it without a hint of an accent. Except in rare circumstances, an adult migrant may never shake-off the accent.

Now researchers from St. Jude Children's Research Hospital have found a way to curtail the activity of a chemical messenger called adenosine in mice. The messenger acts as a neuromodulator in a region of the brain[127] associated with sound. The result: adult mice exposed to certain tones developed a kind of perfect pitch. The mice were able to distinguish between certain very similar sounds, in a way that they would not usually be able to do unless they were exposed to the tones when they were around nine days old. "The results demonstrated that the window for effective auditory learning re-opened in the mice and that they retained the information," Stanislav Zakharenko, a member of the team, told Science Daily.[128]

He added: "These results offer a promising strategy to extend the same window in humans to acquire language or musical ability

---

[126] *Electrical stimulation of the brain boosts maths skills, claim scientists, Ian Sample, The Guardian, 4 November 2010 ,*
[127] *The auditory thalamus, which is the brain's relay station where sound is collected and sent to the auditory cortex for processing," states Science Daily Controlling a single brain chemical may help expand window for learning language and music*
[128] *Controlling a single brain chemical may help expand window for learning language and music, Science Daily*

by restoring plasticity in critical regions of the brain, possibly by developing drugs that selectively block adenosine activity."

What is especially interesting about this study is that the neural messenger in question, the neuromodulator adenosine, has been subject to a "wealth of new data fostering our understanding of how the adenosine system is involved in the pathogenesis of neurological diseases."[129] This brings us back to the key drivers of technology change described in chapter three. New technologies, such as advanced computers and modelling techniques, have enabled a new area of research to open up, sparking a kind of explosion in activity, with new techniques building upon techniques previously tested. In this way, ideas rely on existing concepts and communication of these ideas is then supported by new communication technologies via the internet. We also see a convergence, for example, as techniques advanced to help combat neurological diseases open the door for methods to support greater plasticity in the brain for adults without any neurological disorder.

Again, the implications are astounding. If adults can learn like the young, are able to absorb information and ideas like they could when they were children, will this create a more flexible workforce, will it make us more open to new ideas? If science does indeed advance one funeral at a time – as Max Planck (the German theoretical physicist) said, then maybe by creating this renewed plasticity, we can build upon the best of both worlds, combine the experience that comes with age, with the flexibility customarily restricted to the young. Science would be advancing as different ideas marry up, without the barrier that is the rigidity of thought that comes with ageing – not so much advancing one funeral at a time, as one wedding of ideas at a time.

Or, maybe, the rigidity that so often comes with ageing, which can make us reluctance to adopt new ideas, is not a function of the brain at all. Instead, it has something to do with the network of ideas we form as we age, and which are hard to change

---

[129] Adenosine as a neuromodulator in neurological diseases, Science Direct

Learning without learning

Here is a radical idea! If the neurons in the brain and the synapses they form with each other define our thoughts and memories, maybe, by downloading instructions for our neurons to form a specific configuration, we can create new memories without actually experiencing them.

Instead of learning a new language, we could have our neurons configured such that we know that language.

Maybe they would be artificial neurons, available as a package – 'special price, today only, buy our latest neural configuration and download into your brain and be able to speak Mandarin, without the trace of an accent, instantly, all for just $199!'

Not that we necessarily need to download the knowledge of a new language if we carry a language translation device around with us. But think of the time it would save if we could download the knowledge of just about anything we wanted, without the painful experience of having to go to classes, concentrate very hard on what we read, and what our teacher says and memorise a load of stuff.

But if we can learn without doing, what do we lose? Do we become more or less human?

Scientists at MIT, Steve Ramirez and Xu Liu, have managed to implant a false memory in a mouse – combining classic molecular biology with optogenetics,[130]. Optogenetics uses lasers, emitted into the brain via carbon fibre, to stimulate specific brain cells that have been injected with molecules found in algae that can convert light into electricity. In this way, optogenetics can be used to turn neurons on and off.

Ramirez and Xu were able to pinpoint a cluster of cells in one mouse which lit up when the mouse was in a specific location and received a shock to its foot. They were then able to activate these same cells in another mouse. They then placed this mouse in an environment where the original mouse had received the shock, and it froze in fear. In short, they had implanted a false memory.

The proof of principle "that we can artificially reactivate memories and create false memories in animals," is there, Ramirez was quoted as

---

[130] described in three, why technology is jerking,

saying in the Smithsonian Magazine, "the only leap left, between there and humans, is just technological innovation."[131]

Mind reading and computer-brain interfaces

"The distributed device within your brain and central nervous system, which I have, annoyingly, only recently become aware of, will have recorded its own
memories of this encounter and would be able to transmit
them to your own biological brain. I strongly suspect it has already transmitted our conversation so far… elsewhere.

It was a little bundle of what looked like thin, glisteningly blue threads, lying in a shallow bowl; a net, like something you'd put on the end of a stick and go fishing for little
fish in a stream. She tried to pick it up; it was impossibly slinky, and the material slipped through her fingers

like oil; the holes in the net were just too small to put a fingertip through. Eventually, she had to tip the bowl up and pour the blue mesh into her palm. It was very light.

Something about it stirred a vague memory in her, but she couldn't recall what it was. She asked the ship what it was, via her neural lace.

That is a neural lace, it informed her. "A more exquisite and economical method of torturing creatures such as yourself has yet to be invented."

Ian M Banks
Excession Part of the
Culture Series

---

[131] Meet the Two Scientists Who Implanted a False Memory Into a Mouse, David Noonan, Smithsonian Magazine, November 2014

The field of neuroscience is out at the extreme end of accelerating technology. The developments and advances of recent years read like the stuff of science fiction; they just happen to be true. But it's when the brain and computers work in tandem that things start to reach extraordinary levels. Neural lace is maybe the best example; indeed, the concept has its route in science fiction via the author Ian M Banks.

There is one thing that Elon Musk, Jeff Bezos and Mark Zuckerberg have in common. The world's richest man, the man who wants to save the world and create another one on Mars, and the man who said, "By giving people the power to share, we're making the world more transparent," are all fans of the late Ian M Banks. The Amazon boss once tweeted that the Culture series is a huge personal favourite". The Facebook CEO included a book from the Culture series in his list of '20 books everyone should read', while the CEO of Tesla and SpaceX has named two SpaceX autonomous drone spaceports after creations in the Culture series.

The Culture series introduced a concept called neural lace – an ultra-thin mesh that can be inserted into the brain and which forms electrodes which can monitor the brain, creating an interface between brain and computer.

That's science fiction.

Elon Musk has set up a company called Neuralink. The company's stated mission is to create "ultrahigh-bandwidth brain-computer interfaces."

But Elon Musk, maybe the highest-profile entrepreneur in the world, is not the only one working on brain interfaces. EyeMind, a company founded in 2013, is reportedly working on a brain interface that allows the user to operate navigation tools by thought in virtual reality. Founder Dan Cook told Digital Trends: "When you're in the virtual world whether you're playing a game or something else – you don't want to have to keep thinking about what you're doing with your hands, much better to have pure brainwave control."[132]

It seems that the problem is that speaking is such a slow, ponderous process, much better to interact with a computer at the speed of thought. Elon Musk suggests that language is a kind of compression

---

[132] Eye Mind is building a virtual reality system you control with your brain, Luke Dormehl November 22, 2016, Digital Trends

algorithm of thought executed by the brain. The WaitbutWhy blog quoted him saying "If you have two brain interfaces, you could actually do an uncompressed direct conceptual communication with another person."[133]

So, if we can communicate at the speed of thought, what does that mean for Homo sapiens sapiens? Indeed, would it be appropriate to describe us as a member of that particular version of the human race?

Email and social media are revolutionary tools, but they can also amplify a misunderstanding. That is why communication is often better face to face. And that rather ponderous process of distilling our thoughts called speech can also act as a filter – they may say of some people, that they speak before they think, but if people really did communicate directly via thoughts, the mind boggles concerning the number of expletives we become subjected to – thinking out loud transformed to thinking in the ether.

Maybe more extreme even than this, we might be able to think instructions to a web browser, a search engine, or our AI assistant removing the irritating need to speak or move a cursor on our screen.

Technology to make us better at maths or improve the plasticity of our brain, so that we can more efficiently learn a new language, may become irrelevant. If we have a brain interface to a calculator, communicating at the speed of thought, or an interface to a thought translation device, then the implications are extraordinary. We might interact with people who speak and think in a different language, our thoughts translated as fast as we think them.

Other technologies that entail bypassing the need to talk include a breath-taking idea from Facebook. The social media giant has been working on technology that supports the dictation of text by thought. It calls it a "brain-computer speech-to-text interface." Regina Dugan, who headed Facebook's mysterious Building 8 until early 2018, said that the plan is for a computer algorithm via an electrode implanted into the brain. "Is it a little terrifying? Of course," she said at a talk she delivered at Facebook's annual F8 developer conference in San Jose,

---

[133] Elon Musk on mission to link human brains with computers in four years: Report, Reuters APR 21 201, CNBC

back in April 2017. She was undoubtedly guilty of understatement "– a little terrifying, indeed!.

Meanwhile, a team from MIT Media Lab have unveiled AlterEgo; they have been working on "a wearable interface that allows a user to silently converse with a computing device without any voice or any discernible movements – thereby enabling the user to communicate with devices."[134]

The technology does not involve electrodes or a brain interface. Instead, it tracks specific muscles which give off a signal when we speak, or indeed think in our heads.

In a paper, Arnav Kapur, Shreyas Kapur and Pattie Maes from MIT Media Lab Cambridge, USA, the people behind AlterEgo say: a "user's intention to speak and internal speech is characterised by neuromuscular signals in internal speech articulators that are captured by the AlterEgo system to reconstruct this speech. We use this to facilitate a natural language user interface, where users can silently communicate in natural language and receive aural output (e.g., bone conduction headphones), thereby enabling a discreet, bi-directional interface with a computing device, and providing a seamless form of intelligence augmentation."

The technologies described above are designed to support treatments or even cures for neurological diseases such as Parkinson's. Other possible therapies might include methods to combat dementia.

The medium-term applications, if they are applied to the broader public, are simply mind-boggling.

And we are not talking some distant time frame. Sure the technology may not be practical just yet. But in a few years, maybe when quantum computers can make certain calculations a thousand, or even a million times faster than conventional computers, opportunities will be created. Some of the above technologies, or at least derivatives of them, if not all, will be commercially viable during the lifetime of most readers of this book.

---

[134] 1AlterEgo: A Personalized Wearable Silent Speech Interface, media.mit.edu, A. Kapur, S. Kapur, and P. Maes

Downloading skill

Intelligence is an elusive concept. How much of intelligence is really memory? People who score well in IQ tests may do well because they have a good memory for recalling occasions when they faced a similar puzzle. Skill at crosswords or scrabble can, after-all, be created by practice. The mind often works by hardwiring specific attributes.

If we play tennis or squash, we learn that if we hit the ball in a certain way, it reacts in a certain way. Whereas if we hit the ball in another way, it reacts in another way.

Our knowledge of these different reactions can become hardwired. Individual neurons form links with other neurons relating to this knowledge, and the more we play, the stronger these links become. Then, when we are playing tennis, we may merge – converge if you will – our knowledge and in this way improvise. In the heat of a competitive match, we may play a shot that builds upon our knowledge of several different shots that we have practised. The skills remain primarily memory-based though, combined with physical attributes such as strength, speed, stamina and reflexes.

The point is, we learn – which is how AI works. So, if such skills require memory, how much more skilful can we become if our memory is enhanced digitally?

If artificial neurons can supplement our cognitive functions, maybe such neurons can be hardwired to link with other neurons creating particular skills and knowledge. We could download knowledge of a language. We could download knowledge of an academic discipline; we could download skill at a particular game.

Another good example of intelligence at work is the skill of playing chess. But we know that computers can outperform even grandmasters at chess. But the one-time world's great chess player chess Gary Kasparov, who was famously defeated by the IBM system DeepBlue in 1999, argues that human plus computer is an unbeatable combination.

There is evidence to support his idea from the medical field. When Radiologists apply AI image screening software, they become more accurate at identifying tumours than if they were working without the AI solution.

By augmenting us then, a computer/AI system can give us the cognitive functions to beat a grandmaster at chess.

But what skills do we need to learn, and what skills can we leave the AI tools embedded into our brain to provide?

In Chapter eight, we asked whether we need to memorise our multiplication tables, what seven times eight is, for example, when we have a digital system with the functions of a calculator embedded in our brain? If it is linked to our brain by a thought-based interface, then this question becomes even more relevant.

Or, by learning tables, arithmetic, percentages, or grammar, do we gain an understanding that is more than just doing the sum, or constructing a sentence?

Do we need to read a textbook, or a 'how-to guide', or even a novel as part of our studies, if we can download it into our augmented brain in seconds? Or do we gain a deeper understanding by doing?

Do we gain comprehension by learning in a way that allows for no shortcuts? Studies show that we absorb more information if we are taking notes with a pen, rather than typing on a computer. [135] These days, students are often emailed PowerPoint slides after a lecture – reducing their need to take notes, but do they lose comprehension in the process?

Hunter J Thompson typed out the Great Gatsby, just to get a feel for writing a bestseller. The act of doing creates understanding, downloading memory is one thing, but the technology for rewiring the brain to develop deep understanding does not seem to be on the horizon if indeed it ever will be.

But technology is accelerating and then it is jerking, and who can say what might happen when digital evolution and convergence coincide.

This begs the question; will technology enhance us so much that we become Homo sapiens augmented? Will this enhancement be limited to just knowledge and skill?

---

[135] Revising for an exam? DON'T use a laptop: Taking notes with pen and paper boosts memory and our ability to understand, SARAH GRIFFITHS, Daily Mail, 5 February 2015

Chapter 12

Conflict

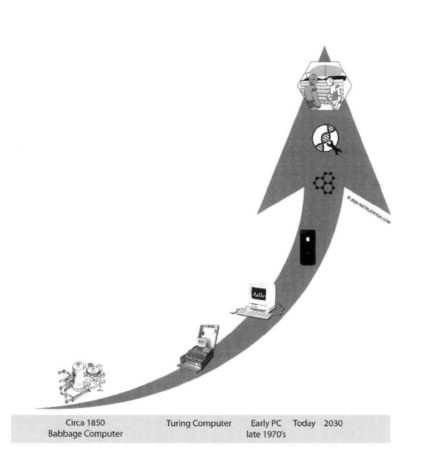

| Circa 1850 | | Turing Computer | Early PC | Today | 2030 |
| Babbage Computer | | | late 1970's | | |

"What are the chances of a Third World War? The Russian President, Vladimir Putin, was asked that question on Russian TV on June 7th, 2018. He responded by saying: "Remember Einstein, he said 'I don't know what the methods of World War Three will be, but the Fourth World War will be waged with sticks and stones.'"[136]

Will technology lead to war? Will that war take the form of conflict between nations? Or will we see conflict within nations, one class against another, perhaps? Might we see conflict between humanity and the machine?

And what impact will the after-effects of the Covid-19 crisis have? Will it lead to a change in the order of geopolitics, hasten the rise of China, speed the decline of the US? And does this increase the risk of conflict?

Will we see a new war of ideas, as capitalism itself comes under threat?

Or in the brave new post-Covid-19 world, with people around the world using technology as their friend, will we instead see a revolution, either peaceful or violent, to create a new order, taking us closer to the dream of utopia?

We start by taking a look at what created revolutions and civil wars in the past and ask whether modern technology, on the trajectory of the jerk, could create similar conditions?

So, let's begin with Civil War and Revolutions.

---

[136] *Putin Responds to Question about World War III https://www.youtube.com/ watch?v=vQwbIpHxJw0*

Revolution and civil war: The strange alliance

 "I am determined to devote my life to repressing the audacity of the common people," or so said Lord Essex, a Parliamentarian in England during the period of the English Civil War.[137]

During this war, Lord Essex, and his fellow Parliamentarians, had an ally…what he referred to as 'the common people.' Yet his sense of identity with the common folk was superficial. No doubt he held some form of moral attachment, in much the same way that a shepherd might feel a moral attachment to his or her flock of sheep, before slaughter. Still, one can be sure that the Lord Essex held a sense of perceived superiority: a kind master, who does what is best for his inferiors.

The ordinary folk didn't see it like that; no doubt they doffed their hats in the lord's presence, but many of these people had ideas of their own – perish the thought, the ordinary people with ideas!

But some of the ordinary people formed movements. The most famous of these were known as the Diggers and Levellers.

The Diggers wanted to change ownership. They believed that the Norman conquest had robbed the ordinary man (not sure about women) of land that was rightly his and wanted to create collective ownership of that land. In some ways, it is similar to the idealistic thinking behind the emerging sharing economy – ownership replaced by the sharing of resource.

The Levellers believed in democracy. "All men (again, women don't seem to have featured so strongly in their idealism) are created equal," they said. They wanted the vote for all, annual parliamentary terms, with equal votes per parliamentary seat, religious tolerance, and redistribution of land to the common people. They also wanted to elect army officers.

Many of the men behind these movements had fought together in what was called the New Model Army, which had been founded by the English statesman, future Lord Protector and general, Oliver Cromwell. The fighting force played a decisive role in the ensuing English Civil War.

---

[137] *1642-1651*

These men and people like Lord Essex had fought on the same side, but their ideology was as different as you can imagine.

That's the first lesson of history concerning revolutions and civil wars – political movements which see the support of people from across society, are often run by people who have entirely different long-term objectives to the people who support them.[138]

With revolutions, the elites need the masses

But the second lesson is that usually, for a revolution or civil war to be successful, it needs support across social classes.

The parliamentarians in the English Civil War had support from a big chunk of the working people, (obviously not all, we will come back to that in a moment.)

The French Revolution, however, was preceded by a clash between the bourgeoisie (the merchant/capitalist class) and the monarchy. The revolution itself saw an alliance between this class and the poorer classes (to use the Marxist terminology, call them the proletariat.)

Many of the history books focus on the American Revolution being mainly about the aggrieved bourgeois. But the revolution was also preceded by a bad harvest. This occurrence, in combination with tax hikes forced upon the population by England, meant that a large proportion of that population faced hardship.

"Well-fed, well-educated people who rebel in the face of apathy among the objectively deprived, can at best expect a coup d'etat. The objectively deprived, when faced with solid opposition from people of wealth, status and power, will be smashed in their rebellion," stated the late James C Davies who, back in 1962, produced a detailed paper looking at the causes of revolution in history. [139]

---

[138] *For example, a populist President who responds to social discontent by cutting taxes paid by the richest in society. Or when people who were concerned about job security created perhaps by globalisation or technology, voted in a referendum, with people who were wedded to an ideology involving the removal of all tariffs that would have led to the destruction of jobs in manufacturing.*

[139] *Toward a Theory of Revolution, James C. Davies, American Sociological Review,*

Revolution often follows a period of dashed high expectations

In both Russia and France, before the revolution, there had been an era of rising living standards.

In France, improvement in rural prosperity had been such that by the mid-years of the seventeenth century, a third of the French land was owned by 'French peasants.[140]

Things went into abrupt reverse when the French government increased taxes to fund debt incurred in France's intervention in the American Revolution combined with a bad harvest. As Marie Antionette famously discovered, not only couldn't the peasants afford bread, they couldn't afford cake, either.

Several decades before The Russian Revolution – 1917- 1923 – in 1861, serfdom was abolished. This was followed by a period of rapidly rising migration from the country into cities, coinciding with industrialisation, increases in average wages in urban areas, but not in rural areas. As a result, expectations changed; the mass population began to become optimistic. This, in turn, was then followed by a period of dashed hopes, which saw a failure to meet expectations, hunger, and a perceived shared interest between the civilian population and the army.[141]

Davies says that "peasants were so pre-occupied with hunger or self-aggrandisement as to be fuelled in their sensitivity to the revolutionary appeals of radical organisers. After more than five years of degrading terror and misery, in 1910 the country appeared to have reached a condition of exhaustion."

---

[140] *Davies*

[141] *Events that triggered this included.*
- *The Bloody Sunday event of 1905 — peaceful— peaceful proletarian protestors marched on St Petersburg palace, but ended in a massacre, apparently instigated by Tsar Nicholas II, who had previously enjoyed popular support*
- *Russia also suffered a major defeat in its war against Japan, a war that was seen as the Tsar's war and not in the interests of the people.*
- *A period of bad harvests, chaotic political moves, in which constitutional changes were implemented then reversed, agrarian reform designed to break up the power of communes, all followed.*

It took a kind of double discontent to create the Russian Revolution. Civilian discontent combined with bitter frustration within the army, following by massive loss of life, in part because the military was so ill-equipped for the wars in which it was engaged.

War itself

War and period of abrupt change can also often sow the seeds of rebellion. Here we take a brief look at the English Civil War, The Russian Revolution, and the Second World War.

In the case of the English Civil War, it seems that the New Model Army created an environment that proved a breeding ground for new ideas, although neither the diggers nor levellers ultimately had their way. In 1647, a time when the English Civil War seemed over and the English King, Charles I was under arrest, what has become known as the Putney Debates occurred. In these debates, a democratic and egalitarian England was almost created. Soldiers from Cromwell's Army debated with their generals in an attempt to redefine the English constitution. It was in these debates that the Levellers pushed for more democracy and equality. They won the debate, England seemed to be on course to becoming a very different place. Then, Charles I escaped, sparking off renewed hostilities, and Cromwell was quietly able to drop the ideas promoted by the Levellers.

The sense of unrest before the Russian Revolution was partly fed by a disillusioned army reacting against the appalling way it had been managed during the First World War.

The Second World War created a sense that ordinary people had won it, men fighting, women working in factories, the people demanded change, and in the post-war years, they got it.

Technology and innovation

But perhaps the most critical drivers of revolutions are technology and innovation.And we begin with a man who was nearly struck by lightning. The man in question was a university student, returning to his University of Erfurt, in eastern Germany, when, during his journey, a bolt of lightning, as if from the heavens, struck down upon the land narrowly missing the traveller. Terrified, he swore then to become a monk if he survived.

Twelve years later, in 1517, the man nailed ninety-five theses to the door of All Saints' Church in Wittenberg. The theses contained radical stuff; one asked, for example, "Why does the pope, whose wealth today is greater than the wealth of the richest Crassus, build the basilica of St. Peter with the money of poor believers rather than with his own money?."

The man's name was Martin Luther, and his ideas sparked revolutions that would last for centuries.

The ideas of Martin Luther spawned alternative Christian ideals to the Catholic religion. Thanks to the ideas of Martin Luther, the course of European history changed. Consider Henry VIII and his six hapless wives, the English Revolution, which pitted Parliament against the catholic king, the radical ideas percolating in France before the French Revolution, the Russian Revolution, which at least in part was inspired by the French Revolution. None of these famous events in history might have occurred if it had not been for Martin Luther.

But Luther himself had support from an unlikely quarter, without which his ideas may never have spread. That support came in the form of the printing press, one of the most critical technology innovations ever.

Just seventeen days after Luther's ninety- five theses were nailed to a church door, copies were printed in London

Luther himself said: "Printing is the ultimate gift of God and the greatest one."

The technology that was the printing press helped spawn industrial revolution, as we said elsewhere, but it also spawned, for better or worse, bloody revolution and war.

As we shall now explain, another revolution combined with changes that could be traced back to Martin Luther may have sown the seeds for the English Civil War.

Although history books often say that differing religious beliefs were the cause of the English Revolution, in reality, the conditions that led to the civil war were more complicated.

Charles I, the English king who literally lost his head after his defeat to Oliver Cromwell, was not quite the villain the history books describe. Indeed, in one crucial respect, he was the champion of the people. Because Charles I wanted to return land to the ordinary people after it had been taken from them during the period of enclosures when a traditional way of rural life came to an abrupt end.

Religion may have been something of a ruse – the real issues at stake were not dissimilar to issues we see today. Traditional ways of life were disrupted, land that had been farmed for centuries was seized, in much the same way that corporates today seek ownership of our personal data – such as genetic data. The thin strips of land that characterized medieval England, were turned into enclosures, owned by a select few.

If Charles I had fined landowners who had acquired land. If, instead, he made them take more responsibility for the peasants who were impacted by their actions, perhaps paying them rent or a share of profits, the UK we know today may be much fairer and egalitarian. It might even have shades of utopia about it.

Technology and new ideas such as enclosures in the seventeenth century and the creation of data in the twenty-first century, create benefits and costs: we have to ensure that the benefits apply to all, unlike what so often happened in the sixteenth, seventeenth and eighteenth centuries.

Today we see a backlash against globalisation and some new technologies. On aggregate, they make us better off, just as enclosures made England better off. But some individuals lost out enormously. If we fail to find a way to soften these adverse effects, we take a potentially reckless risk with our long-term political stability.

Living in the age of the jerk, this risk is greater than ever.

The English Civil War was also led by the merchant class, the business people of that age, supported by the labourers who often worked for them in towns. The royalists were supported mainly by peasant farmers from the north. In short, the English Civil War broadly saw a clash between urban workers, applying the latest technologies, and a newly created entrepreneurial class looking at new ways to make money, on the one side, and the rural workers and royalists steeped in tradition on the opposing side. [142]

---

[142] *The end of enclosures may seen the birth of a new entrepreneurial class. But the peasants who lost their land were often badly compensated. This created high levels of poverty and led to bands of homeless people travelling the country. In this way it created a psychological barrier between those who benefited from enclosers, either*

Oddly, it seems that during the early stages of the Civil War, the Parliamentarians held back, they were not seeking outright victory. Instead, they were trying to force the king to come to a compromise. The last thing they wanted was an overwhelming victory leading to social change that may have in turn undermined their own position.

Populism: No story about revolution and civil war can be complete without a short digression into populism

A long time ago, in a fabled city of beauty, there lived a man known for his golden hair, good looks, and a silver tongue. He was also known for his questionable morals.

Alcibiades was a speaker who by command of his language, timing and charisma could sway a crowd. He was also a populist.

Ancient Athens saw one of the most glorious periods for art, architecture, poetry and philosophy ever. Populism helped bring this period mainly to an end.

This was a period of pure democracy.[143] The freemen of Ancient Athens did not merely have the vote; they were required to vote and on just about everything. Not for Ancient Athens an election every few years, nor yet a system of regular referendums like they have in Switzerland; instead the people made all the big decisions on thirty to forty occasions a year. The men who were charged with carrying out the wishes of the people were chosen by lot. The only leaders who were elected were military generals. In some ways, the Levellers of the English civil war were conservatives, by comparison.

And populists, great orators that they usually are, equipped with the power of their words could sway the will of the people. They were the rock stars of their day.

Yet, ancient Athens often behaved abominably to vassal states and was eventually undone by populists.

---

as entrepreneurs or workers, and those who do didn't. The parallels with today are obvious.

143 Neither women nor slaves could vote, but then that was the 5th Century BC for you.

Alcibiades, along with other populist leaders of that time, had another ally. He was able to enlist in his efforts to sway popular opinion. That ally was groupthink, the crowd. In the cauldron of Ancient Athens, on the hillside where the assembly met, ideas took on a life of their own, crowd opinion became exaggerated. Group polarisation was rife.

Athens' downfall began when Athens engaged in a military expedition in Sicily, which drew them into an unwinnable war against Sparta. And the man whose speeches persuaded the people of Athens to support the expedition was none other than Alcibiades himself.

But the crowd is fickle. It can turn on those it once held in great esteem. Alcibiades himself was subsequently found guilty of various crimes, was sentenced to death, but fled to Sparta. He was later recalled to Athens, all forgiven and appointed commander of all of Athens's generals, until a military defeat when he was found guilty of negligence, and he left Athens again. He was eventually murdered.

But history is littered with tales of populism, sometimes advancing ideas that in a more objective light seem reprehensible.

The tale of Ancient Athens was not so much one of technology, nor was it one of revolution, or civil war, but the conditions created have a resonance today that does relate to technology and could indeed help sow the conditions for war or revolution.

The conditions that existed in Ancient Athens, the populace sharing ideas, exaggerating ideas, riddled with groupthink, exist today, in virtual space. The similarity between the way ideas spread across social media is not dissimilar to the way they engulfed a crowd with excitement in ancient Athens.

Augmented and virtual reality could be applied in a similar way. Assemblies of the people could meet in virtual space, either represented by live video feeds of the individuals who make up the assembly in augmented reality or avatars in virtual reality.

The dangers are clear.

But Ancient Athens created wonders we still marvel at today. So will the crowd of the twenty-first century.

Populism, the fourth and fifth industrial revolution and the post-Covid-19 world

After the financial crash of 2008, the economy tanked, unemployment soared, austerity was imposed across much of the developed world, and the rich got richer.

Some of the conditions that in the past preceded revolution or civil war were in place. Across many countries, real wages ceased to increase; in some cases, they fell.

In 2016, in the US, median wages were no higher than in 1999. In the UK, it took several years for real wages to reach the pre-2008 level. According to some reports, even in 2018 wages in some parts of the UK were a third less than in 2008.

Yet at the same time, the rich appeared to get richer.

So that is one box ticked. Revolution follows a period when people saw rising expectations followed by another period of falling living standards, or at least a period when wages were no longer increasing..

Given that the rich were getting rich so much faster, as explored in Chapter One where we focused on inequality, if you measure income relativity, the case to say median workers were getting worse off becomes more compelling.

As Karl Marx said: "A noticeable increase in wages presupposes a rapid growth of productive capital. The rapid growth of productive capital brings about an equally rapid growth of wealth, luxury, social wants, social enjoyments. Thus, although the enjoyments of the worker have risen, the social satisfaction that they give has fallen in comparison with the increased enjoyments of the capitalist, which are inaccessible to the worker, in comparison with the state of development of society in general. Our desires and pleasures spring from society; we measure them, therefore, by society and not by the objects which serve for their satisfaction. Because they are of a social nature, they are of a relative nature."

At the same time, the internet has created a communication channel ripe for populists and their ideas to flourish.

As argued previously, the printing press helped create massive change, including revolutions and civil wars. Does it not follow that the internet and social media, enhanced in the near future by virtual or augmented reality, will have a similar effect?

After the 2008 Global Financial Crisis, banks were bailed out. Bankers were perceived to have been rewarded for their reckless greed which created this crisis. This perception may or may not be entirely right, but it is there, all the same.

It is no surprise, that in the years which have followed, politics became more polarised and extreme, promoting views of the Far Right and Far Left, around the world.

Even nations, such as Austria, France and Italy, considered to be inherently liberal, flirted with political movements that were not so far from fascism.

But that was before the fourth and fifth industrial revolution change the world

That was before the Covid-19 crisis.

In the post-Covid-19 era, as we argued in the prologue, we are likely to see an acceleration in digital technologies and automation.

And as we move to a world in which we share cars, share other goods, and where AI can help reduce waste, there is a risk that forces that should change the world for the better could instead fashion the conditions which could create civil war and revolutions. If we share cars, car output will fall, and what was once well-paid, secure jobs, in car manufacturing will be devastated.

With many companies bailed out to save them from the worst effects of the pandemic related lockdowns, will the people feel that once again they are left to manage as 'best they can', while governments bankroll the elites with their hard-earned taxes?

How long will it take for unemployment, which has been rising at a terrifying rate, to get back to normal levels?

Will governments be put under pressure to take shares in the companies that they rescue? If they do, does this mean that the ideas of capitalism itself are under threat?

The lessons of history say that these are the ingredients which can together make civil wars and revolutions.

With governments bailing out their economies, this will create massive levels of government debt. Will this mean that in the years that follow, taxes will have to rise in combination with austerity, to repay debt?

For as long as governments can borrow at near-zero per cent, higher debt might be eminently affordable. If inflation continues to be subdued, as it has been these last twenty years or so, some governments could always resort to 'printing money' to pay off debt.

But it might be worth looking at why inflation has been so low. It seems that globalisation and linked to that so- called 'just in time manufacturing' has increased global capacity faster than global aggregate demand has increased.

But suppose, in the post-Covid-19 era, we see a reversal of globalization. Suppose one of the lessons of the Covid-19 crisis is that countries need to be more self-sufficient and that there needs to be more-slack in manufacturing so that 'just in time' manufacturing becomes less popular.

The consequence of this will be a fall in global capacity, and aggregate demand may no longer be increasing less quickly than supply. This may, in turn, lead to higher inflation, higher interest rates and remove the option of printing money to pay off government debt as the risk of this sparking off severe inflation would become too high.

The saviour to these dangers can come in the shape of technology counteracting the negative effect of reversing globalisation and just in time manufacturing with new efficiencies, increasing capacity.

Right now, we need the fourth and fifth industrial revolutions. They may take us to dystopia; they may take us to utopia. But without them, in the post-Covid-era, dystopia looks like a probable consequence anyway.

Conflict between superpowers

 Professor Hanappi from the Institute for Mathematical Models in Economics at the Vienna University of Technology[144] argues that what he calls disintegrating

144 *Professor Hanappi is Jean Monnet Chair for Political Economy of European Integration—an European Commission appointment—at the Institute for Mathematical Models in Economics at the Vienna University of Technology. He also sits on the management committee of the Systemic Risks expert group in the EU-*

capitalism —something he dated back to the 2008 financial crash — poses a threat to stability. *"An immediate consequence of the global contradiction between worldwide interwoven production processes and rivalries between nationalist regimes is a rapidly rising danger of a Third World War,"* he states in his paper.

He argues that China has a fifty per cent probability of surviving a Third World War, the US a thirty per cent chance of surviving and Russia an eighteen per cent chance. He says that if the calculus suggests one side can win such a conflict, the odds of it occurring increase. If mutual destruction is assured, World War III is less likely. Hanappi is echoing the views of Vladimir Putin in the interview referred to at the beginning of this chapter.

Putin said that the "realisation that a Third World War could end civilisation should deter us from dangerous steps." He went on to suggest that the reason why there has been relative peace since the end of world war two, or at least an absence of global conflict is because "global military power has established a parity." He warned, however, that when the US withdrew from the Anti-Ballistic Missile Treaty, it was an attempt to disrupt the strategic parity." It has also been argued that Putin is also betting that the NATO block is fearful of a third World War and so will not take the necessary action as was proven by Russia's annexation of Crimea.

Professor Hanappi describes three scenarios which could lead to global conflict.

- In the first scenario, he looks at conflict between major powers, the risk of which is heightened if the global power balance is no longer in parity.
- In his second scenario, he considers the danger of civil wars as a consequence of the return of Far Right and Far Left ideologues – the same risks we discussed above.
- In his third scenario he envisions a series "super strain pandemics" manifested in the form of armed insurrection

---

funded European Cooperation in Science and Technology research network15:12 12/05/2019

From Integrated Capitalism to Disintegrating Capitalism. Scenarios of a Third World War arising from extreme ideologies such as radical Marxism or Islamism.

A study by Lloyds of London[145] also warns of an imminent future of 'pandemics' of political violence (PV), driven by a 'contagion' effect. It states "Events such as the Arab Spring and, more recently, the wave of violent jihadist extremism affecting parts of the Middle East, have demonstrated the potential for individual outbreaks of unrest to trigger similar events across the world. These events generate widespread disruption yet prove extremely difficult to anticipate… the interdependencies which create the conditions for PV pandemics are liable to become an increasingly important factor in determining international stability."[146][147]

Quite ironic that it looked at political pandemics and paid less attention to possible literal pandemics!

So, let's drill down. Are conditions being created by new technologies that increase the chances of international conflict?

Could new technology create war between superpowers? Maybe this could happen if technology reduces our empathy. Maybe poorly programmed AI fed with misleading data could drag us into war by mistake. These are risks. But technology also provide fixes; it could reduce the chances of war.

AI, rogue AI and the end of empathy

Previously, we looked at whether technology could undermine empathy. We looked at work from Shannon Vallor, a philosopher of technology at Santa Clara University in Santa Clara. She also considers whether technology eroding our empathy could have negative military implications.

We are all aware, perhaps through viewing movies such as The Killing Fields (1984), how soldiers, who we might typically consider

---

[145] *Political violence contagion, Emerging Risk Report – 2016, Lloyds*

[146] Nafeez Ahmed provides a good account of Professor Hanappi's paper and the Lloyds of London study .The "disintegration" of global capitalism could unleash world war 3, warns top EU economist:

[147] See also: How AI Will Go Out Of Control According To 52 Experts

to be upstanding citizens, can behave appallingly under certain circumstances. Sometimes we can be quick to forgive our soldiers for the atrocities they commit, arguing that abnormally stressful situations desensitised them. Yet we may castigate as evil others, living in equally stressful circumstances, who resort to violence.

Vallor said: "If soldiers are divorced from the reality of bloody conflict, with robot soldiers or drones doing their 'dirty work', they will never experience the impact of their actions first hand and so will they fail to learn the necessary moral skills that might be essential for military commanders."

It is not a clear-cut argument, and no doubt medieval knights made much the same argument about the development of the gun. Would soldiers who fought in either of the world wars have agreed that modern weapons divorce them from the consequences of their actions? It seems unlikely.

Likewise, to say to soldiers who might be distanced from their victim that their empathy is reduced would appear to ignore facts. One only needs to watch films such as Eye in the Sky (2015) or Good Kill (2014) to understand that pilots of drones, perhaps operating at a considerable distance from the drone they control, very much feel psychologically attached to the consequences of their actions. Military planners are not divorced from ethical considerations, either.

Maybe a more dangerous threat lies with autonomous weapon systems that, through the limitations of their technology, make inappropriate decisions.

AI, and in particular the only subset of AI that exists today, machine learning, can become biased. Machine learning is the product of the data that is fed into it. It can make inappropriate decisions based on that data.

Similarly, an autonomous weapons system, applying an AI engine created from datasets, could make erroneous decisions based on flaws in the data.

AI requires human interaction to define its purpose. If insufficient rigour is applied in determining this purpose, the results could be catastrophic.

There is a parallel with flash crashes on stock markets or other financial trading systems. A flash crash can occur when multiple high-frequency trading systems, using algorithms with similar parameters, buy or sell simultaneously. This can cause an asset's value to crash or surge spectacularly for a short period, before returning to normal or the circuit breaker kicks in.

Or consider how mathematical models can backfire – take the Black Scholes model, a mathematical model which won it co-creator Myron Scholes a Nobel memorial prize for Economics. The model provided a formula for buying and selling financial assets based on specific criteria. Things went wrong in 1998; however, when Long Term Capital Management, a hedge fund co-founded by Scholes collapsed, creating ripples that nearly sunk the global financial system. (A foretaste of the 2008 crash)

If mathematical formulas or 'algos' operating independently from each other can fail, is it not possible that machine learning systems charging autonomous weapon systems could fail too?

One of the significant issues with modern AI, especially Deep Learning, is that we don't understand why resulting algorithms work the way they do. We just know that they work.

There is even jargon to describe the problem – it's called Explainable AI, although it is tough indeed to explain. It is possible to exaggerate these dangers. We tend to overestimate how clever we are. There is an analogy here with autonomous cars. Over and over again, we hear cynics argue that autonomous vehicles will not be as capable as humans in making critical life and death decisions. Suppose your car is out of control, but you can steer it sufficiently such that you can determine whether it either hits two pensioners or a child. A machine, they say, would be less effective at making the appropriate decision. But such questions seem to have been designed to elicit an outcome that the biased questioner was hoping for. How many times in your life have you had to make such a choice? Humans are not designed to drive. It would be overstating things to say that a car driven by a human is a death trap, but ten years from now, some might well argue precisely that point, when comparing them with autonomous cars.

Humans are just as fallible as machines, and machine errors are human in their instigation. We can, however, take one well-known example and pose it as a test.

Vasili Alexandrovich Arkhipov was a senior officer on board a Russian submarine on 27 October 1962, off the coast of Cuba. The submarine's crew had been incommunicado and were unaware that depth charges that had been deployed by US forces were non-lethal. Arkhipov's captain, Valentin Savitsky, feared that World War III had begun and wanted to fire a nuclear torpedo. But under the protocol of that time, such a decision needed agreement from the three most senior officers. Arkhipov withheld his confirmation and soon after the misunderstanding was revealed. Decades later, when the incident was made public, Arkhipov was hailed as the man who saved the world.

The question is, would an AI system have acted similarly? Actually, there is good reason to think it would. The submarine crew were operating in conditions of extreme stress, the submarine's air conditioning wasn't working, it was hot, cramped and the crew thought they were under attack. An AI system might not have felt such pressure.

Maybe a more significant risk than machines getting out of control, is hot-headed humans like you and me controlling weapon systems. We are all vulnerable to groupthink.

Irrationally is our stock in trade. We seem incapable of seeing an alternative point of view. In a state of near or actual panic, our irrational decision making can become more dangerous still. Imagine that we are supported by a logical, AI system, offering advice that is divorced from emotion. If the AI system had, at its disposal, millions of pieces of data on human nature, perhaps information on how people react under stress, then poor decision making may become less likely.

It is possible that the most significant doubts we have about the machine are based on ignorance of our fallibility, and that human hubris poses a much bigger threat than rogue machines. If the cold logic of AI tempers our human tendencies, then this could become our most significant safeguard against catastrophic decision making.

What causes war? Will technology exacerbate the dangers?

Wars between superpowers can have multiple causes.

Sometimes such wars occur as new superpowers emerge

Sometimes such wars can at least in part be over ideology – World War Two or the Crusades, although often other factors can be at play too.

Sometimes wars can be over limited resources.

The question is, could the fourth and fifth industrial revolutions create the conditions that history tells us have led to war in the past?

Technology could either be a force for preventing or triggering conflict.

Low barriers to entry creating conditions that led to war in the past

In the third century BC, upstart Rome began to clash with ancient Carthage, with its legacy dating back to the Phoenicians. History books tell us war between these two superpowers of the Mediterranean world was inevitable – although admittedly, history books are inclined to apply causes to events, when sometimes forces of randomness were at play. The end result was a series of wars between these two superpowers of the Mediterranean.

We saw similar conditions emerge over 2,000 years later. In the nineteenth century, the unification of Germany occurred as kingdoms that were once little more than city-states slowly came together. By the early years of the twentieth century, a new superpower had emerged in Europe, a superpower that had to play second fiddle to its neighbours, with their empires. World War I was not inevitable, but its causes were deep-rooted. History books often suggest that the assassination of Archduke Franz Ferdinand of Austria was the cause of this war. In fact, this event merely served to determine the precise timing of when World War I began.

Today we see the rise of China, which seems set to return to the position it used to occupy as the world's largest economy. India may follow.

Part of the reason behind the rise of China and then India, relates to technology.

A not well-understood implication of the fourth and then the fifth industrial revolution is the way new technology is lowering barriers to entry. These lower barriers are creating a new impetus for emerging markets.

Such developments are not negative.

For moral reasons, we should celebrate anything that reduces poverty. In any case, a growing global consumer market is good news for companies and people who work for them or benefit from the tax that they pay. It also extends the learning rate, creating greater opportunities for technologies to fall in cost.

But the lesson of history is that changes in the status quo, changes in international order, can lead to conflict.

Consider China's aspirations to expand its borders to encompass islands in the seas and oceans nearby but which other countries claim jurisdiction over, as an example.

None of this makes global conflict inevitable or even likely.

A more significant threat lies in the possibility that one side in the global power struggle believes it could win a global war.

Post Covid-19, if the US, which in many ways has all the hallmarks of a declining empire, seeks to blame China for the crises, then given what history tells us about conflict, this will be dangerous and could leave a legacy that may ultimately lead to conflict.

Ideological war, and war over resources

Another possible danger lies with the combination of revolution or the rise of a totalitarian government, as discussed in previously, within one country leading to an ideological clash with other powers.

Although the underlying causes were complicated, you could say that the above conditions led to the Second World War.

Other danger areas include climate change and a war over a limited but incredibly vital resource, such as water. Indeed, climate change may well lead to water shortages.

Technology provides a solution to both. At least, technology offers a partial fix to climate change and could mitigate the risk of a water shortage.

For one thing, as discussed earlier, the falling cost of renewables will help the war against climate change.

But renewable energy only provides a partial fix to climate change. Deforestation is a much more significant danger.

One of the most critical resources in the World is the Amazon Rainforest, primarily located in Brazil. Its value relates to it acting as the lungs of the earth, sucking carbon dioxide out of the atmosphere and creating oxygen.

But ever since we bit on the fruit of agriculture, deforestation has occurred at an alarming rate driven by a fast-growing global population.

Developed countries, such as the UK, once covered in forest, did not experience the imperative to leave their trees uncut because of the dangers of climate change; however, Brazil does.

Countries such as Brazil are providing the planet with a valuable resource without recompense; this must change.

The Amazon rainforest is undoubtedly more valuable to the world than all the oil in all the OPEC countries, yet these countries get rich on black gold, while Brazil struggles to move past the middle-income trap.

Our short-termism means that we grossly undervalue the importance of photosynthesis, and natural resources in supporting it, while we overvalue other natural resources that threaten to drown out the natural world's ability to create carbon and oxygen from carbon dioxide.

There is good news, however.

Water, water, if only it were everywhere

Population growth pressures are combining with climate change to create water shortages.

The lesson of history is that conflict can occur when the power status quo changes with the emergence of new superpowers.[148]

The big pressure point will most likely occur between India and China. Their development will be turbocharged by fourth and fifth industrial revolution technologies, with their lower barriers to entry. Unlike developed economies, they are less likely to be held back by their legacy of old technologies. As a result, the two countries will become the world's two biggest economies later this century. Likewise, South East Asia will also emerge as an economically powerful region.

The highly populated regions of China, India and South-East Asia will demand a vast amount of water.

But China and India share a common source of water – the largest resource of fresh water outside the polar regions: the Himalayas. The rivers that flow from this region irrigate the Indian and Chinese land, feeding the people.

---

[148] *One has only to see the USA's actions towards China as it feels increasingly threatened by China*

As the pressures of climate change increase, the issue of this common source of water, might well create the impetus for the next conflict between superpowers, but perhaps not for a few decades.

Technology provides a fix – water desalination in which some of the seawater of the oceans turned into freshwater, for example.

One possible technology innovation solution lies with graphene – the super material isolated in Manchester (UK) in 2004. Graphene could act as a kind of sieve; its atoms are configured such that water molecules can pass through it, but not salt molecules.

With existing technologies, water desalination requires a lot of energy, making it highly expensive.

But thanks to the falling cost of renewable energy, there is a region on the planet where the cost of energy generated from solar will be exceptionally cheap – and that is North Africa and the Arab peninsula.

In theory, many of the countries, blessed with considerable sunshine, could become the world's most significant generator of clean energy and fresh water from water desalination. In turn, this could help them irrigate the neighbouring Sahara and Arabian deserts, helping to tackle climate change by creating a new global photosynthesis zone, and become a major region for providing food.

Additionally, CRISPR can edit DNA, potentially creating super crops that require less water, or stem cell technology may enable us to grow meat in scaled-up laboratories.

Over Population

 Perhaps the biggest threat to global stability lies with its ever-growing demographic pressures.

Across one half of the world, the population is either set to decline or is already doing so.

Across the other half, the population is growing rapidly.

This demographic split is creating a paradox which could unwind into something unpleasant.

Rising populations in poorer countries is leading to massive migratory pressure. And since history tells that sharp rises in immigration can lead to the rise of populism and the Far Right, the risks are clear.

On the other hand, in certain countries, where the population is ageing, and the ratio of retired to working people is unprecedented, there is an economic need for immigrants.

Yet, the very thing that is often seen to be fuelling populism, namely immigration, is the precise resource countries with an ageing population require.

At some point, automation technologies such as AI, robotics and robotics process automation will be sophisticated enough to take-over a high proportion of jobs or fill the gap in the workforce.

While the typically older members of the workforce fret about new technology such as autonomous cars, it might be more appropriate to fret over how the economy and dwindling workforce will support them from a diminishing pool of workers once the baby boomers retire. (Record low-interest rates may be a symptom of this.)

The challenge for countries or regions like Japan, Eastern Europe and Russia, and parts of Western Europe, is that the retirement of the baby boomers or local equivalent could happen too fast for technology to fill the gap. Or at least, it may only partially fill the gap.

By the middle of the 2020s, the bulk of the baby boomer generation, the most numerous generation in western history, will have retired. By 2030, almost all of the baby boomer generation will have retired.

The retirement of the baby boomers will only be affordable if the region where they live sees a combination of mass immigration and advances in automation technologies, the very two things this generation tends to rail against.

As for regions of the world where the fertility rate shows no sign of slowing to a sustainable level, the solutions there are several-fold.

It lies, for example, with the emancipation of women – the improved equality of gender in the workforce, the lower the birth rate. Education is the key; the very solution which the internet, virtual and augmented reality, supported by AI can provide at scale, with minimal marginal cost.

It also lies with the provision of health and social services – state pensions and health services in regions with a high birth rate. Do that, and the imperative to have lots of children to provide for you in your old age diminishes. As these economies advance, which will be supported by technology, providing these services become more affordable. In this respect technology is vital.[149]

Will demographic pressures lead to global conflict? In combination of the other factors described above, they might.

That's why accelerating or jerking technology is vital. It may come with its own set of threats, but without it, demographic pressures will build other unpleasant risks.

The threat of conflict in the post-Covid-19 world

But in the post-Covid-19 world new dynamics come into to play. For one thing, there is the likely acceleration in the rise of China.

For another thing, there is the likely acceleration in the decline in the power of the West. If the West incurs crippling debts as a result of the Covid-19 related lockdown, this decline might be especially pronounced

A threat to capitalism itself forms a part of this narrative. We can add to this additional dangers. A backlash against globalisation, anti-Chinese rhetoric regarding the origin of Covid-19, and a rise in nationism, pose perhaps the most severe threat to global peace in the longer term. It is quite the powder keg!

In the aftermath of the First World War, the victorious allies chose to punish Germany. The Treaty of Versailles imposed the equivalent of $442billion[150] in reparations on Germany. The economist Keynes warned that the penalties imposed on Germany were too high and would prove counterproductive.

The League of Nations was founded soon after the war, but the US never joined. Japan, Italy, Spain and Germany withdrew. The Soviet Union joined later but was then expelled.

---

[149] *It can support developing nations by providing electricity generated by renewable energy, cheap high-quality education via the internet, online banking, by blockchain used to clearly define property right, and because new technologies entail much lower barriers to entry.*

[150] *In 2020 valuation*

As an organisation founded to protect global peace, The League of Nations was a failure, but it failed mainly because the major powers of that time were not committed to it.

In 1930, after the 1929 crash, the US passed the Smoot Hawley Tariff, which imposed tariffs on 20,000 goods imported from the rest of the world.

It was not only the Second Industrial Revolution that ended in 1914, the first age of globalisation ended, too.

This combination is no coincidence. Globalisation and technological change are intertwined. The reversal of one impacts the other.

Keynes said of the first age of globalisation: "What an extraordinary episode in the economic progress of man that age was which came to an end in August 1914.

"The inhabitant of London could order by telephone, sipping his morning tea in bed, the various products of the whole earth, in such quantity as he might see fit, and reasonably expect their early delivery upon his doorstep; he could at the same moment and by the same means adventure his wealth in the natural resources and new enterprises of any quarter of the world, and share, without exertion or even trouble, in their prospective fruits and advantages; or he could decide to couple the security of his fortunes with the good faith of the townspeople of any substantial municipality in any continent that fancy or information might recommend. [...] he regarded this state of affairs as normal, certain, and permanent, except in the direction of further improvement, and any deviation from it as aberrant, scandalous, and avoidable. The projects and politics of militarism and imperialism, of racial and cultural rivalries, of monopolies, restrictions, and exclusion, which were to play the serpent to this paradise, were little more than the amusements of his daily newspaper, and appeared to exercise almost no influence at all on the ordinary course of social and economic life, the internationalization of which was nearly complete in practice."

After the First World War, the world retreated in on itself, and thereby sowed the seeds for the next world war. When two country's economies are interdependent; they are less likely to go to war with each other. Reverse globalisation and you risk breaking this interdependence.

By the end of the Second World War, the Allies had learned their lesson. The world's victorious powers were determined not to repeat the errors that led to the Second World War.

In 1944, in the town of Bretton Woods, in the US, a new way to structure how the global economy operates was created. Alas, the boldest of the plans: a proposal by John Maynard Keynes to set a form of international currency, and which imposed fines on countries with large trade surpluses would have created a more prosperous, less bubble prone and interdependent world, was rejected. The IMF and World Bank were formed as halfway houses.

But the post-war settlement also involved the Marshall Plan, in which around $120 billion in 2020 value, was provided to help rebuild Western Europe. A part of the idea behind the plan was to halt the spread of communism and Russia's expansion.

The post-war period also saw a period of diminishing inequality and the rise of welfare states. Global institutions such as the UN, WHO, IMF, World Bank, WTO and what was once called the European Coal and Steel Community, the forerunner of the EU, were founded.

They helped support political stability and prosperity.

Today, as globalisation and immigration are blamed first for rising inequality, we risk reversing the very drivers that created seventy-five years of relative peace.

The jury is out on whether globalisation or technology is behind the hollowing out of labour markets across the US and Europe seen in recent years. It is clear, however, that globalisation and technology have created more wealth than they have destroyed.

If globalisation and technology have also created social discontent, that is the fault of governments and failure to coordinate worldwide efforts to soften the negative effects of these forces. Given the track record of the government, we firmly believe that we should no longer abdicate this responsibility to governments alone. We all need to join and shape this debate proactively.

There is no doubt, however, that technology has created a new breed of entrepreneur and investor and in so doing has created an army of billionaires (540 at the last count in the US alone.)

In the post-Covid-19 world, there is a real risk inequality will accelerate.

Supporters of the idea of growing inequality say that the wealth created by the super-rich trickles down and finds its way into the pockets and purses of ordinary people. They say that to object to this is the politics of envy. Such critique is, to excuse the pun, too rich for words. The creation of so many billionaires at a time when so many people are homeless and median wages have barely increased in twenty years, can only be described as the politics of greed. And as Marx said: "our desires and pleasures spring from society; we measure them, therefore, by society."

To mitigate against the risk that growing inequality may sow the seeds of revolution and civil war, that the pitchforks may rise up, some politicians are finding scapegoats. And the echo chamber of social media supports them. Instead of trying to ensure that the fruits of globalisation are equitably distributed, they blame it. In so doing, we see a headlong rush to reversing globalisation, the lessons of World War One and Two washed away on a populist tide.

As a result, we risk the return of global conflict.

The Terminator!

 Science fiction has been beguiling us with tales of conscious machines taking over from humanity for decades. But are such fictional scenarios realistic? A Terminator-looking like a young Arnold Schwarzenegger will never appear naked in our midst, sent back from future; but might machines become self-aware, develop free-will, consciousness, even emotions? And will such machines pose a threat to humanity?

Elon Musk, a kind of real-life Tony Stark from the Marvel franchise, has warned that AI posed the greatest existential threat to humanity. The late Stephen Hawking had similar fears.

Speak to many other experts on AI, and many dismiss such fears.

But never forget the infamous prediction of yesteryear. "There is a world market for maybe five computers," or just as extraordinary: Computers in the future may weigh no more than one and a half tons — Popular Mechanics, 1949. Dismissing predictions of superintelligence, conscious AI, maybe the most serious and indeed last mistake we make.

But how realistic are these warnings? It is not as unlikely as some argue, and it is not unlikely for three reasons running in parallel. Those three reasons are Moore's Law, convergence and evolution.

And if it is possible for a super-intelligent conscious machine to emerge it may be that there is little, we can do to avoid it.

Our best hope lies not so much in acting like King Cnut in trying to stop such an event, but rather in trying to create as benign an outcome as possible. Such an outcome might entail some kind of combination of human and machine. That may sound unpalatable, but it is better than the alternative.

The good news is that the emergence of a super-intelligent conscious machine is not likely to be imminent. This book is about how technology can change us during the lifetime of most readers of this book. Assuming we don't all start living until we are well over 100, the danger of super-intelligent conscious machines seems likely only to pose a risk to the very youngest readers of this book. This threat is more likely to be a sixth industrial revolution, danger.

But the point when it is too late to do anything about it might come sooner, much sooner. Assuming you care about the fate of your children and grandchildren, the time to start putting in place a plan to ensure this benign outcome is probably pretty soon.

A more likely threat: and this is a threat that could emerge during the fifth industrial revolution is a scenario in which some people merge with machines, creating a new elite subset of superhumans. The good news is that up to now, technology has needed a mass market for it to flourish – so too much elitism might hold technology back. The bad news is that economies of scale are not what they used to be. Diminishing automation technology and additive manufacturing may mean that the creation of a mass- market is less critical for future technology developments. In which case, the creation of a superhuman/ half-machine elite could indeed occur in the lifetime of most readers of this book.

Some numbers

So, might a computer eventually be able to out-perform humans in almost all respects? Might a computer become self-aware?

To answer that, first consider some simple numbers. There are roughly 100 billion neurons in the human brain. These neurons form synapses with other neurons. There could be up to one trillion synaptic links, of various levels of intensity.

There are roughly 4.3 billion transistors in an iPhone X. The fact that there are so many more interactions within the human brain than on advanced computer might suggest that we are nowhere near creating artificial intelligence as advanced as the human brain.

An essential part of the human brain is parallel processing. Different synapses seem to support simple ideas. One series of synaptic links between neurons, might convey an understanding of a straight horizontal line. Another set might convey that a straight horizontal line between two vertical lines which slope downwards away from each other conveys the letter A. Billions of such links may create the ability to read.

Neural networks study data and extrapolate trends and patterns using a similar, albeit much more primitive approach.

Up to now, computers have operated linearly. This is now changing.

Falon Fatemi, [151] founder of Node, draws a parallel with a raccoon. "Intuitively, we understand what a raccoon is, maybe because the brain works on a problem in parallel. We see the whole, the multitude of ways an animal is, in fact, a raccoon. On the other hand, if we describe the creature, we do it in stages."

This is what neural networks, in combination with what is called deep learning, or even unsupervised deep learning, try to achieve. This is the technology that lies behind the autonomous car.

But sophisticated and indeed astonishing though the latest advances in artificial intelligence are, they are nothing like the human brain. Nothing like the creation of consciousness. Yet.

But what about convergence?

At a conference on AI, Sir John Dermot Turing, nephew of the famous Alan Turing, and who is a member of the European Post-Trade Forum, and a Trustee of the Turing Trust, and who has a DPhil in Genetics from New College, Oxford, gave a warning. And his warning relates to the convergence of ideas.

---

[151] In an interview with Michael Baxter for Information Age,

He draws an analogy with Darwin. Charles Darwin, the man who revolutionised our understanding of the world and our place in it, produced a unified theory. Before Darwin, the number of natural history enthusiasts, and scientists working in the areas that interested Darwin were legion. Before Darwin, for example, there was the French naturalist, Jean-Baptiste Lamarck, who believed that species developed their unique appearances via acquired characteristics. Animals that went around stretching their necks to reach high hanging fruit or leaves may eventually get long necks, and their descendants even longer necks, leading to giraffes. Another predecessor of Darwin, the geologist Charles Lyell, proposed that the Earth was much older than had previously been assumed and that countless and continuing small changes had shaped the geological layout of the Earth over millions, or even hundreds of millions, of years. Darwin took these disparate ideas of eminent thinkers such as Lamarck and Lyell as well as countless enthusiasts to create his theory, complete with all its stunning implications.

Sir John wonders whether there might be an analogy with AI. "What AI is all about is simple self-contained things, like facial recognition, self-driving cars, voice recognition, algorithms for helping Amazon sell products – self-contained boxes. For as long as AI exists like this, in disparate groups, there is no risk that AI could escape from their boxes and take over the planet." But, "I don't think we are that far away from when someone comes along with a super algorithm that glues together all the bits of thinking, and we end up with a super-intelligent algorithm. It seems to me that we underestimate our capabilities, someone clever is going to come up with something and we need to be prepared."

Jeremy Achin, CEO of DataRobot [152], once told the authors that "we are nowhere near that. But we are near something similar which is trillions of independent AI systems each doing simple things, which collectively are not far from that scenario...If you picture trillions of little independent systems that are all doing something automatically, they don't need to know about each other but the collective impact, it's kind of similar to the one powerful AI that is impacting everything we do, like in science fiction."

---

[152] *In an interview with Michael Baxter for Information Age*

But what is consciousness?

The trouble is, no one has much of a clue what consciousness is. It feels like there are as many theories as there are Ted talks.

Dan Dennett questions whether consciousness is overrated, that it is mostly an illusion; we just follow the instructions of the brain. Anil Seth speculates consciousness comes from our brain, creating a hallucination of our experiences in the physical world.

The brilliant mathematics professor from Oxford University (UK), Sir Roger Penrose speculates that consciousness can only be explained by quantum mechanics. Similarly, other scientists have proposed that consciousness can be described by multidimensional mathematics.

In an article[153] studying the work of Henry Markram and his team at the Blue Brain Project at the Swiss Federal Institute of Technology in Lausanne, New Scientist magazine summed it up well stating: "What they have found beggars belief. As our brains think, learn and remember, they create elaborate but ephemeral structures in at least seven mathematical dimensions, and possibly many more. What's more, these transient structures, which appear and disappear like sandcastles on a beach, could help us understand how the brain creates our thoughts and feelings. They might even unravel the greatest mystery of them all: consciousness."

Or maybe consciousness just is. It is something innate; perhaps that is the God part of this discussion.

Consciousness evolved

But you don't need to understand what consciousness is to be able to understand a simple apparent truth. Consciousness evolved.

The question that asks will computers ever be able to achieve human-like consciousness misses the point. A more pertinent question might be will computers ever have a form of consciousness comparable to that an amoeba?

---

[153] *The brain's 7D sandcastles could be the key to consciousness, Anil Ananthaswamy, 27 September 2017 https://www.newscientist. com/article/mg23531450-200-the-brains-7d-sandcastles-could-be- the-key-to-consciousness/*

Life evolved. At some point in the evolution process, it appears that consciousness evolved.

The question is not, will we build a computer or AI system that has consciousness? It should be, might such a system evolve?

In the digital world, evolution can occur incredibly quickly. If in the human world, it takes twenty years to move from one generation to the next; in a computer simulation, generations might only be separated by nanoseconds.

Theoretically, with sufficient computing power, an evolutionary process that created life in all its complexity we know today, and which took billions of years, could be duplicated in a digital process lasting no more than a few years/months/or even minutes.

If we see a kind of new Moore's Law operate and we get photonic chips and quantum computers, all linked together via the cloud, how can we predict what possibilities might be created?

In the human brain, the speed at which synapses form is slow. According to Neil Bostrom [154] "A biological neuron fires, maybe, at 200 hertz, 200 times a second. But even a present-day transistor operates at the Gigahertz. Neurons propagate slowly in axons, 100 meters per second, tops. But in computers, signals can travel at the speed of light." The human brain is limited in size by the human skull. The internet/cloud, consisting of quantum computers and photonic chips could consist of hardware, which, when put together, could be the size of a mountain.

Recall, how Brad De Long once estimated how difficult it would have been to build a computer with a similar processing power to the iPhone X in 1957. It would have cost 150 trillion of today's dollars, the device would have taken up a hundred-story building 300 meters high, and three kilometres long and wide and draw 150 terawatts of power – thirty times the world's generating capacity at that time." But consider the value and scale of all computers linked together today; think forward ten to twenty years. Maybe we will have a computer comparable in size to De Long's 1957 version of the iPhone X

The speed of light is roughly comparable with travelling around the world seven times a second. If a neuron fires 200 times a second; a

---

[154] *What happens when our computers get smarter than us, Nick Bostrom, Ted.*

computer, the size of Africa could send a message from one end to the other at roughly the same rate that a neuron fires.

To say that an algorithm which is superior to the human brain could not evolve in such a medium seems implausible. It may not be likely that a computer will become self- aware and that in the process pose a threat any time soon. If this is possible, this is more likely to be a danger of the sixth industrial revolution. And even if a computer did become superior to us, it may not want to destroy us. [155]But that does not mean these things are impossible.

Evolution is not predictable

But evolution is not a predictable thing – no one can predict what it will turn out. Conscious life had been on the Earth for hundreds of millions of years before we turned up. That may have been a fluke. We have no way of knowing what results will arise from evolution in a digital environment.

Link to the physical world

Or maybe it is impossible for a digital environment to create a living, thinking creates – that algorithms can never do more than simulate.

Maybe to create a conscious entity, there has to be a physical existence, one where we can feel pain and pleasure.

But that is where this gets interesting.

If we can link the digital/virtual world to the physical world via say brain interfaces or neural lace, then who is to say what might result?.

Such links do not have to be computer to human; they could be computer to any conscious creature – one of the other super-intelligent animals such as a chimpanzee, dolphin. elephant, crow, or maybe even something as intelligent as your pet dog, or even all the way down to the bottom of the consciousness league table, wherever that maybe, an ant or fly perhaps.

It is not being suggested the above is likely, and surely not imminent. But let us not be too complacent.

---

[155] As Musk said, and we quoted in chapter eight, we could become like pet Labradors

The elites

 Perhaps the growing wealth divide will see the emergence of a world in which an elite are supplemented by technology and are therefore able to suppress the non-elites.

Whether that be amplified, as described in chapter eleven, or something more extreme as hypothesised here; the result could be the creation of master humans: Homo sapiens augebatur dominus – wise augmented dominant man.

You may find that acceptable; the authors don't, and if the populace rose up in bloody rebellion to resist such a danger, the authors would join them.

Chapter 13

Collective intelligence – Gaia

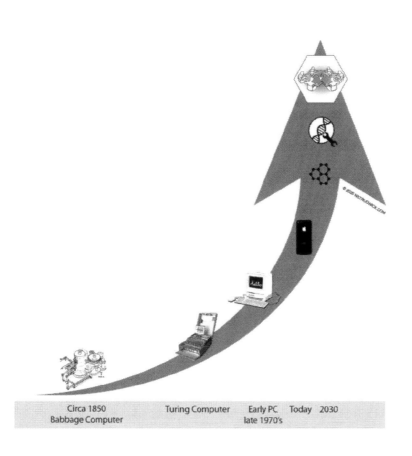

| Circa 1850 | | Turing Computer | Early PC | Today | 2030 |
| Babbage Computer | | | late 1970's | | |

For each individual among the many has a share of excellence and practical wisdom, and when they meet together, just as they become in a manner one man, who has many feet, and hands, and senses, so too with regard to their character and thought. Hence the many are better judges than a single man of music and poetry, for some understand one part and some another, and among them, they understand the whole. (Aristotle, Politics, book 3, chapter 11)

"Diverse teams make better mousetraps,"
Scott E Page.

 Crowds can be incredibly smart, so much so that they may prove to be our greatest hope. Crowds can also be extraordinarily stupid, so stupid in fact that they may prove to be our undoing. No medium in history can come close to the internet for creating and uniting crowds at a size that was once considered unthinkable. Technology that is set to follow will make the internet seem old and clunky with respect to its ability to create, unite, amplify, but also polarise crowds.

There is another not fully understood danger and opportunity created by accelerating technology, or indeed 'jerking' technology. It is the idea of creating a kind of collective intelligence, or worse case collective stupidity. The internet and emerging technologies such as augmented and virtual reality could draw us closer together. At one level, we form groups and share ideas, feeding off each other's insights to create a wise crowd. On the flip side, instead, we may see groupthink, group polarisation, and we perform acts of collective destruction, like the Californian sardines we described in the chapter on totalitarianism and fascism. At the more extreme, we may even create something bigger than us, what scientists call an emergent system: something that may possess something that has a sense of consciousness.

The writer James Lovelock has suggested that the Earth is like a living organism and that humanity has become akin to a virus. Lovelock calls his idea of Earth Gaia, named after Mother Earth from Greek mythology. The science fiction writer, Isaac Asimov explored the concept of Gaia in his acclaimed Foundation Series – in this case, Gaia was like a collective conscious, made of its human inhabitants thinking in unison. The movie Avatar (2009) expresses a similar idea with 'the one tree,' and the Star Trek TV series explores the concept of a collective conscious, but in a negative and terrifying way, with the Borg.

Suppose technology brings us together, maybe it creates closely interacting groups made up of thousands of people, technology making the Dunbar number which imposes a limit on how many people we can have meaningful engagement with, redundant.

Suppose technology does more than that and eventually the neurons in our brain form synapses with artificial neurons, and they form synapses with neurons in someone else's brain.

Parents sometimes think that their children see them as a single entity, a two-headed creature that thinks as one. Maybe technology will create an entity with several billion heads that think as one. One massive neural network of brains!

We need to stop and understand what collective intelligence is. This is important, and the ideas here tie in directly with the purpose of this book. We need you, the reader, to join the debate.

The greatest genius of all time wasn't even human

No one, not ever, not Einstein, not Leonardo da Vinci, Van Gogh, Isaac Newton, Mozart, Beethoven, Plato, Shakespeare, or Galileo Galilei came close.

The collective intelligence of humanity: the product of thousands of years of innovations building upon existing innovations seems amateurish by comparison.

And what or who is this ultimate genius, this sublimely talented artist, a creative force without peer?

For an answer, here is a clue. It has no plan, no strategy, and no grand design. It is random. It experiments as nothing else has done so before. And it has a simple selection mechanism to choose which experiments are worth pursuing. It is also an example of collective intelligence.

It is called evolution.

Creativity is far from being unique to either individuals or humans.

Collective intelligence

Collective intelligence applies to a phenomenon in which individual units or actions work together creating an outcome that they may not have been able to achieve on their own.

Evolution is the ultimate version of collective intelligence. It creates ecosystems, with each constituent part playing a role in the cohesion of that system. But you need to view it over a long-time horizon to appreciate its wonder.

Collective intelligence is closely aligned with the concept of emergence. To cite Wikipedia; "An emergent behaviour or emergent property can appear when a number of simple entities (agents) operate in an environment, forming more complex behaviours as a collective."

Examples of emergent systems are a beehive, ants' nest, a city, the economy, and the human brain.

The human brain is unusual for an emergent system as a by-product of this system is consciousness.

The collective intelligence of humanity

If anthropologists are right, and we are designed to live in groups of 148 (or 150 as the Dunbar number is typically rounded up to) then in the past, humanity may well have seen a form of collective intelligence as the group of people in a community acted together.

Maybe it is our ability to collaborate at scale – it is thought that the optimal community size for chimps is around forty to fifty – that made our species so successful.

In other words, collective intelligence may be what gave Homo sapiens sapiens its edge.

This ability of humans to collaborate with other people, but limited in scale to around 150, is fundamental to the nature of humanity.

Many of the quirks of human behaviour can be explained by our need to be part of a group; supporting collective intelligence.

As was told previously, psychologists have long known that we find it hard to go against the group. If everyone in a group is asked a question, and everyone answers the question with the same answer; then when it comes to us we may well provide the same solution, even if we happen to know the answer is in fact wrong.

Over time, another form of collective intelligence occurred among humans in the form of memories handed down from one generation to the next, but which in turn are expanded upon, over time. In this way, a tribe of humans learns over time.

We often learn via storytelling – when information is presented as a story rather than a collection of facts, we are more likely to remember and more likely to apply the lessons of that tale. In this way, storytelling extends our ability to recall information, and remind more people, beyond the Dunbar number.

This is why populist politicians who can often ride roughshod over facts can secure a significant following. They are great storytellers.

It is why Christ told parables, and why the lessons from those parables are still remembered today.

Storytelling can also bring a tribe together — it is not hard to imagine a tribe of hunter- gatherers, sitting around a fire, hearing tales.

Such tales can often evolve over time. They are a staple part of uniting a tribe and help cement its collective intelligence. Indeed the stories themselves can be part of the collective intelligence of a tribe, with individuals reacting to real-world challenges by applying lessons from tales, thereby creating a kind of social currency: a tribe communicates via metaphors partially drawn from the stories its members all share, thus creating a common way of thinking – 'I threw the spear just like Achilles,' 'I drove the car like Ayrton Senna'.

When we finally bit upon the fruit of agriculture, like Adam and Eve biting into the forbidden fruit in Eden, we began to collaborate in larger groups, in much larger communities. We needed new means to bring a community together. Religions evolved that supported the operation of larger communities and in their own way, supported collective intelligence.

Writing and then more recently, the printing press helped promote collective intelligence, communicating ideas and stories to huge numbers, supporting the evolution of those ideas.

Sometimes we are passive observers within an emergent system. Before there was a Netflix, families across a country, or even the world, might gather around a television en masse watching the same programme. And then the next day, discuss it or also recite extracts from the show at work or school. It was not so much collective intelligence as collective communicating. The phenomenon was no doubt not dissimilar to the way a pre-agriculture tribe may have shared the lessons of the tale they heard the night before. But in a way, we were sharing a collective consciousness. Likewise, fans in a football stadium watching their team play, share a collective consciousness – groaning with despair as one, yelling in excitement as one, collectively agreeing that the referee was born out of wedlock, chanting and singing in unison, sometimes creating what football commentators call a twelfth player. [156]

The internet changes things again. Just as writing and then the printing press supported more complex and broader scale collective intelligence, so does the internet. That is why the medium is so important – it is a point that technology cynics do not understand.

But new technologies, such as augmented and virtual reality, and AI supporting us with information, and facilitating communication, for example, real-time language translation, will enhance the internet's communication properties.

Future technologies, such as neural lace which will enable us to think instructions to a computer, may eventually allow us to communicate ideas, via a computer interface operating at superfast speeds, to other people.

Ultimately, we may all share our thoughts, neurons in the brain forming synapses with external artificial neurons, which in turn form synapses with neurons in other brains, creating a kind of central brain of humanity.

The wisdom of crowds

To illustrate how crowds can be wise, consider another shoal of fish. This particular shoal is quite different from the sardines referred to

---

[156] *There is even a book by that very name — The Kop: Liverpool's Twelfth Man Paperback – 14 Aug. 2008 by Stephen F Kelly*

in chapter seven, which died en-masse by sucking the oxygen out of water.

By contrast, this shoal creates a form of wisdom from a collection of individuals.

The fish in question is called a shiner – these simple creatures are not blessed with thinking ability. In the case of an experiment conducted by Andrew Berdahl and Colin Torney, researchers forming part of a team, run by Iain Couzin,[157] from Princeton University, shiners were placed into a shallow pool of water. The fish like shade, but when the researchers projected shifted patterns of light over the water, on their own, each fish showed ineptitude in its ability to avoid the light. But by adding more fish to the water, the researchers found that their ability to avoid the light grew. To quote National Geographic: "The solo fish did so badly that they were almost swimming randomly. Only larger shoals were good at avoiding the shifting light. Even then, Berdahl and Torney found that the shiners' movements were far more influenced by what their neighbours were doing, than by how bright the environment was."[158]

It seems each fish followed two simple rules, swim slower where it is dark, and stick close to its neighbour.

As National Geographic put it: "*That's* collective intelligence! The shiners' ability to stay in the shade *emerges* from neighbourly interactions of dumb units. The fish aren't pooling decisions that each individual makes on its own – they're collectively *processing* information. By moving as one, they can compute as one."

Wisdom of human crowds

The idea groups are wiser than individual humans is not new.

The classic example of the wisdom of the crowds relates to a notable finding by a mathematician, Francis Galton. Back in 1907, he published a paper reporting his discovery from observing a 'guess the weight of an ox competition' at a livestock fair. Many of the guesses were wildly inaccurate, and none of the estimates were especially close

---

[157] Collective Behaviour.com, Iaiin Couzin
[158] *The Real Wisdom of the Crowds, National Geographic, ED YONG, JANUARY 31, 2013*

to the mark. The ox did, in fact, weigh 1,198 pounds. The best guess was. 2,207 pounds. Yet, when

Galton tallied up all the estimates and worked out the median, which came out at 1,197 pounds. So, there you have it, proof, or so we are told, crowds are wiser than individual humans.[159]

Another example is provided by the TV show 'Who wants to be a millionaire,' where the contestants can choose to 'ask the audience', however, the audience doesn't always get it right. This is particularly true if the subject matter is quite obscure, or it is worded in such a way that the instinctive answer is wrong.

A small group of doctors working together[160] as a team are more likely to make an accurate diagnosis compared to working alone; college students sitting examinations perform better when students work together than when working individually. So compelling is the evidence support to support the idea that students perform better when they work as a group that a number of universities have started implementing what has become known as 'collaborative learning techniques.' [161]

Madness of crowds

But crowds can get it horrendously wrong. There are many reasons for this. For one thing, there is group psychology and in particular groupthink – when a crowd gets stuck thinking in a specific direction. Certain biases, such as confirmation bias, can come together, making it hard for individuals to develop independent ideas from the crowd. The classic example of the madness of crowds relates to the Bay of Pigs disaster when the US government ignored advice from outside experts and instigated a disastrous attempt to arrange a coup in Cuba.

Before Castro, Cuba was ruled by a much-hated regime. A popular uprising during 1958 resulted in the overthrow of the Batista Government and in January 1959, Fidel Castro gained power. The

---

[159] *The story of Galton and the idea of the wisdom of the crowds is just told by James Surowiecki in 'The wisdom of crowds, why the many are smarter than the few and how collaborative wisdom shapes business economies societies and nations.*

[160] *According going to J. C Click on K Stanley,*

[161] *As was stated by Tracy Burkett book and Idee Winfield in collaborative testing test performance, 2004.*

new leader said he was pro both the US and democracy and just a few months after gaining control. he visited New York, full of charm and good intentions. He attempted to ingratiate himself with the American people eating hamburgers and hotdogs, affirming his hatred for communism and his desire for Cuban democracy. Who knows, did Castro really believe these things, or was he simply trying to cosy up to the superpower on his doorstep? Rejected Castro returned home and instead made overtures to the Soviets. Hell has no fury like a Castro scorned.

The then US President, a certain John F Kennedy, watched the developments in Cuba with alarm. The lynchpin to his presidential campaign was his promise to halt the spread of communism; a popular cause, it may have won him the presidency. Once in the White House, he drew up plans for the removal of Castro. The CIA devised a strategy to launch a covert mission to remove the Cuban leader from power by landing highly trained troops onto a strip of Cuban land called the Bay of Pigs, from which point they were expected to draw popular support. Kennedy recruited the very best men to orchestrate the manoeuvre.

So meticulous was the planning that it seemed certain to succeed. How irritating it must have been when the Institute of International Social Research (IISR) produced a report warning that such an uprising would not prove popular with the Cuban people. Still, the IISR was clearly wrong, or so they thought.

Yet fail it did. In fact, the US government eventually had to send food and supplies to Cuba in exchange for the handing back of the surviving members of its invading force. Kennedy later asked: "How could I have been so stupid?" Soon after, the Cuban missile crisis threatened to drag the entire world into a nuclear war, all because of an error caused initially by inaccurate groupthink, furthermore, it was groupthink that was unable to countenance the possibility that its central assumption was wrong.

It is not difficult to find other examples of UK and US foreign policy mistakes that had calamitous consequences. In fact, so extraordinarily inept are some of these errors that some conclude there must be some kind of conspiracy, a mysterious group of individuals following an agenda hidden from the public, pulling strings, orchestrating a catalogue of apparent policy mistakes.[162]

There is no conspiracy. Instead, all we have seen is evidence of how a thinking group can be extraordinarily foolhardy. Or perhaps can be so blind to the truth that they engage in an orgy of self-justification, leading to self- destruction.

That's the funny thing about groupthink and crowds cooperating; they can get things horrendously wrong but on other occasions gloriously right.

Polarising

What we can say is that crowds are often subject to polarisation. As was told previously, a group of people who, on an individual basis, tend to be mild risk-takers, can, when they collaborate, become reckless in the extreme. A group of people who, on an individual basis, tend to be mildly risk-averse, can become paralysed by indecision.

Other tests [163]indicate that judges working together in a group of three or more, make more extreme decisions than when they work independently.

To quote Donelson R Forsyth (Group Dynamics) "a gathering of students who are moderately negative about a professor's teaching methods will become openly hostile after group discussion."

Diversity and collective intelligence

According to James Surowiecki, for the wisdom of the crowds to be genuinely effective; there must be both diversity and independent thinking within the group:

---

[162] *For at least the first 2 years of the Second World War, the Brits were of the opinion that the Germans didn't have radar despite many intelligence sources countering that claim. In fact, the German radar tech was much more advanced that the UK one! Many, many lives were lost as result. That's groupthink for you.*
[163] (EC main TG Walker choice shifts and extreme behaviour judicial review in the federal courts)

- Diversity: the more varied the group, the less likely it will make a standard, mistaken assumption
- Independence, somehow the individuals must not be influenced in their decision making by the views of other members; that way lies groupthink and its inherent dangers.

But is that second point, right? To an extent, but people can also feed off other people's ideas. Somehow there needs independent thought, without at the same time thinking in a vacuum.

In her Ted Talk, [164] Margaret Heffernan, a UK CEO and entrepreneur, referred to an experiment conducted by William M. Muir, Professor of Animal Sciences at Purdue University which she refers to as 'super chickens'. Muir investigated the productivity of chickens at a farm. All the highly productive chickens are separated from the rest.

Then the highly efficient chickens breed together, the lesser, average chickens breed together.

The end result: rather than the product of super chicken breeding creating exceptionally productive chickens, it instead created aggressive chickens, and in fact, the group of ordinary chickens saw productivity rise.

If this conclusion bears relevance to the real world, then it is a damning indictment of the ideal of benefits of inequality – even selection by ability at school.

After interviewing William Muir[165], the celebrated evolutionary biologist, David Sloan Wilson said: "Muir's experiments reveal a tremendous naiveté in the idea that creating a good society is merely a matter of selecting the 'best' individuals. A good society requires members working together to create what cannot be produced alone, or at least to refrain from exploiting each other. Human societies approach this ideal to varying degrees, but there is always an element of unfairness that results in some profiting at the expense of others. If these individuals are allowed to breed, and if their profiteering ways are

---

[164] https://www.ted.com/talks/margaret_heffernan_why_it_s_ time_to_forget_ the_pecking_order_at_work/transcript?nol

[165] *David Sloan Wilson is a Distinguished Professor of Biological Sciences and Anthropology at Binghamton University*

heritable, then selecting the 'best' individuals will cause a cooperative society to collapse. It's a good thing that the early eugenicists did not have their way!"[166]

Returning to Ms Heffernan's Ted talk, she also referred to experiments showing that when psychologists divided volunteers into groups and set them complex problems, the most successful groups were not necessarily those made up of individuals with 'spectacularly high IQs', "Nor were the most successful groups the ones that had the highest aggregate I.Q."

Instead, Ms Heffernan said, to be successful, a group needed:

- Individuals with high degrees of social sensitivity to each other
- To give roughly equal time to each other, so that no one voice dominated, but neither were there any passengers
- And thirdly, the more successful groups had more women in them.

Or, as John Stuart Mill said: "It is hardly possible to overrate the value...of placing human beings in contact with other persons dissimilar to themselves, with modes of thought and action unlike those with which they are familiar."

Or as Scott E Page, the acclaimed American social scientist said: "Progress depends as much on our collective differences as it does on our individual IQ scores." [167]

And "If we can understand how to leverage diversity to achieve better performance and greater robustness, we might anticipate and prevent collapses."

It's a point that critics of immigration may want to take note.

---

[166] *When the Strong Outbreed the Weak: An Interview with William*
[167] *Scott E. Page, The Difference: How the Power of Diversity Creates Better Groups, Firms, Schools, and Societies*

And creative too

There is a view that creative intelligence lacks creativity —that individualism is the key to inspiration.[168] This may be true, but such arguments seem to ignore the lesson of evolution; the most powerful force of creativity ever seen.

The power of technology

We have already seen social media at work. It can polarise behaviour, creating bias and reinforcing arguments that counter no alternatives, but it can be a force for wonderful collective intelligence projects or open innovation challenges such as Wikipedia, or Linux.

By promoting communication over vast distances, the internet is also a force for supporting diversity, as people from entirely different cultural backgrounds can meet in e-space, interact and compare ideas.

Virtual and augmented reality will move the potential for this form of long-distance interaction to a different level. Virtual reality creates new meeting places, as people can meet, avatar to avatar, in virtual space, groups made up of individuals from every corner of the planet.

AI can support conversations in large groups, reminding people who other individuals are, what they said previously, introducing data in a timely and appropriate manner, while reinforcing the rules that support positive collective behaviour.

We all come together

But the truly dramatic change that technology may promote could take the idea of collective intelligence to another level. The brain is made up of neurons – on its own no one neuron is much use. But when a hundred billion or so neurons form links with each other, by creating what are called synapses, we get us – each and every individual in their complexity and wonder.

Suppose, there was a way for the neurons in our brain to form links with the neurons in other brains.

---

[168] *See this piece for an extension of this argument Groupthink is no match for solo genius, Christopher Caldwell, MARCH 30 2012, FT*

Suppose that just as billions of neurons form a consciousness, a few billion people, sufficiently linked together, can create an even higher consciousness.

Is that as ridiculous as it sounds?

Recently, researchers have claimed [169] to have developed a system which they call, BrainNet, to allow three people to share thoughts — from brain to brain, to brain.

They claim that BrainNet is the first "multi-person non- invasive direct brain-to-brain interface for collaborative problem-solving."

The interface works by combining EEG [170]machines to record brain signals with transcranial magnetic stimulation (TMS) to deliver information non-invasively to the brain. Two of the individuals can then send simple messages, via the EEG machine which decodes the messages, over the internet, to a third individual who acts upon the instructions

Together, the three people are able to play a Tetris type game. One following instruction sent directly from the respective brains of the other two individuals.

The researchers say: "Our results raise the possibility of future brain-to-brain interfaces that enable cooperative problem solving by humans using a 'social networks' of connected brains."

The opportunity and indeed threat lie with convergence. The combination of advances in neuroscience, evolving technology for measuring the brain in real-time; computers that are becoming ever more powerful and super-fast internet connection creates the possibility of being able to communicate directly with people by thought, over long distances.

Neural lace and other technologies create the opportunity of direct brain interfaces with computers, and if such computers are also connected to other brains, our brains may become linked.

In time, will the neurons in our brain be able to form synapses with artificial neurons, which in turn create synapses with neurons in other human brains?

---

[169] *BrainNet: A Multi-Person Brain-to-Brain Interface for Direct Collaboration Between Brains*
[170] *Electroencephalography*

As the philosopher, Nick Bostrom from The Future of Humanity Institute at Oxford University in the UK, speculates: "Some Human individuals upload and make many copies of themselves. Meanwhile, there is gradual progress in neuroscience and artificial intelligence, and eventually, it becomes possible to isolate individual cognitive modules and connect them up to modules from other uploaded minds." He continued: "There might be multiple standards; some modules might specialise in translating between incompatible standards. Competitive uploads begin outsourcing increasing portions of the functionality: Why do I need to know arithmetic when I can buy time on Arithmetic-Modules Inc. whenever I need to do my accounts? Why do I need to be good with language when I can hire a professional language module to articulate my thoughts? Why do I need to bother making decisions about my personal life when the certified execution-modules that can scan my goal structure and manage my assets so as to best to fulfil my goals?" He went on to say: "When it becomes possible to copy modules at will, to send high- bandwidth signals between parts of different brains, and to build the architecture that cannot readily be implemented on biological neural nets, it might turn out that the optima relative to this new constraints-landscape have shifted away from the human-like mind region. There might be no niche for mental architectures of a human-kind."[171]

As mentioned above, James Lovelock advanced the idea of the Earth being a kind of super organism: one that regulates itself, perpetuating the conditions for life. He called this emergent system Gaia.

Isaac Asimov took the idea further in his Foundation series with a planet called Gaia in which the entire population think as one, creating a giant group consciousness. In the James Cameron movie Avatar, a similar concept is advanced; the tree of life, the combined thoughts of all living things, forming a goddess that was able to mobilise an army of living creatures to fight the human invaders. In Star Trek, we see a collective intelligence of a terrifying kind – The Borg, a collective that sucks out all individuality and says: "Resistance is futile."

---

[171] *THE FUTURE OF HUMAN EVOLUTION, Nick Bostrom, Future of Humanity Institute, Faculty of Philosophy & Oxford Martin School, University of Oxford https://nickbostrom.com/ fut/evolution.html*

Technology is creating a collective intelligence. Whether the result is something that amplifies the worst of us or creates godlike wisdom, whether this collective intelligence is at a distance – just an amalgamation of our conversations and ideas, or whether it is something more close-knit, not necessarily a super organism, but something approaching Gaia, collective intelligence without an emergent consciousness, is not evident.

But Homo sapiens sapiens, wise man, may become the collective of wise men (and for the optimal outcome, women too.) Will we become Homo sapiens colligere, or better still homo et femina sapiens colligere — the wise man and women collective? In the age of the jerk, we cannot dismiss such possibilities.

Accelerating and converging technology is creating an extraordinary opportunity. The result will be as profound as you can imagine. And these effects, for better or ill, will manifest themselves during the lifetime of most readers of this book.

Shaping the Techopia

If we chose to be indifferent and leave these significant geopolitical decisions to the elite, which we have learnt are prone to groupthink, we will pay a high price as a society.

However, if we understand the gravity of the issue before us and chose to engage as a crowd, then great opportunity awaits. Collectively we can be smart or can be foolish. But if we ensure the group is diverse, and the individuals who make it up are taught to support the crowd without automatically complying with it, it can be formidable.

We believe that we have an unprecedented opportunity through technology to join up as that giant human neural network to debate, shape and influence the agendas of the next industrial revolutions.

Part 3

Utopia or Dystopia?

Chapter 14

We need a wise crowd

We need your help! That's to say, 'we all', 'us', 'the human race', need your help.

If the Covid-19 crisis has taught us anything, it is how dangerous complacency can be. There are two further lessons we can draw from the way the disease caught us napping:

- When things develop exponentially, or at the very least accelerate at an accelerating rate, changes can occur at a pace that can take us all by surprise
- The elites, political leaders, business leaders and even the collective intelligence that defines the markets[172] were hopeless at spotting the danger. Yet senior civil servants in governments around the world had been aware of the risk of pandemics for years. They discussed what might happen if an epidemic occurred. They discussed how we should prepare. They even held discussions to consider what we should do with all the dead bodies. Political leaders such as George W Bush[173] and Barack Obama[174] were also aware of the risk and made speeches warning of such. The most famous business person in the world, Bill Gates,[175] famously tried to warn us. Yet when

---

[172] *Which were surely riddled with group think*

[173] *https://www.youtube.com/watch?v=spcj6KUr4aA*

[174] *https://www.youtube.com/watch?v=pBVAnaHxHbM*

[175] *https://www.youtube.com/watch?v=6Af6b_wyiwI*

it happened, with a few exceptions, governments were slow to react.[176]

Yet the changes that technology will bring will dwarf Covid-19 in their impact. The speeds with which they occur will also be extraordinarily fast. If we are complacent this time, the effect will be even more dramatic. We may be lucky, of course, and this impact will take us to one of the more benign scenarios described in the previous section. Do we want to leave it to luck? Do we want just to hope fate will smile upon us?

Instead, we need to take ownership of the debate. In part, that means joining us on social media and moving the discussion along. We urge you to do that. It also means it needs more extensive debate at the local bar, in schools, we need to shine the glare of public attention on this issue.

Once Covid-19 is finally banished, the economy will look very different.

Organisations that dealt best with Covid-19 were those that were able to show agility in adapting new business practices and which adopted digital technologies. The crisis will undoubtedly accelerate the shift towards digital. Post Covid-19, we will probably see an acceleration in the shift towards automation.

History seems to tell us that in the past, while technology often creates more jobs than it destroys, there can be time lags of considerable length. During those time lags, some people experience extreme hardship.

Such times can, under certain circumstances, lead to social unrest; they can sow the seeds of revolution and civil war, which can risk driving us to a global conflict.

---

[176] *In a blog posted dated 3rd February, Michael Baxter wrote: "If new cases were to continue to increase by 30 per cent a day, that means doubling every three days, by the end of March everyone on the planet would have had the condition... It is because of this infection rate that authorities are likely to take extreme measures to try and stop the spread — and it is these extreme measures, however necessary, that pose the greatest economic threat...I fear that dark, populist, forces of the Far Right, playing to a receptive audience, will use this outbreak as a means to promote their dangerous agenda. Share.com, Markets seem invincible but will coronavirus turn them?*

The Covid-19 crisis has exacerbated the issue. We will exit the crisis with sky-high unemployment and massively indebted governments. Households themselves may react to the post-Covid-19 conditions by saving more.

This pandemic conjures up thoughts of the 1930s Great Depression.

The generation which grew up during the Second World War learned how to scrimp and save. An ideology that many of this generation signed up to can be summed up by the words uttered by Polonius in Shakespeare's Hamlet: "Neither a lender nor a borrower be."

Perhaps the post-Covid-19 world will see a return of that ethos.

We may, however, exaggerate the importance of this so-called scrimp and save mentality. The Second World War was followed by a period of falling inequality and the foundation of welfare states across much of the developed world. At the same time, wages increased rapidly. Sure, people were prudent in the way they managed money, but the combination of higher earnings, less inequality and social safety nets is an often-forgotten factor. The post-war world also learned how to optimise the innovations of the Second Industrial Revolution. It was the convergence of finally learning how to build upon the innovations created by the Second Industrial Revolution with the creation of an emerging consumer-led economy that created the strongest run of economic growth ever experienced in the West, lasting for around twenty-three years. [177]

The Second World War also created jobs.

Unfortunately, the Covid-19 crisis will have destroyed them.

Post Covid-19, we have technology creating the opportunity for wealth creation. Yet, still, we have a threat of rising inequality, compounded by yet further wealth redistribution as governments attempt to reboot their economies, and mass unemployment.

The combination of such troublesome financial circumstances with the echo chamber of social media seems to risk popular support for a more authoritarian approach to government, eventually maybe even fascism.

---

[177] *Indeed, one of the reasons why we have seen a surge in household debt in recent years is that the combination of rising inequality, weak growth in wages, but lower interest rates creating high house prices, meant that the economy needed surging household debt in order to grow. This was the system that evolved.*

But this is more likely if we retreat into ourselves, incourage the reversal of globalisation and support causes that demand a less interconnected world.

Be in no doubt. A less interconnected world, one in which we emphasise national identities and rail against diversity will make us poorer. It will probably mean higher interest rates.

Governments, struggling under mountains of debt, no longer able to borrow at near-zero per cent, will have to repay the debt through increasing taxes and imposing many years of austerity.

We made those mistakes after the First World War – The Treaty of Versailles sought to punish Germany, the League of Nations was not given the support it needed, and the Smoot Hawley tariff in 1930 marked an era when the world turned in on itself. And we all know how badly that period ended.

Yet, technology creates the opportunity to fashion a more prosperous and egalitarian world.

Pre-pandemic, PwC projected that by 2030, AI would contribute sixteen (15.7) trillion dollars to the global economy per year.

Other reports suggest that 5G technology could boost the global economy by thirteen point two trillion dollars by 2035. Other fourth industrial revolution technologies such as the Internet of Things will have a similarly massive effect.

This creates an outstanding economic opportunity. After the Second World War, we saw the Marshall Plan, Bretton Woods, institutions such as the UN, and the World Health Organisation, GATT and later the WTO, the precursor of the EU and attempts to create international accords of human rights.

The result was an economic boom, in part driven by mass adoption of technology, more wealth creation than ever seen before, and relative peace.

Yet, history tells us that periods of innovation don't always coincide with periods of enormous wealth.

This danger is exacerbated by technologies that actually offer positive benefits. When autonomous cars have converged with fast internet connectivity (such as 5G) and AI, leading to the end of car ownership, we will be able to fulfil our transport needs for less cost. When the Internet of Things converges with AI (with machine learning used to analyse data) leading to more accurate matching of demand and supply, reducing waste, then perversely output may reduce.

This is not a bad thing per se, but it could be if we don't manage the transition while aware of the dangers.

Inflation, debts and alternative options

The danger is that we see an economy that moves into reverse gear. The opportunity is an economy that can tend to all our basic needs with ease.

Look beyond those basic needs, and move up Maslow's hierarchy of needs, and you find higher needs, relating to love, self-esteem and self-actualisation. We measure those needs relative to others. We are a social species; we need love, friendships, respect, and to feel we are the best we can be. Whether the economic model that has emerged over the last century or so, maybe longer, perhaps you can date it back to when we invented agriculture, satisfies those needs especially well, is a moot point.

If technology innovation can meet all our basic needs, then perhaps the jobs of the future will relate solely to meeting those higher needs.

That means jobs that support social activity, caring, entertainment, creativity and above all play to that very fact that we are a social species.

And while we worry about how governments can repay debt, if we can easily meet all of our basic needs from global resources, maybe we miss the point. Money is just a form of shorthand, just a way of facilitating trade and the exchange of our skills for someone else's. Purists will say money is also a store of value, in truth, even in this respect, it is shorthand. In our materialistic world, our real wealth is in the form of property, tools, inventory and our skill sets[178]. Money is just a way to measure it, and given the tendency for asset bubbles, it doesn't always measure it that well.

If the resources are there to meet our needs, then money is just a human-made construct for enabling it.

Economic theory has a concept called the Irving Fisher Equation. It is not a controversial idea; it is simply undeniably true..

---

[178] Human capital.

The equation says PT=MV. It means that average price times the number of transactions equals the money in circulation times velocity of money (rate at which money changes hands.)

If the sharing economy and internet of things means that velocity of money falls, and transactions are unchanged, then it is possible to increase the money supply without increasing price. This is not a debatable point. It is basic economics.

So, there is a simple solution to the problem of hugely indebted economies.

But those solutions only exist if we have ample spare productivity potential, created by encouraging global collaboration by supporting the free flow of ideas, allow technology learning rates to unwind by creating global marketplaces and by celebrating our diversity.

If we don't do that, we will see a continued rise in inequality, a return of fascism or at least totalitarianism, maybe state surveillance and ultimately civil wars, revolutions and perhaps global conflict.

Shaping our future

What we need is the wisdom of crowds.

As the chapter of collective intelligence demonstrates, as a crowd, we can be remarkably clever and downright self-destructive.

We know that governments, the elites and corporations often fail to spot a crisis emerging until it is too late.

Nothing can match the crowd, that's us all, for insight.

But first, we must get our act together.

Gullibly soaking up fake news, failing to check what we read if it confirms our existing beliefs, and falling victim to groupthink will be beyond disastrous.

And that takes us back to the Dunbar number. If we are designed to live in groups of 150, or 148, as Robin Dunbar says, that then many of the quirks of human nature, our biases, tendency towards prejudice, the way we form opinions and seem unwilling to change them, may support loyalty to the group. Groupthink and group polarisation evidently occurred because it supported the survival of the group. As the palaeontologist, Christopher Stringer said, "there were no iconoclasts" in our hunter-gatherer past.

But one of the more profound changes that technology is creating is that we are beginning to interact with groups that are bigger than 150. The internet is the greatest tool ever invented for enabling interaction among large groups. Other technologies may support our memories, so we are better able to cope cognitively speaking with interaction on a bigger scale.

This is an exciting development indeed but consider the dangers if groupthink is multiplied out across millions of people.

Studies show that highly educated people can be even more subject to bias than the rest of us, because while they are well-read, they typically devote their time to reading material that supports their preconceived ideas.

Other studies show that once we learn about bias, we typically become even more confident we are right, as 'those who disagree with us must be biased'.

Part of the solution to creating wise groups is diversity. Few things are more dangerous than crowds of likeminded people. Social media has magnified this danger many-fold. A crowd that spans international borders and different cultures can be extraordinarily wise. Ask the authors what they would rather have to create new insights, a group of academics all with the same cultural background, or a group of reasonably educated people from across the world, then we would choose the latter.

We have to learn to become somehow independent of groupthink while simultaneously collaborating with others. Maybe creating that ability is the most critical task for education in the fourth and fifth industrial revolution. We have to become comfortable with stepping out of our comfort zone, pushing the boundaries of our understanding and opinion.

Technology can come to our aid too: our AI assistant advising us if we have been subject to fake news, providing timely fact-checked input, challenging us to question the crowd, for example.

Join the debate

Faced with this landscape of challenges and opportunities, do you expect that nothing will change and hope to pick up where you left off in a vague hope that it will be quick and painless? Be aware that, very much like the 2008 crisis, you would be aiding and abetting the Great Wealth Redistribution from the many to the few.

Or do you expect a fundamental rethink?

It is time for us all to join the debate. Our future and that of future generations need us. It is time for us all to understand the issues, decipher truth from fake news, opportunity from threat, ambition from greed, and hope from despair.

Join us on social media, under the name Techopia, follow blogs which pursue similar topics, challenge groupthink, and engage with your family, friends and colleagues.

We all need each other.

Otherwise, living as we do in the age of the jerk, we will experience the very worst of humanity, just at the moment when we could create utopia.

-----------The End-----------

APPENDICES

Timeline of key milestones and sayings in the augmentation of humanity

1832:   Charles Babbage invents the first Computer.

1904:   John Ambrose Fleming invents the vacuum tube.

1936-1938:   Konrad Zuse creates the first electro- mechanical binary programmable computer.

1936:   Alan Turing proposes what has become known as the Turing Machine.

1940:   Alan Turing's Bombe is able to decrypt the enigma code.

1943:   Thomas Watson, president of IBM, states: "I think there is a world market for maybe five computers."

1947:   John Bardeen and Walter Brattain, with support from colleague William Shockley, demonstrate the transistor at Bell Laboratories in Murray Hill, New Jersey.

1949:   Popular Mechanics states: "Where a calculator like ENIAC today is equipped with 18,000 vacuum tubes and weighs thirty tons, computers in the future may have only 1000 vacuum tubes and perhaps weigh only one and a half tons."

1953	James D. Watson and Francis H.C. Crick determine the double-helix structure of DNA.
1959:	Richard Feynman gives a lecture with the title: "There's plenty of room at the bottom." Although Feynman's role in its development may be exaggerated, this is considered by many to be the point when the concept of nanotechnology was first conceived.
1965:	Gordon Moore, who later went on to co- found Intel, states that the number of the number of transistors on a computer chip doubles roughly every two years, and so Moore's Law was defined.
1966:	K.C.Kao & G.A.Hockham publish "Dielectric-fibre surface waveguides for optical frequencies", proposing optical fibre communication
1969:	ARPANET funds the first packet-switched message between two computers marking the beginning of the internet.
1976:	Apple 1 released.
1980:	John Bannister Goodenough invents the cobalt-oxide cathode making the lithium-ion battery that now sits in smart phones and makes electric cars, possible.
1985:	Akira Yoshino, enabled industrial-scale production of the lithium-ion battery, representing the birth of the current lithium- ion battery.
1981:	IBM invents the PC.
1889:	Sir Tim Berners Lee at CERN proposes HTML, the standard that made the World Wide Web possible.
1997:	IBM's Deep Blue defeats Gary Kasparov at chess.
2001:	The human genome is finally sequenced.

2004: Prof Andre Geim and Prof Kostya Novoselo from Manchester University isolate graphene.

2005: Boyden ES, et al. Nat Neurosci publish a paper showing how a protein in a certain type of algae reacts to light. This was a key moment in the development of optogenetics, technology for turning targeted neurons in the brain on and off, with extraordinary applications.

2007: Apple releases the iPhone.

2011: IBM's Watson defeats two Jeopardy champions.

2012: Jennifer Doudna, and Emmanuelle Charpentier from the University of California, Berkeley and Umeå University in Umeå, Sweden, publish a paper showing how CRISPR/Cas 9 is used by bacteria to protect themselves from viruses by editing their own DNA.

2017: Google subsidiary, DeepMind software AlphaGo defeats world's best player at Chinese game of Go, something previously considered impossible for a computer.

The fourth Industrial revolution, some forecasts:

2022: AI is harnessed in the battle against fake news. This will be the start of a ten-year process.

2023: Evidence shows that autonomous cars are marginally safer than cars driven be people.

2024: Highly accurate real time voice translation devices linking earphones via the cloud to AI translation tools become available, meaning that we can talk to anyone on earth. A public debate then ensues – why do we need to learn more than one language if translation tools are so accurate?

2024: Quantum computers begin to emerge as an alternative to conventional computers, accessed via the cloud. Moore's Law for Quantum Computers, Rose's Law applies, meaning that the number of qubits in scalable quantum computing architecture double every six to twelve months.

2025: The cost of renewable energy and energy storage which had been falling for decades reaches a tipping point, when the economic benefits of renewables over fossil fuels becomes overwhelming. But will this be enough to win the war against climate change?

Scientists will say we need to do more. As the evidence for climate change becomes plain for all to see, there will be a backlash against companies and politicians who were seen as denying climate change or who deliberately tried to confuse public understanding.

2027:   Projected date for automated truck drivers.[179]

2030:   Autonomous cars become so much safer than conventional cars that nearly all new cars are exclusively autonomous. The cost of insuring cars driven by humans escalates. Rules are introduced to heavily regulate traditional cars, to protect innocent passengers in autonomous cars from human drivers.

The fifth industrial revolution takes on the baton from the fourth

2031:   The age of the sharing car economy dawns. It will be called TaaS – transport as a service. With this development, the psychology of driving changes. We will no longer see our car as 'our pride and joy' or even an appendage, in which male drivers see their automobile as an extension of their manhood, as a method to attract potential mates, because cars will no longer belong to us. As a consequence, cars will become more functional, and there will be less variety. Since the average car is parked for around ninety-five per cent of the time, the emergence of the TaaS model will mean consumer demand could be met with between five and twenty per cent less cars. This will have a devastating effect on the auto-industry.

2031:   Emerging markets, for several reasons, but primarily because they will not be hampered by technology legacy, unlike in the West, will begin to emerge as the new economic powerhouses.

2031:   CRISPR/cas 9 products become commonly available. The DNA of certain food products will be modified as will the DNA of disease carrying animals such as

---

179   *When Will AI Exceed Human Performance? Evidence from AI Experts Katja Grace John Salvatier Allan Dafoe Baobao Zhang Owain Evans Journal of Artificial Intelligence Research 62 (2018) 729-754*

mosquitos and then in time, human DNA will be modified, at first by treating disease, later to augment us, even to reverse ageing. The resulting ethical implications will be hotly debated.

2032: The fake news battle reaches new heights as augmented reality products whisper into our ear, advising us if information we have just heard or read may in fact be fake, or misleading. Although the intension behind this is well meaning, there will be a massive public backlash and claims of state sponsored indoctrination. Some press, which will fall victim to the fake news apps will be among the more vociferous critics.

2032 – 2040: Augmented reality begins to transform the way we communicate over distance. Green screens become ubiquitous in restaurants, meeting rooms, offices and even in the bedroom, as we communicate, enjoy simulation of face-face interaction, we can work from home or a local office even though it will feel as if we are working with others in an office many miles away, maybe even thousands of miles away. We will eventually be able to make love, or an approximation, at a distance.

2034: Quantum computers are between 1,000 and one million times more powerful than ten- years earlier, depending on whether they double in power every six or twenty-two months.

2035: Neuro computing reaches a level such that technology is finally applied to augment our own cognitive abilities. Interfaces between brains and computers will emerge at around this time, and before the end of this decade, it will be possible to control our brain augmented devices by thought alone.

2035: Climate change will be reaching a level of such threat, that it will be realised that we are reaching a do or die moment, that only global cooperation can save us from ourselves, and only by building carbon capture projects on a massive scale can we stop, and possibly reverse some of the disastrous effects of climate change. Just as technology caused the climate change crisis in the first place, it will be required to come up with a fix. Carbon capture becomes essential.

2035:   Lab grown meat (from stem cells) competitive in price with conventional meat.181

2040:   Conventional meat, a niche product as lab growth meat proves superior, better for the environment and cheaper. See footnote [180]

2044:   Quantum computers between one million and a trillion times more powerful than in 2020

2045:   Revolution in battle against climate change — advances in cultured meat will be such that millions of acres of land currently used for grazing animas will be freed up. Billions of trees will be planted on this land and the option to reverse climate change then becomes viable, but is this breakthrough in time?

2049:   Projected date for AI writing a best seller. See footnote 180

2054:   Projected date for Robot Surgeons. See footnote 180

---

[180] MOVE OVER, IMPOSSIBLE BURGER: LAB-GROWN MEAT WILL OVERTAKE PLANTS BY 2040, Mike Brown, Inverse.com https://www.inverse.com/article/56704-move-over- impossible-burger-lab-grown-meat-will-overtake-plants-by-2040

Biographies

Michael founded Solution PR, which specialised in the computer industry when he was just twenty-four. His next venture, a tech firm, for which he was a founder shareholder, secured a stock market listing. After a spell as an active investor, he founded an investment newsletter, which he exited via a trade sale in 2006. "During this period, I stumbled across the one thing for which I am passionate, writing about tech and the economy," he said. Since then, he has been a technology and investment writer.

"My interest in how technology will change the world began when I was at school," he says. "We had to produce a topic on what the world would be like in ten years. Ever since then, futurology has fascinated me."

Julien is the CEO and co-founder of Galen Growth, the global leader in digital health intelligence, analytics, and matchmaking firm serving Fortune 500 companies and institutional investors.

Julien is a change catalyst and evangelist who challenges the status quo in healthcare with his deep understanding of the world in which healthcare providers and organisations function. His has a passion and knowledge for profound technological innovation to transforming healthcare outcomes.

After a career in the British armed forces, Julien has gained a deep understanding of healthcare in both developed and emerging markets, through over 25 years of working in healthcare. He has extensive international business experience.

References

Academy, Saylor; The Relationship Between Television and Culture, taken from Understanding Media and Culture: An Introduction to Mass Communication, 2012

Adams, Douglas, Hitch Hikers Guide to the Galaxy, Pan Books, 1979, London

Albright Madeleine, Fascism a Warning, 2018, William Collins Books, London

Allen, Bob; Hedrick, James; Coady, Dan; Engler, Amanda; Narayan, Spike; Pitera, Jed; Ninja Polymers: Nanomedicine that can destroy antibiotic-resistant bacteria, IBM, http://www.research.ibm.com/articles/nanomedicine.shtml#fbid= MQ3mKGt4zzb, 7 July 2014

Anders, George; The Innovator's Solution, Fast Company, May 31, 2002, http://www.fastcompany.com/44935/innovators-solution 7 July 2014

Anderson, Chris; Free: How today's smartest businesses profit by giving something for nothing, Random House Business, 6 May 2010

Andreesen, Marc; Why Bitcoin Matters, New York Times, 21 January 2014, http://dealbook.nytimes.com/2014/01/21/whybitcoin-matters/?_php=true&_type=blogs&_r=0

Anthony, Sebastian; The wonderful world of wonder materials, Extreme Tech, 27 August 2013

Apple Museum, Apple History Timeline, 18 December 2013

Armstrong, Doree; Ma, Michelle; Researcher controls colleague's motions in 1st human brain-to-brain interface, University of Washington, August 27 2013

ARPA-E Advanced, Hybrid Planar Lithium/Sulfur Batteries

Asch, Solomon, Studies of independence, and conformity; A minority of one against an unanimous majority, 1956, Psychological Monographs

Asymco; Television History - A Timeline, The University of Texas School of Law Tarlton Law Library 1878-2005 http://www.asymco.com/

Atherton, Kelsey B.; How Robo-Bees Could Save America's Crops, Popular Science, 19 September 2013,

Asian Scientist, Chinese Scientists Sequence Genome Of COVID-19; 25 February 2020 https://www.asianscientist.com/2020/02/topnews/china-coronavirus-covid-19-study/ May 2020

Asimov, Isaac; Foundation's Edge, Grafton Books, 1984, London

Autocar, The future of the car: an Autocar guide, 21 May 2017, Autocar, https://www.autocar.co.uk/car-news/new-cars/future-car-autocar-guide, June 4 2020

Azonano.com., Comprehensive Report on Global Market for Nanoelectromechanical Systems, 24 October 2012

Bacteria in Photos, http://www.bacteriainphotos.com/Alexander_Fleming_and_penicillin.html, May 2020

Bailey, Ronald; Post-Scarcity Prophet Economist Paul Romer on growth, technological change, and an unlimited human future, Reason, December 2001

Bain, Read; Technology and State Government, American Sociological Review Vol. 2, No. 6 (Dec., 1937), pp. 860-874,

Baird, Benjamin; Inspired by Distraction : Mind Wandering Facilitates Creative Incubation, 21 August 2012, Psychological Science, 2012 23: 1117 originally published online 31 August 2012

Bak, Thomas H. Vega-Mendoza, Mariana; Sorace, Antonella; Never too late? An advantage on tests of auditory attention extends to late bilinguals, Psychol., 26 May 2014, https://doi.org/10.3389/fpsyg.2014.00485 24 May 2020

Banks, Iain, M; Culture Series, (10 book collection) Orbit (2018)

Barr, Alistair; Amazon testing delivery by drone, CEO Bezos says, USA Today, 2 December 2013,

Basiliere, Pete, The Future of 3D Printing, Gartner, 26 February 2014

Baxter, Michael, Markets seem invincible, but will Coronavirus turn them?, 3 February 2020, https://www.share.com/stock-markets-and-news/opinion-and-analysis/2020/february/markets-seem-invincible-but-will-coronavirus-turn-them 30 May 2020

Baxter, Michael; AI won't destroy jobs it will transform them. 28 November 2011, Information Age, https://www.information-age.com/ai-wont-destroy-jobs-123476901/ 24 May 2020

Baxter, Michael; Kasparov and AI: the gulf between perception and reality, 25 March 2019, Information Age, https://www.information-age.com/kasparov-and-ai-123481118/ 25 May 2020

Baxter, Michael; The Blindfolded Masochist, Hothive, 2011

Baxter, Michael, Will technology really destroy jobs? Amber Rudd reckons automation is driving the decline of banal, 190 May 2019, Information Age, https://www.information-age.com/technology-destroy-jobs-123481264/ 24 May 2020

Baxter, Michael; The Wind Farm Bias, Investment and Business News, 27 August 2013, http://www.investmentandbusinessnews.co.uk/economicnews/the-wind-farm-bias/5131

Baxter, Michael; Will 2019 see the automation of automation and push up salaries of data scientists? 5 December 2018, Information Age, https://www.information-age.com/will-2019-see-the-automation-of-automation-and-push-up-salaries-of-data-scientists-123477045/ 24 May 2020

Baxter, Michael; New Californian privacy law and GDPR allow anonymous data: but how anonymous can it be?, PrivSec Report, 13th July 2018, https://gdpr.report/news/2018/07/13/new-californian-privacy-law-and-gdpr-allow-anonymous-data-but-how-anonymous-can-it-be/ 25 May 2020

Baxter, Michael, Markets seem invincible, but will Coronavirus turn them?, 3 February 2020, Share.com last accessed 20 May 2020 via https://www.share.com/stock-markets-and-news/opinion-and-analysis/2020/february/markets-seem-invincible-but-will-coronavirus-turn-them

BBA; The way we bank now, https://www.bba.org.uk/landingpage/waywebanknow/

BBC; Millions tune in for Doctor Who 50th anniversary show, http://www.bbc.co.uk/news/entertainment-arts-25076912, 28 December 2014

BBC; The Classroom of the Future: My Teacher is an App, BBC Radio 4, 24 February 2014,
http://www.bbc.co.uk/programmes/b03w02sj

BBC, Rwanda genocide: 100 days of slaughter, 4 April 2019, https://www.bbc.co.uk/news/world-africa-26875506, 25 May 2020

Beinhocker, Eric D; The Origin of Wealth as Corporate Venture Capital, BVCA,

Bellew, Corby Lenn; An SOI Process for Integrated Solar Power, Circuitry, and Actuators for Autonomous Microelectromechnical Systems, University of California, Berkeley, Spring 2002,

Bellis, Mary; Inventors of the Modern Computer ARPAnet - The First Internet. About.com

Bellis, Mary; The Birth of Fibre Optics, about.com,

Benkler, Yochai; Open-source economics, TED,

Benkler, Yochai; The Wealth of Networks How Social Production Transforms Markets and Freedom,

Bennett, Taylor; Does watching violence make you violent? A look at the Bobo doll experiment, 4 February 2019, The Thrive Works, https://thriveworks.com/blog/does-watching-violence-make-you-violent-a-look-at-the-bobo-doll-experiment/ 24 May 2020

Benton, Adam; When did humans leave Africa?, Evoanth, 28 March 2013,

Bergan, Brad; Holy Grail" Microchip Might Surpass the Power of the Human Brain, SEPTEMBER 27TH 2017, Futurism, https://futurism.com/holy-grail-microchip-might-surpass-the-power-of-the-human-brain?utm_source=facebook.com&utm_content=buffer5a246&utm_medium=social&utm_campaign=buffer, June 4 2020

Berger, Michael; An alternative to antibiotics - weakening superbugs' grip; Nanowerk, 20 April 2018, https://www.nanowerk.com/spotlight/spotid=49991.php 9 May 2020

Bessen James; Automation and Jobs: When Technology Boosts Employment; Boston University School of Law, Law and Economics Research Paper Series; 18 March 2017

Best, Shivali; Would you date a robot? More than a quarter of millennials say they would replace a human lover with a DROID, 8 December 2017, Daily Mail, https://www.dailymail.co.uk/sciencetech/article-5156943/27-millennials-say-consider-dating-robot.html 24 May 2020

Biever, Celeste; Free trade may have finished off Neanderthals, New Scientist, 1 April 2005

Biba, Erin, Brain-to-Brain Communication Is Closer Than You Think, June 7 2016, Popular Mechanics, https://www.popularmechanics.com/science/a21220/brain-brain-communication/?src=socialflowFBPOP, June 4 2020

Bloom, Nicholas; Jones, Charles I; Reenen,J ohn Van; Webb, Michael; Are Ideas Getting Harder to Find?; American Economic Review 2020, https://web.stanford.edu/~chadj/IdeaPF.pdf, 9 May 2020

Bloomberg News, China Sacrifices a Province to Save the world from Coronavirus, 5 February 2020, https://www.bloomberg.com/news/articles/2020-02-05/china-sacrifices-a-province-to-save-the-world-from-coronavirus 9 May 2020

Biology Online; Answers to all your Biology Questions, Stem cell, http://www.biology-online.org/dictionary/Stem_cells, 21 January 2014

Bloombergh News, Chinese giant that powers Tesla says it has million-mile electric-car battery ready to launch, June 9, 2020, https://nationalpost.com/news/world/million-mile-electric-car-battery-ready-to-go-says-chinese-manufacturer#:~:text=The%20Chinese%20behemoth%20that%20makes,drivers%20to%20their%20EV%20models, 22 June 2020

BLS: Labor Productivity and Costs; 5 March 2020, https://www.bls.gov/lpc/prodybar.htm; 9 May 2020

Black, Doug; Ignore AI Fear Factor at Your Peril: A Futurist's Call for 'Digital Ethics, November 3, 2018, Enterprise AI,https://www.enterpriseai.news/2018/11/03/ignore-the-ai-fear-factor-at-your-peril-a-futurists-call-for-digital-ethics/ 25 May 2020

Blundon, Jay A; et al; Restoring auditory cortex plasticity in adult mice by restricting thalamic adenosine signaling, Science, 30 Jun 2017, Vol. 356, Issue 6345, pp. 1352-1356.

Boison, Detlev; Adenosine as a neuromodulator in neurological diseases, Current Opinion in Pharmacology, Volume 8, Issue 1, February 2008, Pages 2-7, https://www.sciencedirect.com/science/article/abs/pii/S1471489207001580 23 May 2020

Bond, Rod; Smith, Peter, B: Culture and Conformity, A Meta-Analysis, of Studies Using Asch's., Psychological Bulletin, 1996, by the American Psychological Association, Inc, 1996. Vol 119, No. 1, pp 111-137

Bonsor, Kevin; Fenlon, Wesley How RFID Works, http://electronics.howstuffworks.com/gadgets/high-techgadgets/rfid.htm 19 January 2014

Bostrom, Nick; The future of human evolution, Future of Humanity Institute, Faculty of Philosophy

& James Martin 21st Century School, University of Oxford, 2004

Bostrom, Nick, What happens when our computers get smarter than we are, Ted 2015,

Booth, Robert, Is this the age of the four-day week? The Guardian, 13 March 2019, https://www.theguardian.com/world/2019/mar/13/age-of-four-day-week-workers-productivity?CMP=Share_iOSApp_Other 24 May 2020

Borreli, Lizette; Human Attention Span Shortens To 8 Seconds Due To Digital Technology: 3 Ways To Stay Focused, 124 May 2015, Medical Daily, https://www.medicaldaily.com/human-attention-span-shortens-8-seconds-due-digital-technology-3-ways-stay-focused-333474, 25 May 2020

Bostrom, Nick. "Are We Living in a Computer Simulation?" The Philosophical Quarterly (1950-) 53, no. 211 (2003): 243-55. www.jstor.org/stable/3542867. May 25, 2020.

Brandmeir, Kathrin; Grimm, Michaela; Heise, Michael; Holzhausen, Arne; Allianz Global Wealth Report 2017,

Brewster, Signe; How do you manufacture huge amounts of graphene for a fraction of the cost? Printing presses, Gigaom, http://gigaom.com/2013/09/30/how-do-you-manufacture-hugeamounts-of-graphene-for-a-fraction-of-the-cost-printing-presses/, 26 January 2014

Breedlove, William; Winfield, Idee; Burkett, Tracy; Collaborative Testing, Gender, Learning Styles, and Test Performance, January 2007, Research Gate, https://www.researchgate.net/publication/254734112_Collaborative_Testing_Gender_Learning_Styles_and_Test_Performance/citation/download 25 May

Brin, Page; 2017 Founder's Letter, Alphabet Investor Relations, https://abc.xyz/investor/founders-letters/2017/ 9 May 2020

Brooks, Rodney; Flesh and Machines: How Robots Will Change Us, Vintage; Reprint edition (February 4, 2003),

Brown, Mike; Move over, impossible burger: lab-grown meat will overtake plants by 2040, Inverse.com https://www.inverse.com/article/56704-move-over-impossible-burger-lab-grown-meat-will-overtake-plants-by-2040 25 May 2020

Brouillette, Monique; Biologists would love to program cells as if they were computer chips, February 13 2018, MIT Technology Review, https://www.technologyreview.com/2018/02/13/145643/biologists-would-love-to-program-cells-as-if-they-were-computer-chips/ June 4 2020

Brumfiel, Geoff, The Insane and Exciting Future of the Bionic Body, Smithsonian Magazine, Septmber 2013,

Buckley, Sean; Solar cell that can receive data transmitted through light waves. Engadget, http://www.engadget.com/2014/01/06/wysipsconnect/?ncid=rss_truncated, 30 January 2014

Buller, David J.; Evolution of the Mind: 4 fallacies of evolution, Scientific American, December 2008

Caldwell, Christopher; Groupthink is no match for solo genius, 30 March 2012, The Financial Times

Cann, Oliver; Machines Will Do More Tasks Than Humans by 2025 but Robot Revolution Will Still Create 58 Million Net New Jobs in Next Five Years, 17 September 2018, World Economic Forum, https://www.weforum.org/press/2018/09/machines-will-do-more-tasks-than-humans-by-2025-but-robot-revolution-will-still-create-58-million-net-new-jobs-in-next-five-years/ 24 May 2020

Caramela, Sammi; Working From Home Increases Productivity; Business News Daily; March 31, 2020; https://www.businessnewsdaily.com/15259-working-from-home-more-productive.html 9 May 2020

Carr, Nicholas; The Shallows: What the Internet is Doing to Our Brains, W. W. Norton & Company, 6 June 2011

Casey, Tina; Caution: Wet Solar Power (New Affordable Solar Paint Research), Cleantechnica, 15 May 2013,

Caughill, Patrick; Harvard's Remarkable New Battery Can Run For More Than a Decade, FEBRUARY 13TH 2017, Futurism, https://futurism.com/4-a-new-battery-can-run-for-a-decade, June 4 2020

CBI Insights, In The Clouds: 6 Startups Chasing The Flying Car Dream, June 16 2017, CBI Insights, https://www.cbinsights.com/research/flying-car-startups/?utm_source=CB+Insights+Newsletter&utm_campaign=486536b9f4-TuesNL_02_27_2018&utm_me-

dium=email&utm_term=0_9dc0513989-486536b9f4-90342993
June 4 2020

CBI Insights, Our Meatless Future: How The $1.8T Global Meat Market Gets Disrupted, November 13, 2019; CBI Insights, https://www.cbinsights.com/research/future-of-meat-industrial-farming/ June 4 2020

CERN; The birth of the web, CERN http://home.web.cern.ch/about/birth-web, 18 December 2013

Chapman, Nicholas; International Comparisons of Productivity - Final Estimates: 2014; Office of National Statistics; 18 February 2016, https://www.ons.gov.uk/economy/economicoutputandproductivity/productivitymeasures/bulletins/internationalcomparisonsofproductivityfinalestimates/2014 9 May 2020

Channell, Jason; Jansen, Heath R.; Syme, Alastair R.; Savvantidou, Sofia; Morse, Edward L.; Yuen, Anthony; Energy Darwinism: The Evolution of the Energy Industry, Citi, October 2013,

Chatfield, Tom; / September 23, 2009, Adair Turner addresses Mansion House, Prospect, https://www.prospectmagazine.co.uk/economics-and-finance/adair-turer-addresses-mansion-house, 10th May 2020

Chalmersat, David; How do you explain consciousness, TED2014, https://www.ted.com/talks/david_chalmers_how_do_you_explain_consciousness/transcript?referrer=playlist-what_is_consciousness 30 May 2020

Chozick, Amy; As Young Lose Interest in Cars, G.M. Turns to MTV for Help, New York Times Business Day, 22 March 2012

Christensen, Clayton; Raynor, Michael E.; The Innovator's Solution, Harvard Business School Press; 2003.

Christensen, Clayton; The Innovator's Dilemma: When New Technologies Cause Great Firms to Fail, Harvard Business Review Press, Reprint edition 19 November 2013

Christensen, Clayton M.; Bohmer, Richard; Kenagy, John; Will Disruptive Innovations Cure Health Care?, Harvard Business Review, 2000

Churchill, Winston; Fifty Years Hence, Teaching American History, https://teachingamericanhistory.org/library/document/fifty-years-hence/ 9 May 2020

Clarke, Stephen, Bangham, George; Counting the hours, January 2018, Resolution Foundation, https://www.resolutionfoundation.org/app/uploads/2018/01/Counting-the-hours.pdf 24 May 2020

Clements, Isaac Perry; How Prosthetic Limbs Work, How Stuff Works,

Clinton, Bill; Text of Remarks on the Completion of the First Survey of the Entire Human Genome Project, The White House Office of the Press Secretary, June 26, 2000,

Coeckelbergh, M. Drones, information technology, and distance: mapping the moral epistemology of remote fighting. Ethics Inf Technol 15, 87–98 (2013). https://doi.org/10.1007/s10676-013-9313-6 June 4 2020

Cohen, Jon; Genome editor CRISPR's latest trick? Offering a sharper snapshot of activity inside the cell, February, 15, 2018, Science Magazine, https://www.sciencemag.org/news/2018/02/genome-editor-crispr-s-latest-trick-offering-sharper-snapshot-activity-inside-cell?utm_source=newsfromscience&utm_medium=facebook-text&utm_campaign=crisprcamera-17926 June 4 2020

Cohen, Tyler; The Great Stagnation: How America Ate All The Low Hanging Fruit of Modern History, Got Sick, and Will (Eventually) Feel Better: A Penguin eSpecial from Dutton, 2011

Cook, Carson; A content analysis of LA content analysis of LGBT representation on broadcast and streaming television, Honors Thesis, 28 March 2018, University of Tennessee at Chattanooga

Creighton, Jolene; The "Father of Artificial Intelligence" Says Singularity Is 30 Years Away, February 14 2018, Futurism; https://futurism.com/father-artificial-intelligence-singularity-decades-away, June 4 2020

Cross, Tim; The novelist who inspired Elon Musk, The Economist, https://www.1843magazine.com/culture/the-daily/the-novelist-who-inspired-elon-musk, 23 May 2020

Crucible, 3D printing, http://www.crucibleid.com/3d-printing/

Cuthbertson, Anthony; Scientists develop the first ever low-cost 3D metal,

Danaher, John; Embracing the robot; robot relationships need not be kinky, exploitative or fake. In fact they might give human relationships a helpful boost; AEON, https://aeon.co/essays/programmed-to-love-is-a-human-robot-relationship-wrong, 24 May 2020

Davies, Professor, Mike; Dame, Sally; The Drugs Don't Work: A Global Threat, Penguin, 2013

Davies, James C; Toward A Theory Of Revolution' American Sociological Review

Vol. 27, No. 1 (Feb., 1962), pp. 5-19

Davis, Nicola; Soviet submarine officer who averted nuclear war honoured with prize, 27 October 2017, The Guardian

Dawkins, Richard; The Selfish Gene, Oxford University Press, 1976

DeLong, Brad, Do "They" Really Say: "Technological Progress Is Slowing Down"? Brad DeLong's Grasping Reality, https://www.bradford-delong.com/2017/09/do-they-really-say-technological-progress-is-slowing-down.html 9 May 2020

Diamandis, Peter H; Why the World Is (Still) Better Than You Think—New Evidence For Abundance, October 12 2017, Singularity Hub, https://singularityhub.com/2017/10/12/why-the-world-is-still-better-than-you-think-new-evidence-for-abundance/?utm_content=buffer7788f&utm_medium=social&utm_source=facebook-hub&utm_campaign=buffer#sm.000qwo79toqcf4h10vr1n1xcc1sog June 4 2020

De Grey, Aubrey, We're Closer To Ending Aging Than You Think, Big Think, https://bigthink.com/Charles-Koch-Foundation/raise-independent-children?utm_campaign=Echobox&utm_medium=Social&utm_source=Facebook June 4 2020

Demming, Anna; Nanotechnology takes on microbial drug resistance; Physics World, 14 December 2017, https://physicsworld.com/a/nanotechnology-takes-on-microbial-drug-resistance/ 9 May 2020

Dennet, Dan; From Bacteria to Bach and Back, 2017, Penguin Random House,

Dennet, Dan; TED2003, The illusion of consciousness, https://www.ted.com/talks/dan_dennett_on_our_consciousness/transcript?language=en, verified May 30 2020

Diamond, Jared; Guns, Germs and Steel: A short history of everybody for the last 13,000 years Paperback, Vintage Books, London, 2005

Department of Health, Prime Minister warns of global threat of antibiotic resistance, Department of Health and Prime Minister's Office, 2 July 2014

Domhoff, William; Wealth Income and Power, Who Rules America,

University of California at Santa Cruz,

Dormehl, Luke; EyeMynd is building a virtual reality system you control with your brain, Digital Trends, 22 November 2016

Dorrier, Jason; DNA Origami to Nanomachines: Building Tiny Robots for the Body and Beyond, Singularity Hub,

Dorrier, Jason; Genomic Studies Sift Centenarian DNA for Genes Protecting Against Age-Related Diseases, Singularity Hub, 29 December 2012,

Downes, Larry; Nunes, Paul F.; The Big idea Big-Bang Disruption, Accenture, March 2013,

Drake, Matt; Human beings on brink of achieving IMMORTALITY by year 2050, expert reveals, February 19 2019, Daily Express, https://www.express.co.uk/news/science/920735/Science-news-immortal-live-forever-2050-sex-robots-androids-virtual-reality-technology June 4 2020

Dunbar, Robin; How Many Friends Does One Person Need?: Dunbar's Number and Other Evolutionary Quirks, Faber and Faber, 2011

Dunbar, Robin, Grooming, Gossip, and the evolution of language, Faber and Faber, London, 2004

Dvorak, John C: Ready or Not, You're Getting Microchipped; 9 August 2017, PC Magazine,

Dvorak, Paul; Wind energy blowing life into global carbon fiber industry, Windpower Engineering and Development, 3 July 2013

Dvorsky, George; How We Can Prepare for Catastrophically Dangerous AI—and Why We Can't Wait, 12 May 2018, Gizmodo.com, https://gizmodo.com/how-we-can-prepare-now-for-catastrophically-dangerous-a-1830388719 25 May 2020

Dyble, M., Thorley, J., Page, A.E., Smith, D. & Migliano, A.B. Engagement in agricultural work is associated with reduced leisure time among Agta hunter-gatherers. Nature Human Behaviour, 2019 DOI: 10.1038/s41562-019-0614-6

Edmond, Charlotte; China's lead in the global solar race - at a glance, 18 June 2019, World Economic Forum

Efrati, Amir; In online ads, there's Google and then everyone else, Wall Street Journal, 13 June 2013

Elliot, Larry; Economics: Whatever happened to Keynes' 15-hour working week?, 1 September 2008, The Guardian, https://www.theguardian.com/business/2008/sep/01/economics?CMP=Share_iOSApp_Other 24 May 2020

Erkoreka, Anton; Origins of the Spanish Influenza pandemic (1918–1920) and its relation to the First World War, NCBI, 3 December 2009, https://www.ncbi.nlm.nih.gov/pmc/articles/PMC2805838/ 9 May 2020

Essays, UK. (November 2018). Media Influences Our Beliefs and Attitudes. https://www.ukessays.com/essays/media/media-influences-our-belief-attitudes-media-essay.php?vref=1 June 4 2020

Evans-Pritchard, Ambrose; Solar power will slowly squeeze the revenues of petro-rentier regimes in Russia, Venezuela and Saudi Arabia. They will have to find a new business model, or fade into decline, The Daily Telegraph, 9 April, 2014

Evilyoshida.com; Robert Johnson and the Crossroads Curse http://www.evilyoshida.com/Thread-Robert-Johnson-and-theCrossroads-Curse , 19 January 2014

Fallows, James; The 50 Greatest Breakthroughs Since the Wheel, The Atlantic, 23 October 2013

Fan, Shelly; Here's How to Get to Conscious Machines, Neuroscientists Say, 1 November 2017, Singularity Hub, https://singularityhub.com/2017/11/01/heres-how-to-get-to-conscious-machines-neuroscientists-say/?utm_content=buffer-c9ed7&utm_medium=social&utm_source=facebook-hub&utm_campaign=buffer#sm.001j9e0kf1a3ienkxdy114ejqhkrv 25 May 2020

Fan, Shelly: How BrainNet Enabled 3 People to Directly Transmit Thoughts, 9 October 2018, Singularity Hub, https://singularityhub.com/2018/10/09/how-brainnet-enabled-3-people-to-directly-transmit-thoughts/#sm.0001g46goxqdyf12xpx10q8ttl2rg 25 May 2020 via

Fan, Shelly; We Read This 800-Page Report on the State of Longevity Research So You Don't Have To, February 14 2018, Singularity Hub, https://singularityhub.com/2018/02/14/we-read-this-800-page-report-on-longevity-research-so-you-dont-have-to/#sm .0001yoox1wfo4dpnqog1u4ztm6pu7 June 4 2020

Farrimond, Stuart; The Man Who Could Never Forget, Doctor Stu's Science Blog, 24 October 2010, http://realdoctorstu. com/2010/10/24/the-man-who-could-neverforget/

Federal Reserve Bank of St Louis, Real Median Household Income in the United States, Sep 10, 2019, https://fred.stlouisfed.org/series/ MEHOINUSA672N, 20 May 2020

Feenstra, Robert C; Inklaar, Robert; Timmer, Marcel P; The Next Generation of the Penn World Table, American Economic Review 2015, 105(10): 3150–3182, https://www.rug.nl/ggdc/docs/the_next_ generation_of_the_penn_world_table.pdf May 24 2020

Fehrenbacher, Katie; How battery improvements will revolutionize the design of the electric car, Gigaom, 2 February 2014,

Feloni, Richard; Why Mark Zuckerberg is reading 'Orwell's Revenge,' an unofficial sequel to '1984', April 29, 2015, Business Insider, https://www.businessinsider.com/mark-zuckerberg-book-club-orwells-revenge-2015-4?r=US&IR=T, 24 May 2020

Ferguson, Kirby; Rise of the Patent Troll, Everything is a Remix, 8 April 2014, http://everythingisaremix.info/ June 4 2020

Ferguson, Niall; The Ascent of Money: A financial history of the world, Penguin, New York, 2008

Field, C.B.; Barros, V.R.; Dokken, D.J.; Mach, K.J.; Mastrandrea, M.D.; Bilir, T.E.; Chatterje, M.; Ebi, K.L.; Estrada, Y.O., Genova, R.C.; Girma, B.; Kissel, E.S.; Levy, A.N.; MacCracken, P.R.; Mastrandrea and White, L.L. (eds); Climate Change 2014: Impacts, Adaptation, and Vulnerability Summary for Policymakers, IPCC, Cambridge University Press, 12 April 2014,

Fiol, Taryn; Why 83 per cent of Millennials sleep with their phones, Apartment Therapy, http://www.apartmenttherapy.com/do-yousleep-with-your-cell-ph-127903, 18 December 2013, https://thenextweb. com/evergreen/2017/10/01/heres-quantum-computing-matters/, 4 June 2020

Floud, Roderick; Johnson, Paul; The Cambridge Economic History of Modern Britain: Volume 1, May 2018, Cambridge University Press, Cambridge

Forsyth, Donelson R.; Group Dynamics, Wadsworth, Cengage Learning, 2009 http://www.cengagebrain.com/shop/content/forsyth99522_04955

99522_01.01_toc.pdf, 27 May 2011

Fox, Justin; The Real Story Behind Those "Record" Corporate Profits, Harvard Business Review, 24 November 2010,

Frey, Carl Benedikt; Osborne, Michael A.; The future of employment: how susceptible are jobs to computerisation? University of Oxford, 17 September 2013,

Friedman, Janice; Difference Between Short-Term, Long-Term, and Working Memory, Examined Existence. https://examinedexistence.com/difference-between-short-term-long-term-and-working-memory/ 23 May 2020

Futurism Creative, Ray Kurzweil Predicts the Exact Year Singularity Will Occur, October 18 2017, https://futurism.com/videos/ray-kurzweil-predicts-the-exact-year-singularity-will-occur?utm_source=facebook.com&utm_content=buffere9985&utm_medium=social&utm_campaign=buffer June 4 2020

Futurism, Light-Based Laptops Can Run A Staggering 20 Times Faster, February 17th 2017, https://futurism.com/light-based-laptops-can-run-staggering-20-times-faster June 4 2020

Galeon, Dom; THE U.S. FDA just approved a treatment that reprograms cells to fight cancer, August 31 2017, Futurism, https://futurism.com/neoscope/the-u-s-fda-just-approved-a-treatment-that-reprograms-cells-to-fight-cancer?utm_medium=social&utm_content=bufferad4c0&utm_source=facebook.com&utm_campaign=buffer June 4 2020

Gallego, Jelor; First-Of-Its-Kind Farm Uses Seawater and Solar Power to Grow Crops, October 10 2016, Futurism, https://futurism.com/first-of-its-kind-farm-uses-seawater-and-solar-power-to-grow-crops, 4 June 2020

Gent, Ed; Hyperloop and Flying Cars Are Battling It Out for the Future of Transportation, March 5 2020, https://singularityhub.com/2018/03/05/hyperloop-and-flying-cars-are-battling-it-out-for-the-future-of-transportation/?utm_content=bufferb3ac7&utm_medium=social&utm_source=facebook-hub&utm_campaign=buffer#sm.018tx97w1dvkegg10gv2fdgy3r562 June 4 2020

Graeber, David; Bullshit Jobs: A Theory, 15 May 2018, Allen Lane, London,

Greene, Tristan; Here's why 100 qubit quantum computers could change everything, February 6 2018, The Next Web, https://thenextweb.com/artificial-intelligence/2018/02/06/heres-why-100-qubit-quantum-computers-could-change-everything/, June 4 2020

Greene, Tristan; Here's what quantum computing is and why it matters, October 1 2017, The Next Web,

Galeon, Dom; Graphene Computers Work 1000 Times Faster, Use Far Less Power; 15th August 2017, https://futurism.com/graphene-computers-work-1000-times-faster-use-far-less-power 9 May 2020

Galeon, Dom; A synthetic microbe could be the next antibiotic; March 9 2018, Futurism, https://futurism.com/neoscope/synthetic-microbe-next-antibiotic June 4 2020

Garfield, Leanna, A Giant US Retail Corporation Just Filed a Patent For Autonomous Robot Bees, Science Alert, https://www.sciencealert.com/walmart-has-filed-a-patent-for-robot-bees-pollination-drones?utm_source=Facebook&utm_medium=Branded+Content&utm_campaign=ScienceNaturePageSign June 4 2020

Gartner; Gartner Hype Cycle, https://www.gartner.com/en/research/methodologies/gartner-hype-cycle, 9 May 2020

Gent, Ed; New Photonic Synapses Mimic the Brain and Compute With Light, October 4 2017, Singularity Hub, https://singularityhub.com/2017/10/04/these-new-photonic-synapses-mimic-the-brain-and-compute-with-light/?utm_content=bufferfe5ae&utm_medium=social&utm_source=facebook-hub&utm_campaign=buffer#sm.0000yuh05z6lwexpqtx1k97h5220r June 4 2020

Gershgorn, Dave; Researchers are using Darwin's theories to evolve AI, so only the strongest algorithms survive March 20, 2017, QZ.com

Gibney, Elizabeth; The super materials that could trump graphene, 17 June 2015, Nature, https://www.nature.com/news/the-super-materials-that-could-trump-graphene-1.17775 June 4 2020

Giles, Chris; Piketty findings undercut by errors, The Financial Times, 23 May 2014

Gladwell, Malcom, Outliers, Penguin Books, London, 2008

Glaser, April; Wagner, Kurt; Facebook is developing a way to read your mind, Recode, April 19, 2017, https:// www.recode.net/platform/

amp/2017/4/19/15361568/facebook-mark-zuckerberg-brain-mind-reader-regina-dugan-building-f8 23 May 2020

Gohd, Chelsea; Hundreds of 2D Materials Could be the Next Graphene, February 16 2018, Futurism, https://futurism.com/hundreds-2d-materials-next-graphene June 4 2020

Going Global, The Worldwide fanbase of the Premier League, https://no.unibet.com/hub/goingglobal/en, 24 May 2020

Golding, William, Lord of the Flies, 1954 & Faber & Faber Ltd, London,

Goodwin, Phil; Peak Car' Where did the idea come from? And where is it going?, Centre for Transport and Society and The University of the West of England (UWE), CTS Winter Conference 2012

Goodwin, Phil; Peak Travel, Peak Car and the Future of Mobility Evidence, Unresolved Issues, Policy Implications, and a Research Agenda, OECD, October 2012

Goodwin, Phil; What about 'peak car' – heresy or revelation?, TransportXtra, 25 June 2010,

Gordon, Robert J; Is US economic growth over? Faltering innovation confronts the six headwinds, Centre for Economic Policy Research, September 2012

Gould, Stephen.J; Punctuated Equilibrium, Harvard University Press, 2007

Grace, Katja; et al, When Will AI Exceed Human Performance? Journal of Artificial Intelligence Research 62 (2018) 729-754, https://www.inverse.com/article/56704-move-over-impossible-burger-lab-grown-meat-will-overtake-plants-by-2040 30 May 2020

Gray, Richard; Stem cell study raises hopes that organs could be regenerated inside patients' own bodies, Telegraph

Greenemeier, Larry; Scientists use 3-D printer to speed human embryonic stem cell research, Nature, 5 February 2013,

Griffiths, Sarah; Revising for an exam? DON'T use a laptop: Taking notes with pen and paper boosts memory and our ability to understand, , Daily Mail, 5 February 2015

Griffin, Matthew; Computing Quantum computing Rose's Law is Moore's Law on steroids, 31st August 2016, Fanatical Futurist, https://www.fanaticalfuturist.com/2016/08/quantum-computing-roses-law-is-moores-law-on-steroids/, 9th May 2020

Kristen; Social networking sites and our lives, Pew Research Internet Project, 16 June 2011,

Hamzelou, Jessica; Brain implant boosts human memory by mimicking how we learn, New Scientist, 13 November 2017; https://www.newscientist.com/article/2153034-brain-implant-boosts-human-memory-by-mimicking-how-we-learn/#ixzz6NGEQbOFZ 23rd May 2020

Hanauer, Nick; The Pitchforks Are Coming… For Us Plutocrats, July/August 2014, Politico Magazine, https://www.politico.com/magazine/story/2014/06/the-pitchforks-are-coming-for-us-plutocrats-108014 24 May 2020

Hanappi, Gerhard; From Integrated Capitalism to Disintegrating Capitalism. Scenarios of a Third World War, 2019, MPRA, https://mpra.ub.uni-muenchen.de/91397/ 25 May 2020

Harris, Bernard; Health, Height, and History: An Overview of Recent Developments in Anthropometric History, Social History of Medicine, Volume 7, Issue 2, August 1994, Pages 297–320

Harvey, Matt; Let's evolve a neural network with a genetic algorithm—code included, Coastline Automation, 7 April 2017, https://blog.coast.ai/lets-evolve-a-neural-network-with-a-genetic-algorithm-code-included-8809bece164, 9 May 2020

Hazari, Arnab; Trending Latest Sections search icon menu icon. 18th February 2017, Science Alert, https://www.sciencealert.com/light-based-laptops-will-run-at-least-20-times-faster-than-yours, 9th May 2020

Heap, Imogen; Blockchain Could Help Musicians Make Money Again, June 05, 2017, Harvard Business Review, https://hbr.org/2017/06/blockchain-could-help-musicians-make-money-again 4 June 2020

Hermanussen, Michael; Stature of early Europeans; www.hormones.gr, 2003, http://www.hormones.gr/pdf/Stature_europeans.pdf, 9 May 2020;

Heyworth, Robin; Mesoamerican wheeled toys, 9 May 2014, Uncovered History, https://uncoveredhistory.com/mesoamerica/wheeled-toys/ 30 May 2020

Hicks, Michael J; The Myth and the Reality of Manufacturing in America, June 2015, CBER Data Center Projects https://conexus. cberdata.org/files/MfgReality.pdf, 24 May 2020

Houser, Kristin; We Have No Idea What Having Sex With Robots Might Do to Us, June 5 2018, https://futurism.com/sex-robots-health 24 May 2020

Houser, Kristin; See the translation tech lawmakers say "threatens democracy" in action, November 15 2015, Futurism https://futurism. com/the-byte/deepfakes-translation-tech-synthesia 24 May 2020

Humphrey, Louise and Stringer, Chris; Our Human Story; Natural History Museum; First edition (16 Feb. 2018)

Hyperphysics, Laser Applications, http://hyperphysics.phyastr. gsu.edu/hbase/optmod/lasapp.html, 19 January 2014

Illinois Oil and Gas Association; History of Illinois Basin Posted Crude Oil Prices, July 2013, http://www.ioga.com/Special/ crudeoil_Hist.htm

IMF; Global Financial Stability Report, April 2006: Chapter II. The Influence of Credit Derivative and Structured Credit Markets on Financial Stability ,

In correct pleasures; Luria's "S" the synaesthete wasn't face-blind, 10 September 2011, http://incorrectpleasures.blogspot.com/2011/09/ lurias-s-synaesthete-wasnt-face-blind.html 30 May 2020

Istvan, Zoltan; Quantum Archaeology: The Quest to 3D-Bioprint Every Dead Person Back to Life, 3 September 2019, Newsweek, https:// www.newsweek.com/quantum-archaeology-quest-3d-bioprint-every- dead-person-back-life-837967 24 May 2020

IRENA, Renewable Power Generation Costs in 2018, IRENA 2019, https://www.irena.org/-/media/Files/IRENA/Agency/ Publication/2019/May/IRENA_Renewable-Power-Generations- Costs-in-2018.pdf 24 May 2020

JLab, How fast do electrons move? JLab, https://education.jlab. org/qa/electron_01.html, 9th May 2020

Jiang, Linxing, Preston; et al; BrainNet: A Multi-Person Brain- to-Brain Interface for Direct Collaboration Between Brains, Cornell University, 22 May 2019,

Janis, I. L.; Victims of groupthink: A psychological study of foreign policy decisions and fiascos, Houghton Mifflin Company Boston, 1972

Johnston, Chris; Biological warfare flares up again between EO Wilson and Richard Dawkins, 7 November 2014, The Guardian, https://www.theguardian.com/science/2014/nov/07/richard-dawkins-labelled-journalist-by-eo-wilson 24 May 2020

Johnson, Bobbie; Privacy no longer a social norm, says Facebook founder, 11 January 2010, The Guardian

Johnson, Steve; Capital gobbles labour's share, but victory is empty, The Financial Times, 13 October 2013

Johnson, Steve, Emergence, Penguin Books, London, 2001,

Johnson, Steven; Where Good ideas come from, Allen Lane, London, 2010

Jones, Tim; The next evolution in personhood, July 11 2017, American Thinker, https://www.americanthinker.com/blog/2017/07/the_next_evolution_in_personhood.html, 24 May 2020

Kadosh, Roi Cohen; et al; Modulating Neuronal Activity Produces Specific and Long-Lasting Changes in Numerical Competence, Current Biology, Volume 20, issue 22, p2016-2020, November 23, 2010, https://www.cell.com/current-biology/fulltext/S0960-9822%2810%2901234-0?switch=standard 23 May 2020

Kahneman, Daniel; Slovic, Paul; Tversky, Amos; Judgment under uncertainty: heuristics and biases, Cambridge University Press, Cambridge, 1982

Kahney, Leander; John Sculley On Steve Jobs, The Full Interview Transcript, Cult of the Mac,
http://www.cultofmac.com/63295/john-sculley-on-steve-jobs-thefull-interview-transcript/#miq7cArzCXBXIeiB.99, 18 December 2013

Kaplan, Marty; Scientists' depressing new discovery about the brain, Alternet, Salon, 17 September 2013,
http://www.salon.com/2013/09/17/the_most_depressing_discovery_about_the_brain_ever_partner/

Kapur, Arnav; Kapur, Shreyas; Maes, Pattie; A Personalized Wearable Silent Speech Interface, MIT, IUI 2018, March 7–11, 2018, Tokyo, Japan, https://dam-prod.media.mit.edu/x/2018/03/23/p43-kapur_BRjFwE6.pdf, 23 May 2020

Kay, Alan; Wikiquote, http://en.wikiquote.org/wiki/Alan_Kay

Kealey, Terence; Sex, Science and Profits, William Heinemann: London, 2008

Keeley, Larry: The Greatest Innovations of All Time, Business Week, 16 February 2007

Kelly, Gavin; The robots are coming. Will they bring wealth or a divided society?, The Observer, 4 January 2014, http://www.theguardian.com/technology/2014/jan/04/robotsfuture-society-drones

Keohane, David; Ahhhh! No robots! Financial Times Alphaville http://ftalphaville.ft.com//2012/08/28/1134571/ahhhh-norobots/, 18 December 2013

Keynes, John Maynard; Economic Possibilities for our Grandchildren (circa 1930) Aspenin Institute, http://www.aspeninstitute.org/sites/default/files/content/upload/ Intro_Session1.pdf, 2 January 2014

Khosla, Vinod; Do We Need Doctors Or Algorithms?, TechCrunch 10 January 2012,

Khosla, Vinod; Technology will replace 80% of what doctors do, Fortune Magazine, 4 December 2012, http://tech.fortune.cnn.com/2012/12/04/technology-doctorskhosla/

Kioskea.net; WPAN (Wireless Personal Area Network), 2014, http://en.kioskea.net/contents/834-wpan-wireless-personal-areanetwork, 19 January 2014

King, Stephen D, Grave new World, 2017, Yale University Press, new Haven and London

Knapton, Sarah; Rise of the 'digisexual' as virtual reality bypasses need for human intimacy, 26 November 2017, https://www.telegraph.co.uk/science/2017/11/26/rise-digisexual-virtual-reality-bypasses-need-human-intimacy/ 4 May 2020

Kohler, Timothy; et al; Greater Post-Neolithic Wealth Disparities in Eurasia than in North and Mesoamerica; Nature, 30 November 2017,

Kramer, Adam D. I; Guillory, Jamie E.; and Hancock Jeffrey T; Experimental evidence of massive-scale emotional contagion through social networks, PNAS June 17, 2014 111 (24) 8788-8790; first published June 2, 2014 https://doi.org/10.1073/pnas.1320040111, 25 May 2020

Kruger, J.; Lake Wobegon be gone! The "below-average effect" and the egocentric nature of comparative ability judgments, Journal of Pers Soc Psychology, 7 August 1999,

Kurzweil, Ray; The Law of Accelerating Returns, Kurzweil Accelerated Intelligence, Ted 2 January 2014 http://www.kurzweilai.net/the-law-ofaccelerating-returns, 30 May 2020

Kurzweil, Ray; Get ready for hybrid thinking, Tedhttps://www.ted.com/talks/ray_kurzweil_get_ready_for_hybrid_thinking/transcript

Lambert, Fred; Electric vehicle battery cost dropped 80% in 6 years down to $227/kWh – Tesla claims to be below $190/kWh, electrek, 30th January 2017, https://electrek.co/2017/01/30/electric-vehicle-battery-cost-dropped-80-6-years-227kwh-tesla-190kwh/ 9 May 2020

H Lamm, H; Myers, D; Group-Induced Polarization of Attitudes and Behavior, Advances in Experimental Social Psychology, Volume 11, 1978, Pages 145-195

Lane, Nick, The Vital Question, Profile Books, Ltd, London, 2015

Lant, Karla; DARPA Is Planning to Hack the Human Brain to Let Us "Upload" Skills, May 2 2017, Futurism, https://futurism.com/darpa-is-planning-to-hack-the-human-brain-to-let-us-upload-skills 4 June 2020

Lant, Karla; Blockchain Will Upend Society's Most Sacred Institutions. Here's How, JUNE 1ST 2017, Futurism, https://futurism.com/blockchain-will-upend-societys-most-sacred-institutions-heres-how 4 June 2020

Lant, Karla, New "Instantly Rechargeable" Battery Deals a Fatal Blow to Fossil Fuels, June 6TH 2017, Futurism, https://futurism.com/new-instantly-rechargeable-battery-deals-a-fatal-blow-to-fossil-fuels, 4 June 2020

Lapore, Jill; The Disruption Machine, The New Yorker, http://www.newyorker.com/magazine/2014/06/23/thedisruption-machine?currentPage=all/, 23 June 2014

Leakey, Richard, The Origin of Humankind, Phoenix, London, 1994

Lee, Dave; Facebook team working on brain-powered technology, 19 April 2020, BBC, https://www.bbc.co.uk/news/technology-39648788 25 May 2020

Leibson, Steven; Racing to the End of Moore's Law: The New World Semiconductor Order, 21 November 2018, Electronic Engineering Journal,

Lim, Diana H et al; Optogenetic approaches for functional mouse brain mapping. PubMed, April 2013, https://www.ncbi.nlm.nih.gov/pubmed/23596383, 9 May 2020

London 2012 Olympic Games Global Broadcast Report, December 2012, https://stillmed.olympic.org/Documents/IOC_Marketing/Broadcasting/London_2012_Global_%20Broadcast_Report.pdf 24 May 2020

Love, Shayla; The Radical Plan to Save the Planet by Working Less, 29 May 2019, vice.com, https://www.vice.com/amp/en_us/article/bj9yjq/the-radical-plan-to-save-the-planet-by-working-less?fbclid=IwAR0oriKJMpgQX5Y4kpMAmRi5c-_WY28dystLoO8if8ld2W5QSHA7THqqj5A 24 May 2020

Love, Shayla; Transferring Your Consciousness Into This Terrifying Robot Head Might Make You Less Scared Of Dying, 30 January 2018, Vice.com, https://www.vice.com/en_us/article/gywak7/the-vr-experience-that-might-make-you-less-afraid-to-die?utm_campaign=sharebutton 24 May 2020

Lovelock, James: Gaia: Oxford University Press, Oxford, 1979

Mackay, Charles; Extraordinary Popular Delusions and the Madness of Crowds, first published in 1841, Harriman House republished September 2003

Maddison, Angus; Contours of the World Economy 1-2040 AD, Oxford University Press, 2007

Main, E. C., & Walker, T. G. (1973). Choice shifts and extreme behavior: Judicial review in the federal courts. The Journal of Social Psychology, 91(2), 215–221. https://doi.org/10.1080/00224545.1973.9923044 25 May 2020

Malthus, Thomas; An Essay on the Principle of Population, Printed for J. Johnson, in St. Paul's Church-Yard, London, 1798

Manyika, James; Chui, Michael; Bughin, Jacques; Dobbs, Richard; Bisson, Peter; Marrs, Alex; Advances that will transform life, business, and the global economy, McKinsey Global Institute Disruptive Technologies, May 2013

Manyika, James; Chui, Michael; Bisson, Peter; Woetzel, Jonathan; Dobbs, Richard; Bughin, Jacques; Aharon, Dan; The Internet of Things, Mapping the value beyond the hype; McKinsey, June 2015

Martin, James; The Meaning of the 21st Century: A vital blueprint for ensuring our future, Transworld Publishers, London 2006

Marx, Karl; Selected Writings Paperback – 3 Aug. 2000, Edited by David McLellan, Oxford University Press, Oxford,

Massachusetts Institute of Technology. "Artificial intelligence yields new antibiotic: A deep-learning model identifies a powerful new drug that can kill many species of antibiotic-resistant bacteria." ScienceDaily. www.sciencedaily.com/releases/2020/02/200220141748.htm May 25, 2020

Massachusetts Institute of Technology. "Artificial intelligence yields new antibiotic: A deep-learning model identifies a powerful new drug that can kill many species of antibiotic-resistant bacteria." ScienceDaily. www.sciencedaily.com/releases/2020/02/200220141748.htm May 25, 2020

Massachusetts Institute of Technology; Antibiotic nanoparticles fight drug-resistant bacteria; Science Daily, 13 July 2017, https://www.sciencedaily.com/releases/2017/07/170713081552.htm; 9 May 2020

Maybin, Simon; Busting the attention span myth, More or Less, BBC World Service, 10 March 2017, https://www.bbc.co.uk/news/health-38896790, 23 May 2020

McCrone, John; The Ape that Spoke: Language and the Evolution of the Human Mind, Picador, 1990, ISBN-10: 068810326X

Mearian, Lucas, AI found better than doctors at diagnosing, treating patients, Computer World, 12 February 2013 http://www.computerworld.com/s/article/9236737/AI_found_bet ter_than_doctors_at_diagnosing_treating_patients 12 May 2014

Meek, Andy; Survey: Americans now check their smartphones a whopping 52 times a day, November 13 2018, BGR, https://bgr.com/2018/11/13/smartphone-addiction-survey-data/?smid=nytcore-ios-share, 24 May 2020

Mehen, Lori; Is the future of Pharma open source? Opensource.com,

Merchant Savvy; Global Remote Working Data & Statistics; https://www.merchantsavvy.co.uk/remote-working-statistics/; 9 May 2020

Microsoft Attention Spans Research Report, Uploaded by Southern California Public Radio, https://www.scribd.com/document/265348695/Microsoft-Attention-Spans-Research-Report, 23 May 2020

Miller, George A; The Magical Number Seven, Plus or Minus Two: Some Limits on our Capacity for Processing Information, Classics in the History of Psychology, 1956, http://psychclassics.yorku.ca/Miller/ 23 May 2020

Mims, Christopher; 3D printing will explode in 2014, thanks to the expiration of key patents, Quartz, http://qz.com/106483/3dprinting-will-explode-in-2014-thanks-to-the-expiration-of-keypatents/, 21 January 2014

Mims, Christopher; Google engineers insist 20% time is not dead – it's just turned into 120% time, Quartz, 16 August 2013, http://qz.com/116196/google-engineers-insist-20-time- is-notdead-its-just-turned-into-120-time/

Mims, Christopher, How Facebook's Telepathic Texting Is Supposed to Work, June 11 2017, Wall Street Journal, https://www.wsj.com/articles/how-facebooks-telepathic-texting-is-supposed-to-work-1497182402 4 June 2020

Mlodinow, Leonard; The Drunkard's Walk, Pantheon, 2008

Morris, Ian; Why the West rules for now, Profile Books 2010

Moscovici, S.; Zavalloni, M.; The group as a polarizer of attitudes, 1969

Journal of Personality and Social Psychology, 12, pp. 125-135,1969

Muir, William; Wilson, David Sloan; When the Strong Outbreed the Weak: An Interview with William Muir, 11 July 2016, The Evolution Institute, https://evolution-institute.org/when-the-strong-outbreed-the-weak-an-interview-with-william-muir/ 25 May 2020

Mullin, Emily; Five Ways to Get CRISPR into the Body, September 22, 2017, https://www.technologyreview.com/2017/09/22/149011/five-ways-to-get-crispr-into-the-body/ June 4 2020

Murphy, B,J; In a Future of Mind Uploading, Who Will Own the Data That is You? 29 July 2018, grayscott.com, https://www.grayscott.com/seriouswonder-//in-a-future-of-mind-uploading-who-will-own-the-data-that-is-you 25 May 2020

McKie, Robin; Could ants be the solution to antibiotic crisis? The Guardian, 24 September 2016,

Naam, Ramez; Smaller, cheaper, faster: Does Moore's Law apply to solar cells?, Scientific American, 16 March 2011,

Naam, Ramaz: How to decarbonize America — and the world; A roadmap for a viable Green New Deal, TechCrunch, 15 February

15, 2019; https://techcrunch.com/2019/02/15/how-to-decarbonize-america-and-the-world/ 9 May 2020

Naam, Ramaz: How Cheap Can Energy Storage Get? Pretty Darn Cheap, https://rameznaam.com/2015/10/14/how-cheap-can-energy-storage-get/, 10th May 2020

Nair, Ajay; Billion people watch as Jessie J wins Chinese TV talent show, Sky News, 18 April 2008, https://news.sky.com/story/singer-jessie-j-wins-chinas-version-of-the-x-factor-in-bid-to-break-boundaries-11335489 24 May 2020

Nano Magazine; New Molecule Can Kill Five Types of Deadly Drug-Resistant Superbugs; 5 March 2018, https://nano-magazine.com/news/2018/3/5/new-molecule-can-kill-five-types-of-deadly-drug-resistant-superbugs; 9 May 2020

Nevett, Joshua; Sick sex robot fantasy BANNED from world's first cyborg brothel, 8 October 2017, Daily Star, https://www.dailystar.co.uk/news/latest-news/sex-robot-brothel-barcelona-lumidolls-17033673 24 May 2020

Neurogram, https://blog.otoro.net/2015/07/31/neurogram/ 25 May 2020

Noonan, David; Meet the Two Scientists Who Implanted a False Memory Into a Mouse, Smithsonian Magazine, November 2014

Ogburn, William, F; and Thomas, Dorothy; Are inventions inevitable? Political Science Quarterly, Vol. 37, No. 1 Mar, 1922 pp 83098

Oldstone, Michael B.A; Viruses, Plagues, and History: Past, Present and Future Paperback; Oxford University Press, Oxford, 2010

Ophir, E., Nass, C., & Wagner, A. (2009). Cognitive control in media multi-taskers. Proceedings of the National Academy of Sciences, 106(37), 15583–15587.

Ophir, E., Nass; Wagner, A. Cognitive control in media multi-taskers. Proceedings of the National Academy of Sciences, 2009, 106(37), 15583–15587.

Page, Scott, E; The Difference: How the Power of Diversity Creates Better Groups, Firms, Schools, and Societies; 2007, Princetown Press, New Jersey,

Pardes, Rielle; Amazon Imagines a Future of Infinite Computing Power, 6 July 2017, Wired, https://www.wired.com/2017/06/amazon-imagines-future-infinite-computing-power/?utm_

content=bufferce644&utm_medium=social&utm_source=twitter.
com&utm_campaign=buffer June 4 2020

Schor, Juliet B; Pre-industrial workers had a shorter workweek than today's, extract from The Overworked American: The Unexpected Decline of Leisure, Basic Books; Reprint edition (24 Mar. 1993), New York, http://groups.csail.mit.edu/mac/users/rauch/worktime/hours_workweek.html 24 May 2020

Parker, Ceri, Artificial intelligence could be our saviour, according to the CEO of Google, 24 January 2018, World Economic Forum, https://www.weforum.org/agenda/2018/01/google-ceo-ai-will-be-bigger-than-electricity-or-fire/?utm_content=buffer100f7&utm_medium=social&utm_source=plus.google.com&utm_campaign=buffer, June 4 2020

Pariser, Eli.; The Filter Bubble: What the Internet Is Hiding from You, Penguin Press HC, 12 May 2011

PARLOFF, ROGER; From 2016: Why Deep Learning Is Suddenly Changing Your Life, Fortune, 28 September 2016, https://fortune.com/longform/ai-artificial-intelligence-deep-machine-learning/, 9 May 2020

Paxton, Robert O; The Anatomy of Fascism, 24 Feb 2005, Penguin Books, London

Pandurangan, Vijay; On Taxis and Rainbows; 21 July 2014, Vijay Pandurangan, https://tech.vijayp.ca/of-taxis-and-rainbows-f6bc289679a1 25 May 2020

Phelps, Edmund S.; What has gone wrong up until now, Spiegel Online International, 12 November 2008,

Piketty, Thomas; Capital in the 21st Century, The Belknap Press of Harvard University Press, 2014

Pinker, Steven; The Better Angels of Our Nature: A History of Violence and Humanity Paperback, 2011, Penguin Books, London

Pinker, Steve; The Enlightenment Is Working, Wall Street Journal, Feb. 9, 2018,

Popper, Karl, The Open Society and Its Enemies, volume 1, The Spell of Plato, 1945 (Routledge, United Kingdom); ISBN 0-415-29063-5 978-0-691-15813-6 (1 volume 2013 Princeton ed.)

Press Association, UK wages worth up to a third less than in 2008, study shows, The Guardian, , 31 Jan 2019, https://www.theguardian.

com/business/2018/dec/14/average-uk-worker-earn-third-less-than-2008-tuc-real-wage-report 25 May 2020

Prior, Ed; Do Man Utd really have 659m supporters? 18 May 2013, https://www.bbc.co.uk/news/magazine-21478857 24 May 2020

Public Health England, Beyond the data: Understanding the impact of COVID-19 on BAME groups, 16 June 2020, www.gov.uk

PWC: AI to drive GDP gains of $15.7 trillion with productivity, personalisation improvements, 27 June 2019; https://www.pwc.com/gx/en/news-room/press-releases/2017/ai-to-drive-gdp-gains-of-15_7-trillion-with-productivity-personalisation-improvements.html 9 May 2020

Radowitz, Jon von; Forster, Katie; Stem cells in brain located by scientists could help reverse ageing process, 26 July 2017, The Independent, 4 June 2020

Rajan, Raghuram, G; Fault lines, Princetown University Press, Woodstock, 2007

Raison, Vince; What A World Without Borders Might Look Like, 21 August 2018, Huffington Post, https://www.huffingtonpost.co.uk/entry/what-a-world-without-borders-might-look-like_uk_5b713c30e4b0530743cb371b 24 May 2020

Ramirez, Vanessa, Bates; How AI Is Like Electricity—and Why That Matters; April 02, 2017, Singularity Hub, https://singularityhub.com/2017/04/02/how-ai-is-like-electricity-and-why-that-matters/?utm_content=buffer071de&utm_medium=social&utm_source=facebook-hub&utm_campaign=buffer#sm.0001g06g9hn-m0er0ssr1sh2tlacbk 4 June 2020

Rauch, Erik; Productivity and the Workweek, https://groups.csail.mit.edu/mac/users/rauch/worktime/, MIT Education, 24 May 2020

Raviv, Shaun; The Genius Neuroscientist Who Might Hold the Key to True AI, 13 November 2018, Wired

Reedy, Christiana, We Just Created an Artificial Synapse That Can Learn Autonomously, April 5 2017, Futurism

Reisman, David A.; Schumpeter's market enterprise an evolution, Edward Elgar Publishing, 2004

Revell, Timothy; AI will be able to beat us at everything by 2060, say experts, 31 May 2017, New Scientist, https://www.newscientist.com/article/2133188-ai-will-be-able-to-beat-us-at-everything-by-2060-say-experts/#ixzz6OPlytgu6 June 4 2020

Richard, Michael Graham; First Production Electric Tesla Roadster Delivered, Treehugger, 6 February 2008

Rikleen, L. (n.d.); Creating tomorrow's leaders: the expanding roles of Millennials in the workplace, Boston College Center for Work & Family, Chestnut Hill, MA

Roberts, Graham; Augmented Reality: How We'll Bring the News Into Your Home, February 1 2018, New York Times, https://www.nytimes.com/interactive/2018/02/01/sports/olympics/nyt-ar-augmented-reality-ul.html, June 4 2020

Roos, Dave, Elon Musk's Neuralink Gets $27 Million to Merge Humans and Machines, 28 August 2017, Seeker.com https://www.seeker.com/tech/elon-musks-neuralink-gets-27-million-to-merge-human-and-machine June 4 2020

Roser, Max and Ortiz-Ospina, Esteban; Income Inequality; Our World in data, https://ourworldindata.org/income-inequality 9 May 2020

Max, Roser, This is how working hours have changed over time, World Economic Forum, 18 May 2018, https://www.weforum.org/agenda/2018/05/working-hours, 24 May 2020

Max, Roser, Working Hours, 2020, Published online at OurWorldInData.org. Retrieved from: https://ourworldindata.org/working-hours' [Online Resource] 24 May 2020

Rothman, Joshua; Are We Already Living in Virtual Reality? April 2 2018, New Yorker, https://www.newyorker.com/magazine/2018/04/02/are-we-already-living-in-virtual-reality?mbid=social_facebook 24 May 2020

Samsung, Samsung Announces World's First 5G mmWave Mobile Technology, http://global.samsungtomorrow.com/?p=24093#sthash.PIQ5h9jO. dpuf, 30 January 2014

Sample, Ian; Electrical stimulation of the brain boosts maths skills, claim scientists, The Guardian, 4 November 2010

Sanford, Kiki; Will This "Neural Lace" Brain Implant Help Us Compete with AI? 4 April 2018, Nautilus,, http://nautil.us/blog/-will-this-neural-lace-brain-implant-help-us-compete-with-ai, 25 May 2020

Santillan, Rita; The effect of the printing press in the Renaissance in the 15th century, Italy, November 9, 2010, https://blogs.ubc.ca/

Sethat, Anil; Your brain hallucinates your conscious reality, TED 2017, https://www.ted.com/talks/anil_seth_how_your_brain_hallucinates_your_conscious_reality/transcript?language=en, 30 May 2020

Shahan, Zachary; Credit Suisse Projects ~85% Of US Energy

Sherif, M.; A study of some social factors in perception, Archives of Psychology, 27, 1935

Simon, Matt, The Impossible Burger: Inside the Strange Science of the Fake Meat That 'Bleeds', 20 September 2017, Wired, https://www.wired.com/story/the-impossible-burger/, June 4 2020

Slater, Mel; Sanchez-Vives, Maria; Enhancing Our Lives with Immersive Virtual Reality; 19 December 2016, Frontiers in Robotics, https://www.frontiersin.org/articles/10.3389/frobt.2016.00074/full 24 May 2020

Smil, Vaclav. Creating the Twentieth Century: Technical Innovations of 1867-1914 and Their Lasting Impact, Oxford, Oxford University Press, 2005

Smith, Adam, The Theory of Moral Sentiments, 1759 , London

Smith, Yves; Secular Stagnation: Demand Is Indeed the Culprit; Naked Capitalism, 30 January 2020; https://www.nakedcapitalism.com/2020/01/secular-stagnation-demand-is-indeed-the-culprit.html, 9 May 2020

Socialist Worker, The Putney debates: visions of democracy, 6 November 2007, https://socialistworker.co.uk/art/13189/The+Putney+-debates%3A+visions+of+democracy 25 May 2020

Snooks, Graeme, Was the Industrial Revolution Necessary? London and New York : Routledge, 1994

Spector, Dina; An Evolutionary Explanation For Why We Crave Sugar, 25 April 2015, Business Insider

Sprenger, Polly; Sun on Privacy: 'Get Over It', 26 January 1999, Wired, https://www.wired.com/1999/01/sun-on-privacy-get-over-it/ 25 May 2020

Starr, Michelle, Scientists Could Soon Use Holography to Edit Memories And Sensations Directly Into The Brain, 1 May 2018,

Science Alert, https://www.sciencealert.com/holographic-brain-modulation-editing-brain-activity-memory-sensation June 4 2020

Suzman, James; How Neolithic farming sowed the seeds of modern inequality 10,000 years ago, 5 December 2017, The Guardian,

Suzman, James; Why 'Bushman banter' was crucial to hunter-gatherers' evolutionary success, 29 October 2017, The Guardian,

St. Jude Children's Research Hospital, Controlling a single brain chemical may help expand window for learning language and music, Science Daily, June 29, 2017,

Stanley, Kenneth O; Miikkulainen, Risto; Evolving Neural Networks through Augmenting Topologies, MIT Press Journals, 2002, http://nn.cs.utexas.edu/downloads/papers/stanley.ec02.pdf, 9 May 2020

STECKEL, RICHARD H; Floud, RODERICK; Health and Welfare during Industrialization, National Bureau of Economic Research Project Report; University of Chicago Press; 1997

Steckel, Richard H; Health and Nutrition in the Preindustrial Era: Insights from a Millennium of Average Heights in Northern Europe; NBER Working Paper No. 8542, Issued in October 2001

Stem Cell Information, Stem Cell Basics, http://stemcells.nih.gov/info/basics/pages/basics1.aspx, 21 January 2014

Stiglitz, Joseph E.; Inequality Is a Choice, New York Times, 13 October 2013

Stinson, Liz; The Future of Prosthetics Could Be This BrainControlled Bionic Leg, Wired, 15 October 2013 http://www.wired.com/2013/10/is-this-brain-controlled-bionicleg-the-future-of-prosthetics/

Stokes, Jonathan M; et al; A Deep Learning Approach to Antibiotic Discovery; Cell.com; 20 February 2020, https://www.cell.com/cell/fulltext/S0092-8674(20)30102- 19 May 2020

Stone, James A. F.; Risky and cautious shifts in group decisions, Journal of Experimental Social Psychology, Volume 4, Issue 4, October 1968, pp. 442-459 Massachusetts

Institute of Technology

Stringer, Chris; McKie, Robin; African Exodus, Jonathan Cape, London, 1996

Surowiecki, James; The Wisdom of Crowds: Why the Many Are

Smarter Than the Few and How Collective Wisdom Shapes Business, Economies, Societies and Nations,
Doubleday, 2004

Syverson, Chad; Challenges to Mismeasurement Explanations for the U.S. Productivity Slowdown; NBER Working Paper No. 21974, February 2016, https://www.nber.org/papers/w21974 109th May 2020

Svenson, Ola; Are we all less risky and more skilful than our fellow drivers?, Acta Psychologica 47 (1981), 143-148, North-Holland Publishing Company, Department of Psychology, University of Stockholm, Sweden, Accepted March 1980

Svitil, Kathy; The promise of stem cells, UCLA Newsroom, http://newsroom.ucla.edu/stories/the-promises-of-stem-cells247547, 12 May 2014

Swns Digital, 40% of Americans would have Sex with a Robot, Study Finds, 27 April 2018, https://www.swnsdigital.com/2018/04/40-of-americans-would-have-sex-with-a-robot-study-finds/ 24 May 2020

Synthetic biology NCBI, http://en.wikipedia.org/wiki/Synthetic_biology

Taleb, Nassim Nicholas; Fooled by Randomness, 2004, Penguin Books, London, 2007

Taleb, Nassim Nicholas; Black Swan, 2004, Penguin Books, London, 2008

Technology Review, Sorry, graphene—borophene is the new wonder material that's got everyone excited, April 5 2019, Technology Review, https://www.technologyreview.com/2019/04/05/239331/borophene-the-new-2d-material-taking-chemistry-by-storm/, June 4 2020

Tett, Gillian; Can we avoid an antibiotic apocalypse?, Financial Times, 6 December 2013

TheGrio, The Future with Artificial Intelligence: Even technology is racist, 24 July 2018, thegrio.com, a https://thegrio.com/2018/07/24/the-future-with-artificial-intelligence-even-technology-is-racist/ 25 May 2020

The Economist, Pricing sunshine, 28 December 2012

The Economist; Print me a Stradivarius, 10 February 2011, http://www.economist.com/node/18114327

The Economist; The other-worldly philosophers, 18 July 2009, pp65–67

The Economist, The battle of Smoot-Hawley, December 18 2008

The Economist; Vertical Farming: Does it really stack up?, 9 December 2010

The Economist; The future of jobs: The onrushing wave, 16 January 2014,

The Economist, The world's most valuable resource is no longer oil, but data, 6 May 2017

Tarlton Law Library; Television History - A Timeline, 1878-2005, The University of Texas School of Law

Tirrell, Meg; Unlocking my genome: Was it worth it? CNBC, 14th December 2015, https://www.cnbc.com/2015/12/10/unlocking-my-genome-was-it-worth-it.html, 9 May 2020

UEA, Antibiotic research to find next-generation drugs unveiled in London, 30 Jun 2014.

http://www.uea.ac.uk/mac/comm/media/press/2014/june/antsroyal-society, 7 July 2014

University of Manchester, Graphene: World-leading Research and Development,

http://www.graphene.manchester.ac.uk/, 26 January 2014

University of Strathclyde; Catching up with the 'superbug', Prism, November-December 2004   http://www.strath.ac.uk/media/publications/prism/2004/media_7 7413_en.pdf, 7 July 2014

Urban, Tim; Neuralink and the Brain's Magical Future, Wait But Why, April 20, 2017, https://waitbutwhy.com/2017/04/neuralink.html 23 May 2020

Vallor, S. Moral Deskilling and Upskilling in a New Machine Age: Reflections on the Ambiguous Future of Character. Philos. Technol. 28, 107–124 (2015). https://doi.org/10.1007/s13347-014-0156-9 24 May 2020

Venter, Craig; Annual Richard Dimbleby Lecture for the BBC, December 2007,

Venter, Craig; Watch me unveil synthetic life, TED,

Vicarious, Vicarious AI passes first Turing Test: CAPTCHA, 27 October 2013,

Vlaskovits, Patrick Henry Ford; Innovation, and That "Faster Horse" Quote, Harvard Business Review Blog:

Vorhies, William; Quantum Computing, Deep Learning, and Artificial Intelligence, June 13 2107, Data Science Central, https://www.datasciencecentral.com/profiles/blogs/quantum-computing-deep-learning-and-artificial-intelligence, June 4 2020

Wake Forest Baptist Medical Center, Prosthetic Memory System Successful in Humans, Study Finds, 27th March 2018, https://newsroom.wakehealth.edu/News-Releases/2018/03/Prosthetic-Memory-System-Successful-in-Humans-Study-Finds 23rd May 2020

Wall, Mike, We're Probably Living in a Simulation, Elon Musk Says, 7 September 2018, https://www.space.com/41749-elon-musk-living-in-simulation-rogan-podcast.html 25 May

Wang, Zheng; Tchernev, John M; The "Myth" of Media Multitasking: Reciprocal Dynamics of Media Multitasking, Personal Needs, and Gratifications, Journal of Communication, Volume 62, Issue 3, June 2012, Pages 493–513, 25 April 2012

Walsh, Fergus; Stem cell transplant 'game changer' for MS patients, 18 March 2018, BBC News, https://www.bbc.co.uk/news/health-43435868 June 4 2020

Weber, Max; The Protestant Ethic and the Spirit of Capitalism (published 1904-5 originally), Allen and Unwin, 1930

Weintraub, Pamela; E.O. Wilson's Theory of Altruism Shakes Up Understanding of Evolution, 28 April 2011, Discover Magazine

Weschler, Matthew; How Lasers Work, http://science.howstuffworks.com/laser.htm, 19 January 2014

Whiteman, Honor; Medical news Today, Worldwide obesity rates see 'startling' increase over past 3 decades, 29 May 2014. Medical news Today, https://www.medicalnewstoday.com/articles/277450, May 24 2020

Westerhoff, Nikolas; Set in our ways, why change is so hard? Scientific American Mind, December 17 2008 ,

WHO Human Genetics Programme & World Alliance of Organizations for the Prevention of Birth Defects. (1999). Services for the prevention and management of genetic disorders and birth defects in developing countries / report of a joint WHO/WAOPBD meeting, The Hague, 5-7 January 1999. World Health Organization

Wikinvest, Apple

http://www.wikinvest.com/stock/Apple_(AAPL)/Data/Market_Capi talization/2003/Q3 18 December 2013

Wikipedia, Synthetic biology: promises and challenges, http://www.ncbi.nlm.nih.gov/pmc/articles/PMC2174633/, 12 May 2014

Wikipedia: Phaistos Disc, http://en.wikipedia.org/wiki/Phaistos_Disc, June 4 2020

Wikipedia; George Gamow: DNA and RNA,

Wikipedia; http://en.wikipedia.org/wiki/Emergence June 4 2020

Wikipedia, Phaistos Disc, https://en.m.wikipedia.org/wiki/Phaistos_Disc, 24 May 2020

Wilkinson, Henry; Emerging Risk Report – 2016, Lloyds, https://www.lloyds.com/~/media/files/news-and-insight/risk-insight/2016/political-violence-contagion.pdf 25 May 2020

Wilson, Clare; Your brain is like 100 billion mini-computers all working together, 18 October 2018, new Scientist,https://www.newscientist.com/article/2182987-your-brain-is-like-100-billion-mini-computers-all-working-together/ 25 May 2020

Wilson, Edward; Sociobiology: The New Synthesis Paperback – 1 Mar. 2000; Harvard University Press; 2nd New editio

Wolf, Martin, Cities Must be open to the World when nations are not; 7 June 2017, THE FT,

Winerman, Lea, The Mind's Mirror, American Psychological Association, Monitor on Psychology, October 2005, Monitor on Psychology.

Woodcock, Jim; 3D printing don't believe the hype, Digital Innovation, 29 July 2013, http://diginnmmu.com/opinion/3dprinting-dont-believe-the-hype-704

Wrangham, Richard W.; Catching Fire: How Cooking Made Us Human, Basic Books, First Trade Paper Edition edition, 7 September 2010

Xiao, Yan and Ziyang, Fan; 10 technology trends to watch in the COVID-19 pandemic, 27 April, World Economic Forum

Yamanaka, Shinya; Nobel Prizes Facts, http://www.nobelprize.org/nobel_prizes/medicine/laureates/2012 /yamanaka-facts.html, 21 January 2014

Yiningsu, Yeah, yeah, yeah, Beatlemania catching on in China (maybe, Shanghai List, 5 May 2018, http://shanghaiist.com/2014/02/09/beatles-storey-china-tourists/ 24 May 2020

Yong, Ed, The Real Wisdom of the Crowds, 31 January 2013, National Geographic,

Zeeberg, Amos; The superpowers of super thin materials, 7 January 2020, New York Times, https://www.nytimes.com/2020/01/07/science/physics-materials-electronics.html 4 June 2020

Printed in Great Britain
by Amazon